CONTRIBUTIONS TO NON-STANDARD ANALYSIS

STUDIES IN LOGIC

AND

THE FOUNDATIONS OF MATHEMATICS

VOLUME 69

NORTH-HOLLAND PUBLISHING COMPANY
AMSTERDAM · LONDON

Symposium on Non-standard Analysis, Oberwolfach, Ger., 1970.

CONTRIBUTIONS TO NON-STANDARD ANALYSIS

Edited by

W. A. J. LUXEMBURG
California Institute of Technology

A. ROBINSON
Yale University

1972

NORTH-HOLLAND PUBLISHING COMPANY
AMSTERDAM · LONDON

Library of Congress Catalog Card Number: 76-183275

PRINTED IN THE NETHERLANDS

PREFACE

The papers collected in the present volume are, in large part, based on lectures given at the Symposium on Non-standard Analysis which took place in Oberwolfach during the period July 19 – July 25, 1970. Participants at the conference were given the option of submitting papers in addition to, or in place of, those read at the Symposium. Accordingly, we have in all cases stated the date at which the manuscripts were received by the editors. The list of papers actually read at the conference is as follows.

J. Hirschfeld:	Ultrafilters and ultrapowers in Non-standard Analysis.
A. Jensen:	A computer oriented version of Non-standard Analysis.
G. Janssen:	Eingeschränkte Ultraprodukte von W^*-Algebren vom Typ II_1.
I. Juhasz:	Non-standard notes on the hyperspace.
L. D. Kugler:	Almost periodicity on groups and semigroups.
D. Laugwitz:	Nichtarchimedische Körper für die Messung von Berührungswinkeln.
W. A. J. Luxemburg:	Some new applications of Non-standard Analysis.
P. A. Loeb:	A non-standard representation of L^∞.
M. Machover:	Infinitesimal paths.
C. W. Puritz:	Choquet's ultrafilters and skies in $^*N$.
A. Robinson:	Nonarchimedean fields.
K. D. Stroyan:	Additional remarks on the theory of monads: compactifications and monadic closure operators.
M. Wolff:	Completion of Cauchy algebras.
L. Young:	Non-standard Analysis and topological vector spaces.

Other participants were: W. Bos, N. Dinculeanu, B. Eifrig, H. O. Flösser, B. Fuchssteiner, E. Heil, J. Jansen, P. W. Pederson, R. Schickhoff, C. Schmieden, A. Wolf, P. Zahn.

We wish to express our thanks to D. Laugwitz who, together with one of us (W.A.J.L.), was responsible for the organization of the meeting in Oberwolfach; to M. Machover who undertook the task of collecting and coordinating the manuscripts; and to the North-Holland Publishing Company who invited us to include this volume in the series "Studies in Logic and the Foundations of Mathematics".

Pasadena, California
and
New Haven, Connecticut
August, 1971

W. A. J. Luxemburg
A. Robinson

CONTENTS

A. ROBINSON, Algebraic function fields and non-standard arithmetic 1
W. A. J. LUXEMBURG, A non-standard analysis approach to Fourier analysis 15
W. A. J. LUXEMBURG, A remark on the Cantor–Lebesgue lemma 41
K. D. STROYAN, Uniform continuity and rates of growth of meromorphic functions 47
P. A. LOEB, A non-standard representation of measurable spaces, L_∞, and L^*_∞ 65
B. EIFRIG, Ein nicht-standard-Beweis für die Existenz eines starken Liftungs in $\mathscr{L}_\infty \langle 0, 1]$ 81
W. A. J. LUXEMBURG, On some concurrent binary relations occurring in analysis 85
G. JANSSEN, Restricted ultraproducts of finite von Neumann algebras 101
C. W. PURITZ, Almost perpendicular vectors 115
L. YOUNG, Functional analysis – A non-standard treatment with semifields 123
I. JUHÁSZ, Non-standard notes on the hyperspace 171
M. WOLFF, Non-standard-Komplettierung von Cauchy-Algebren 179
C. W. PURITZ, Skies, constellations and monads 215
K. D. STROYAN, Additional remarks on the theory of monads 245
G. CHERLIN and J. HIRSCHFELD, Ultrafilters and ultraproducts in non-standard analysis 261
A. JENSEN, A computer oriented version of "non-standard analysis" 281

ALGEBRAIC FUNCTION FIELDS AND NON-STANDARD ARITHMETIC[1])

Abraham ROBINSON
Yale University

1. Introduction. Let $^*Q$ be a non-standard model of the field of rational numbers Q, for a higher order language (see Robinson [1966]). In particular, $^*Q$ may be an ultrapower of Q. Let α be an element of $^*Q$ which is not contained in Q. Then it is easy to verify that α is transcendental over Q. Thus, the field $A = Q(\alpha) \subset {}^*Q$ is the field of rational functions with rational coefficients.

Another method for finding an algebraic function field (of one variable, always) which is a subfield of $^*Q$ is as follows. Let Γ be a plane curve which is given by an equation $F(x, y) = 0$ where $F(x, y) \in Q[x, y]$. Let (α, β) be a non-standard rational point on $^*\Gamma$, i.e. such that at least one of α, β is non-standard. Then $A = Q(\alpha, \beta)$ is an algebraic function field which is also a subfield of $^*Q$. For example, let $F(x, y) = x^2 + y^2 - 1$, so that Γ is the unit circle and let $\alpha^2 + \beta^2 = 1$ where α and β are rational but non-standard. In this case we really obtain nothing new since $Q(\alpha, \beta) = Q(\omega)$ where ω is related to α and β by

$$\omega = \frac{\alpha}{1-\beta}, \quad \alpha = \frac{2\omega}{\omega^2+1}, \quad \beta = \frac{\omega^2-1}{\omega^2+1}.$$

Thus, $Q(\alpha, \beta)$ is again the field of rational functions with rational coefficients. However, it is well known that no such reduction is possible if the curve Γ is of positive genus.

An internal valuation of $^*Q$ is given either (i), by a non-standard prime number in $^*Q$ or (ii), by a standard prime number in Q (and $^*Q$) or (iii), by the archimedean valuation of $^*Q$. We shall refer to these valuations also as valuations of the first, second, and third kind respectively. We avoid the use of the term "infinite prime" because it has incompatible interpretations in non-standard analysis and in valuation theory.

[1]) Research supported in part by the National Science Foundation Grant No. GP-18728.

Let A be an algebraic function field over Q which is also a subfield of $^*Q$ (see above). We shall show that, in certain circumstances, *an internal valuation of* $^*Q$ *induces a valuation of* A *and that, moreover, all valuations of* A *can be obtained in this way.*

In order to avoid repetitions, we shall prove the corresponding assertion immediately for the case where Q is replaced by any algebraic number field (finite algebraic extension of Q) K. In this case also, $^*K$ may, for example, be chosen as an ultrapower of K. An internal valuation of K now is given either (i), by a non-standard prime ideal in $^*K$ or (ii) by the canonical extension to $^*K$ of a standard prime ideal in K or (iii), by the canonical extension to $^*K$ of an archimedean valuation of K. We shall refer to these valuations again as valuations of the first, second, or third kind, respectively.

2. Valuations induced in A. Let K be an algebraic number field, $^*K$ a non-standard model of K, and A an algebraic function field over K which is contained in $^*K$. We consider valuations of the first kind in $^*K$. Thus, let P be a non-standard prime ideal in $^*K$. For any $x \in {}^*K$ we denote by $v_P x$ the order (exponential value) of x at P. Then $v_P x \in {}^*Z$, where $^*Z$ is the non-standard model of the rational integers which is included in $^*K$.

Suppose now that $v_P x$ *is not identically zero on* $A - \{0\}$. Choose $\alpha \in A$ such that $v_P\alpha > 0$ $(\alpha \neq 0)$. Let $\beta \neq 0$ be another element of A. Then we claim that $v_P\beta / v_P\alpha$ is a standard rational number.

We observe first that $\alpha \notin K$ since the non-standard ideal P cannot divide any standard number in $^*K$ (i.e. $v_P x = 0$ on $K - \{0\}$). Accordingly, β is algebraic over $K(\alpha)$, there exists a non-zero polynomial $f(x, y) \in K[x, y]$ such that $f(\alpha, \beta) = 0$. Let

2.1. $f(x, y) = \sum c_{ij} x^i y^j, \quad c_{ij} \in K.$

Since $f(\alpha, \beta) = 0$, there exist distinct non-zero terms $c_{ij}x^i y^j$ and $c_{kl}x^k y^l$ such that

2.2. $v_P(c_{ij}\alpha^i\beta^j) = v_P(c_{kl}\alpha^k\beta^l).$

But c_{ij} and c_{kl} belong to K, so $v_P c_{ij} = v_P c_{kl} = 0$ and $(i - k)v_P\alpha = (l - j)v_P\beta$. Now $l - j \neq 0$ for if $l - j = 0$ then $i - k \neq 0$ and $v_P\alpha = 0$, contrary to our choice of α. Hence

2.3. $v_P\beta = \dfrac{i - k}{l - j} v_P\alpha.$

Thus, $v_P\beta$ is a standard rational multiple of $v_P\alpha$. Putting

2.4. $w_P x = v_P x / v_P\alpha$

we see that 2.4 defines a valuation of A in the additive group of rational numbers, with $w_P x = 0$ for $x \in K - \{0\}$. Thus w_P is a valuation of the algebraic function field A over K. It follows that w_P is discrete, and this can also be seen directly from 2.3. We shall say that w_P (or any equivalent valuation) is *induced by* v_P *in* A. The valuation is, up to equivalence, independent of our particular choice of α (subject to the stated conditions).

Next, we consider valuations of the second kind in $^*K$. Let then P be a standard prime ideal in $^*K$, i.e. the canonical extension of a prime ideal of K to $^*K$. Using the same notation as before suppose that $v_P x$ *is not finite* (in the sense of Non-standard Analysis) for some $x \in A - \{0\}$.

Choose $\alpha \in A$ such that $v_P\alpha$ is positive infinite ($\alpha \neq 0$). Then $\alpha \notin K$ since $v_P x$ is finite on $K - \{0\}$. Let $\beta \neq 0$ be an element of A. As before, there exists a polynomial $f(x, y) \in K[x, y]$ as given by 2.1 such that $f(\alpha, \beta) = 0$. Hence, again, 2.2 is satisfied for two distinct non-zero terms of $f(x, y)$. From 2.2,

2.5. $(i - k)v_P\alpha = (l - j)v_P\beta + (v_P c_{kl} - v_P c_{ij})$.

Now $l - j = 0$ would imply that $v_P\alpha$ is finite, which is contrary to our choice of α. Hence $l - j \neq 0$ and

2.6. $$\frac{v_P\beta}{v_P\alpha} = \frac{i - k}{l - j} + \frac{v_P c_{ij} - v_P c_{kl}}{(l - j)v_P\alpha}.$$

The numerator in the second term on the right-hand side of 2.6 is finite while the denominator is infinite. It follows that the term is infinitesimal. Hence, taking standard parts on both sides of 2.6, we obtain, introducing $w_P\beta$ by definition

2.7. $$w_P\beta = {}^\circ\left(\frac{v_P\beta}{v_P\alpha}\right) = \frac{i - k}{l - j}.$$

Notice that 2.6 also contains some additional information on the proximity of $^\circ(v_P\beta/v_P\alpha)$ to $(i - k)/(l - j)$ since it shows that the difference between these quantities cannot exceed some finite multiple of $(v_P\alpha)^{-1}$ (or, equivalently if $v_P\beta \neq 0$, some finite multiple of $(v_P\beta)^{-1}$).

We claim that $w_P x$, as given by 2.7, is a valuation of A over K in the additive group of standard rational numbers. Indeed, for $\beta \neq 0$, $w_P\beta$ is standard rational, by definition. Also, for $\beta = K - \{0\}$, $w_P\beta = 0$ since $v_P\beta$ is then finite. Also, for $\beta, \gamma \in A$, $\beta \neq 0$, $\gamma \neq 0$,

$$w_P(\beta\gamma) = {}^\circ\left(\frac{v_P(\beta\gamma)}{v_P\alpha}\right) = {}^\circ\left(\frac{v_P\beta + v_P\gamma}{v_P\alpha}\right) = {}^\circ\left(\frac{v_P\beta}{v_P\alpha}\right) + {}^\circ\left(\frac{v_P\gamma}{v_P\alpha}\right)$$
$$= w_P\beta + w_P\gamma,$$

which shows that the rule for the value of a product is satisfied. To consider the value of a sum, we may suppose that $v_P\beta \leq v_P\gamma$ and $\beta + \gamma \neq 0$. We then have $w_P\beta \leq w_P\gamma$ and

$$w_P(\beta + \gamma) = {}^\circ\left(\frac{v_P(\beta + \gamma)}{v_P\alpha}\right) \geq {}^\circ\left(\frac{v_P\beta}{v_P\alpha}\right) = w_P\beta.$$

Thus, w_P is a valuation of A over K. We call it the valuation which is *induced by* v_P *in* A. The valuation is, up to equivalence, again independent of our particular choice of α.

Finally, we have to consider valuations of the third kind in $^*K$. Such a valuation is given by the absolute values $|x|$ provided by an embedding of $^*K$ in the corresponding non-standard model of the complex numbers, $^*C$. The value of $|x|$ depends on the embedding but we shall not indicate this in the notation.

Suppose that $|x|$ *does not remain finite* everywhere on A. That is to say, $|x|$ is infinite for some $x \in A$ and hence, considering inverses, that it is infinitesimal but not zero somewhere on A. We choose a fixed $\alpha \neq 0$ in A such that $|\alpha|$ is infinitesimal. Then $\alpha \notin K$.

Let $\beta \neq 0$ be an element of A. Again there exists a polynomial $f(x, y) \in K[x, y]$ as given by 2.1 such that $f(\alpha, \beta) = 0$. Pick a term $c_{ij}x^iy^j$ such that $|c_{ij}\alpha^i\beta^j|$ is as large as possible. Then $|c_{ij}\alpha^i\beta^j| \neq 0$, and for any other term $c_{kl}x^ky^l$ the ratio

2.8. $$\frac{|c_{kl}\alpha^k\beta^l|}{|c_{ij}\alpha^i\beta^j|}$$

cannot exceed 1. At the same time, this ratio cannot be infinitesimal for all such terms for if it were then $|f(\alpha, \beta) - c_{ij}\alpha^i\beta^j|/|c_{ij}\alpha^i\beta^j|$ also would be infinitesimal. And this is impossible, for this ratio is actually equal to 1 since $f(\alpha, \beta) = 0$. Accordingly, there exists a monomial $c_{kl}x^ky^l$ distinct from $c_{ij}x^iy^j$ such that the ratio 2.8 is not infinitesimal. It follows that the natural logarithm of 2.8 is a finite real number, $-\mu$, where $\mu \geq 0$,

$$\ln|c_{kl}| - \ln|c_{ij}| + (k - i)\ln|\alpha| + (l - j)\ln|\beta| = -\mu.$$

Now $\ln|c_{kl}|$ and $\ln|c_{ij}|$ are finite since c_{kl} and c_{ij} are standard while $\ln|\alpha|$ is negative infinite, since $|\alpha|$ is infinitesimal. Hence

$$(k - i)\ln|\alpha| + (l - j)\ln|\beta| = v$$

where v is finite, and $l - j \neq 0$, otherwise $\ln|\alpha|$ also would have to be finite. Then

$$2.9.\quad \frac{\ln|\beta|}{\ln|\alpha|} = \frac{l - k}{l - j} + \frac{v}{(l - j)\,\text{in}|\alpha|}$$

where the last term on the right-hand side is infinitesimal. We put

$$2.10.\quad w\beta = {}^{\circ}\!\left(\frac{\ln|\beta|}{\ln|\alpha|}\right) = \frac{i - k}{l - j}$$

so that $w\beta$ is standard rational for all $\beta \in A$, $\beta \neq 0$, and we assert that this defines a valuation of A over K. Here again, 2.9 gives a measure for the difference between $w\beta$ and $\ln|\beta|/\ln|\alpha|$ by showing that this difference cannot exceed a finite multiple of $(\ln|\alpha|)^{-1}$ (or, for $\ln|\beta| \neq 0$, if $(\ln|\beta|)^{-1}$).

Let $\beta, \gamma \in A$, $\beta \neq 0$, $\gamma \neq 0$. Then

$$w(\beta\gamma) = {}^{\circ}\!\left(\frac{\ln|\beta\gamma|}{\ln|\alpha|}\right) = {}^{\circ}\!\left(\frac{\ln|\beta|}{\ln|\alpha|} + \frac{\ln|\gamma|}{\ln|\alpha|}\right) = {}^{\circ}\!\left(\frac{\ln|\beta|}{\ln|\alpha|}\right) + {}^{\circ}\!\left(\frac{\ln|\gamma|}{\ln|\alpha|}\right)$$
$$= w\beta + w\gamma.$$

Also, assuming $-\ln|\beta| \leq -\ln|\gamma|$ and $\beta + \gamma \neq 0$, we have $w\beta \leq w\gamma$ and

$$2.11.\quad w(\beta + \gamma) = {}^{\circ}\!\left(\frac{\ln|\beta + \gamma|}{\ln|\alpha|}\right) = {}^{\circ}\!\left(\frac{\ln|\beta|}{\ln|\alpha|} + \frac{\ln|1 + \gamma/\beta|}{\ln|\alpha|}\right).$$

Since $\beta + \gamma \neq 0$ and $1 + \gamma/\beta \in A$, $\ln|1 + \gamma/\beta|/\ln|\alpha|$ is finite. We claim that

$$2.12.\quad {}^{\circ}\!\left(\frac{\ln|1 + \gamma/\beta|}{\ln|\alpha|}\right) \geq 0.$$

Since $\ln|\alpha|$ is negative infinite, 2.12 will be established, if we can show that $\ln|1 + \gamma/\beta|$ cannot be positive infinite, i.e. that it is either finite or negative infinite. By assumption, $\ln|\beta| - \ln|\gamma| \geq 0$, i.e. $|\gamma/\beta| \leq 1$. This shows that $\ln|1 + \gamma/\beta| \leq \ln 2$ and proves 2.12. Hence, from 2.11

$$w(\beta + \gamma) \geq {}^{\circ}\!\left(\frac{\ln|\beta|}{\ln|\alpha|}\right) = w\beta.$$

Finally, since $\ln|\beta|$ is finite for all $\beta \in K - \{0\}$, $w\beta = 0$ for all such β. This shows that wx is a valuation of A over K. We shall say that *wx is induced by the given archimedean valuation.* Once again, wx is, up to equivalence, independent of the particular choice of α.

Examples which show that all three kinds of induced valuations may actually occur can be obtained already for $K = Q$, $A = Q(\omega)$, where $\omega \in {}^*Q - Q$. Choosing ω as a non-standard prime number in ${}^*Q$, we see that $P = (\omega)$ yields a valuation of the first kind which induces a valuation of A. Choosing $\omega = p^\nu$ where p is a standard rational prime and ν is a non-standard positive integer, we obtain a valuation of the second kind which induces a valuation of A, from $P = (\omega) = (p^\nu)$. Finally, for $\omega = \nu^{-1}$, where ν is an arbitrary non-standard positive integer, the archimedean valuation of ${}^*Q$ also induces a valuation of A.

We shall show in the next two sections that, actually, *all* valuations of an algebraic function field $A \subset {}^*K$ are induced. However, it is entirely possible that different valuations of ${}^*K$, and even valuations of different kinds, may induce the same valuation of A.

3. All valuations of $A = K(\omega)$ over K are induced. For K an algebraic number field, as before, suppose first that $A = K(\omega) \subset {}^*K$ where $\omega \in {}^*K - K$ so that $K(\omega)$ is the field of rational functions of one variable with coefficients in K. We shall require the following lemma.

3.1. LEMMA. *Let α be any algebraic integer which belongs to ${}^*K$. If $|\alpha|$ is finite in all archimedean valuations of ${}^*K$ then α must be standard, $\alpha \in K$.*

Proof. Choose a fixed embedding of ${}^*K$ in the corresponding non-standard model of the complex numbers, ${}^*C$. Let $\alpha = \alpha^{(1)}, \alpha^{(2)}, \ldots, \alpha^{(n)}$ be the conjugates of α in ${}^*C$. Suppose that $|\alpha^{(1)}|, |\alpha^{(2)}|, \ldots, |\alpha^{(n)}|$ are all finite. Then we have to show that α is standard.

Let b be a finite upper bound for the $|\alpha^{(j)}|$, $j = 1, \ldots, n$, and let $s_1, \ldots, s_n$ be the fundamental symmetrical functions of $\alpha^{(1)}, \ldots, \alpha^{(n)}$. Then $|s_k| \leq \binom{n}{k}b$, $k = 1, \ldots, n$. Thus, the s_k are finite rational integers in ${}^*Q$. They are therefore standard, $s_k \in Q$, $k = 1, \ldots, n$. Consider the polynomial

$$f(x) = x^n - s_1 x^{n-1} + \ldots + (-1)^n s_n.$$

This is a standard polynomial, whose roots are therefore also standard. But α is one of these roots. Accordingly α is standard. This proves the assertion.

A valuation of $K(\omega)$ is given either by a prime polynomial $p(t) \in K[t]$ or it is the valuation "at infinity". Consider the former case. The corresponding valuation of $K(t)$ will be denoted by V_p. It is obtained as follows. For any $q(t) \in K[t]$, write

3.2. $q(t) = (p(t))^m\, s(t), \quad m \geq 0$

where $p(t)$ is prime to $s(t)$. Then there exist elements $g(t)$ and $h(t)$ of $K[t]$ such that

3.3. $g(t)p(t) + h(t)s(t) = 1.$

The valuation of $q(t)$ is now defined by $V_p q = m$ and by $V_p f = V_p q - V_p r$ for any $f(t) \in K(t)$, $f(t) = q(t)/r(t)$. The corresponding valuation of $K(\omega)$, which will again be denoted by V_p is given by the canonical mapping of $K(t)$ on $K(\omega)$, i.e. by $V_p(f(\omega)) = V_p(f(t))$ for any $f(t) \in K(t)$.

For any $q(t) \in K[t]$ consider $q(\omega) \in K[\omega] \subset {}^*K$. Since $q(\omega)$ is an algebraic number in ${}^*K$, the ideal $(q(\omega))$ can be written as a product of prime powers $\prod P_j^{v_j}$, with starfinite index set (i.e. the index set is "finite" in the non-standard sense).

Suppose first that there is a non-standard prime ideal P_j in the numerator of the prime power representation of $p(\omega)$, i.e. $v_j > 0$. We put $P_j = P$, $v_j = v$, and we consider the valuation v_P in ${}^*K$, which is of the first kind. By assumption, $v_P(p(\omega)) = v > 0$.

We observe that $v_P\omega \geq 0$. For suppose $v_P\omega < 0$ and let

3.4. $p(t) = a_0 + a_1 t + \ldots + a_\lambda t^\lambda, \quad a_j \in K, a_\lambda \neq 0.$

Since $v_P a_j = 0$ for $a_j \neq 0$ we then have $v_P(p(\omega)) = \lambda v_P\omega < 0$, which is contrary to assumption. It follows that $v_P\omega > 0$ and, hence, that $v_P(k(\omega)) \geq 0$ for all $k(t) \in K[t]$.

In particular, for any $q(t) \in K[t]$, we then have $v_P(g(\omega)) \geq 0$, $v_P(h(\omega)) \geq 0$, $v_P(s(\omega)) \geq 0$ where g, h, and s are given by 3.2 and 3.3. Now $v_P(s(\omega)) > 0$ would imply

$$v_P\, 1 = v_P(g(\omega)p(\omega) + h(\omega)s(\omega)) > 0$$

although $v_P\, 1 = 0$. Hence $v_P(s(\omega)) = 0$ and, from 3.2,

3.5. $v_P(q(\omega)) = m v_P(p(\omega)).$

Now let $\alpha = p(\omega)$ for the construction of the valuation w_P induced by v_P in A. We claim that w_P coincides with V_p on A. Indeed, for $x = q(\omega) \in K[\omega]$, we have, from 2.4,

$$w_P(q(\omega)) = \frac{v_P(q(\omega))}{v_P(p(\omega))} = \frac{m v_P(p(\omega))}{v_P(p(\omega))} = m = V_p(q(\omega)).$$

Hence for $f(t) \in K(t)$, $f(t) = q(t)/r(t)$, $q(t)$, $r(t) \in K[t]$

$$w_P(f(\omega)) = w_P(q(\omega)) - w_P(r(\omega)) = V_p(q(\omega)) - V_p(r(\omega)) = V_p(f(\omega)),$$

which proves our assertion.

Suppose next, that for some P_j in the numerator of the prime power representation of $p(\omega)$, P_j is a standard prime ideal and ν_j is infinite, hence positive infinite. Putting $P_j = P$ and $\nu_j = \nu$, we observe that, this time, $v_P\omega$ while not necessarily non-negative is at any rate not negative infinite. To see this, let $p(t)$ be given by 3.4. The numbers v_Pa_j, $a_j \neq 0$, being standard, cannot be negative infinite. If $v_P\omega$ were negative infinite we should again have $v_P(p(\omega)) = \lambda v_P\omega$, so that $v_P(p(\omega))$ also would be negative infinite, contrary to assumption. It follows that no monomial $a\omega^\mu$, μ finite, $a \in K$, can be negative infinite, and hence that $v_P(k(\omega))$ cannot be negative infinite for any $k(t) \in K[t]$.

Let $q(t) \in K[t]$ and let g, h, and s be given by 3.2 and 3.3. Then we claim that $v_P(s(\omega))$ cannot be positive infinite. For if this were the case then $v_P(g(\omega)p(\omega))$ and $v_P(h(\omega)s(\omega))$ would both be positive infinite. Since

$$v_P\,1 = v_P(g(\omega)p(\omega) + h(\omega)s(\omega)) \geq \min(v_P(g(\omega)p(\omega)), v_P(h(\omega)s(\omega)))$$

it would then follow that $v_P\,1$ is positive infinite, which is not true. We conclude that $v_P(s(\omega))$ is finite and, hence, standard, $v_P(s(\omega)) = \mu$, say. By 3.2, then,

$$v_P(q(\omega)) = mv_P(p(\omega)) + \mu.$$

Let $\alpha = p(\omega)$ for the construction of the valuation w_P which is induced by v_P, a valuation of the second kind in A. We claim that $w_P = V_p$ on A and we see that again it will be sufficient to show this for $x = q(\omega) \in K[\omega]$. From 2.7,

$$w_P(q(\omega)) = {}^\circ\!\left(\frac{v_P(q(\omega))}{v_P(p(\omega))}\right) = {}^\circ\!\left(\frac{mv_P(p(\omega))}{v_P(p(\omega))} + \frac{\mu}{\nu}\right) = m = V_p(q(\omega)),$$

since μ/ν is infinitesimal. This proves our assertion.

It only remains for us to dispose of the case that the numerator of $(p(\omega)) = \prod P_i^{\nu_i}$ contains neither a non-standard prime ideal, nor a standard prime ideal with infinite exponent. We claim, first of all that in this case the number of prime ideals in the numerator of $p(\omega)$ must be finite in the absolute sense. Let the set of these ideals be S. At any rate, S is internal. Range all prime ideals of K in a sequence, $\{P^{(j)}\} = \sigma$ without repetitions. If S is not finite then, for every standard natural number μ, there exists a $j > \mu$ such that $P^{(j)} \in S$. On the other hand, S is starfinite, so there must exist a first natural number, μ_0, such that $P^{(j)} \notin S$ for all $j > \mu_0$. Since we have just seen that μ_0 cannot be finite, it must be infinite. But then $P^{(\mu_0)}$ is a non-standard prime ideal which belongs to S, which is contrary to assumption. Thus,

S is finite. Since, in the case under consideration, the prime ideals P_i which belong to S all appear in the prime power representation of $(p(\omega))$ with finite exponents, the numerator of $(p(\omega))$ must be standard, so

$$(p(\omega)) = J_1/J_2$$

where J_1 and J_2 are entire ideals in $^*K$ and J_1 is standard. Let γ be the absolute norm of J_1 then γ is standard and is divisible by J_1, $(\gamma) = J_1 J_3$ say, where J_3 is standard and entire. Hence

$$(p(\omega)) = \frac{J_1 J_3}{J_2 J_3} = \frac{(\gamma)}{J_2 J_3} = \frac{(\gamma)}{(\delta)}$$

where δ is some integer in $^*K$. It follows that $p(\omega) = \gamma/\varepsilon\delta$ where ε is a unit in $^*K$, $\varepsilon\delta = \gamma/p(\omega)$. Now $\varepsilon\delta$ is an algebraic integer, hence, by 3.1 there exists an archimedean valuation of $^*K$ for which the absolute value of $\varepsilon\delta$ (to be denoted simply by $|\varepsilon\delta|$) is infinite. We conclude that $|p(\omega)| = \gamma/|\varepsilon\delta|$ is infinitesimal.

We put $\alpha = |p(\omega)|$ and we construct a valuation wx on A according to the procedure given in section 3 above for valuations induced in A by valuations of $^*K$ which are of the third kind. We are going to show that w coincides with V_p on A. Again it is sufficient to prove $wx = V_p x$ for any $x = q(\omega)$ where $q(t) \in K[t]$, and where g, h, and s are given by 3.2 and 3.3. Then $V_p(q(\omega)) = m$.

Let $p(t)$ be given by 3.4. If $|\omega|$ were infinite then

$$|p(\omega)| = |\omega|^\lambda \left| \frac{a_0}{\omega^\lambda} + \frac{a_1}{\omega^{\lambda-1}} + \dots + a_\lambda \right|$$

would be infinite also. But $|p(\omega)|$ is infinitesimal, so $|\omega|$ must be finite. It follows that $|g(\omega)|$, $|h(\omega)|$, $|s(\omega)|$ also are finite. But then $|s(\omega)|$ cannot be infinitesimal, since, by 3.3,

$$1 = |1| = |g(\omega)p(\omega) + h(\omega)s(\omega)| \leq |g(\omega)||p(\omega)| + |h(\omega)||s(\omega)|$$

so that $|1|$ would be infinitesimal as well. Hence, $|s(\omega)|$ is neither infinite nor infinitesimal, implying that $\mu = \ln|s(\omega)|$ is finite. Using the definition of w by 2.10 we therefore obtain

$$w(q(\omega)) = {}^\circ\left(\frac{\ln|q(\omega)|}{\ln|p(\omega)|}\right) = {}^\circ\left(\frac{m \ln|p(\omega)|}{\ln|p(\omega)|} + \frac{\mu}{\ln|p(\omega)|}\right) = m = V_p(q(\omega)).$$

This completes our argument. We have shown that V_p is always induced by a valuation of $^*K$. We still have to consider the valuation of $K(\omega)$ "at infinity", but this is reduced to the previous case by the substitution $\omega' = \omega^{-1}$. We conclude that *all* valuations of $A = K(\omega)$ over K are induced by valuations of $*K$ of the first, second, or third kind.

4. All valuations of A over K are induced. We now tackle the case of a general algebraic function field A over K, $A \subset *K$. Our argument depends heavily on the following "standard" lemma.

4.1. LEMMA. *Let A be an algebraic function field over a field K, where K is algebraically closed in A. Let S be a set of valuations of A over K with the following property. For every element $\omega \in A - K$ and for every valuation V of $K(\omega)$ over K there exists a $V' \in S$ which reduces to V on $K(\omega)$. Then S is the set of all valuations of A over K.*

Leaving aside the proof of 4.1 for the moment, we show first that it implies the statement which titles this section. In our case, K is certainly algebraically closed in A since it is even algebraically closed in $*K$. We now identify S with the set of valuations which are induced in A by (internal) valuations of $*K$. If $\omega \in A - K$ and if V is a valuation of $K(\omega)$ over K then, as shown in section 3 there exists a valuation v of $*K$ which induces the valuation V on $K(\omega)$ over K. But the same v induces a valuation V' on A over K which reduces to V on $K(\omega)$. We conclude that S consists of all valuations of A over K, i.e. every valuation of A over K is induced by some valuation of $*K$. This confirms our assertion.

In order to prove 4.1, we shall find it convenient to identify the elements of S with the corresponding places (prime divisors). Using a terminology which is suggested by the particular application made above, we call the elements of S *induced* places or *induced* prime divisors. Products of powers of induced prime divisors will be called induced divisors. The set of induced divisors will be denoted by D. Then $S \subset S_0$, $D \subset D_0$ where S_0 and D_0 are the sets of all prime divisors, and the sets of all divisors, in A over K, respectively. Every induced divisor, in particular every induced prime divisor has a *degree* in the usual sense.

Let α be any element of A, (α) the corresponding divisor. Then (α) can be written in the form R/Q where Q and R are elements of D_0 without common factor. If now we exclude from Q and R those prime factors which do not belong to S, we obtain elements of D which will be denoted by Q_i and R_i respectively. If $Q \neq Q_i$ we then have $d(Q) > d(Q_i)$ where $d(X)$ denotes the degree of a divisor X. Suppose now that $D_0 \neq D$ so that $D_0 - D$

contains a divisor C. Then C appears in the denominator of (α) for some $\alpha \in A$. For this α, $Q \neq Q_i$, $d(Q) > d(Q_i)$. Now $d(Q) = n$ where n is the degree of A over $K(\alpha)$. Accordingly, in order to show that $D_0 - D$ is empty, i.e. in order to prove 4.1, we only have to establish that $d(Q_i) = n$ also, for all $\alpha \in A$.

By an induced zero (pole) of an element $\alpha \in A$ we mean an induced prime divisor which belongs to the numerator (denominator) of α.

4.2. LEMMA. *On the assumptions of* 4.1, *an element* $\alpha \in A$ *without induced poles is a constant.*

Proof of 4.2. Suppose $\alpha \in A$ is not a constant. Then there exists a valuation V of A such that $V\alpha < 0$. Let V' be the restriction of V to $K(\alpha)$, and let $V'' \in S$ be an extension of V' to all of A such as exists on the assumptions of 4.1 and 4.2. Then $V''\alpha < 0$, α has an induced pole.

Let Q be an induced entire divisor. An element $\alpha \in A$ will be called an induced multiple of Q if for every prime divisor P which appears in Q with non-zero exponent v, the order (value) of α at P, $V_p\alpha$ is not smaller than v, and if for all other *induced* prime divisors the order of Q is non-negative. Notice that, a priori, α may be a multiple of the induced divisor Q without being an induced multiple of Q. For a given induced Q, the induced multiples of Q^{-1} constitute a K-module $M_i(Q)$. We claim that $M_i(Q)$ has a finite rank, $l_i(Q)$, over K which satisfies the inequality

4.3. $$l_i(Q) \leq d(Q) + 1.$$

The proof of 4.3 as well as the subsequent steps given before for the proof of 4.1 are entirely analogous to the corresponding proofs for ordinary multiples. Compare Van der Waerden [1967].

Since we have supposed that Q is entire, $Q = \prod P_j^{v_j}$ where the P_j are induced and the v_i are non-negative. Let $\delta_j = d(P_j)$ and let π_j be a corresponding prime element of A–i.e. $V_{P_j}\pi_k = 1$ where V_{P_j} is normed with smallest positive element 1–for any one of the P_j. δ_j is, as usual, the degree of the residue class field W_j/J_j over K where $W_j \subset A$ and $J_j \subset W_j$ are the valuation ring and the valuation ideal for P_j, respectively. Let $\delta = d(Q) = \sum \delta_j v_j$ and let $\alpha_1, \ldots, \alpha_\lambda$ be elements of $M_i(Q)$. Then the expansion of any of the a_σ at P_j begins with the v_jth negative power of π_j (at most). Hence, at most δ linear conditions are required on $k_1, \ldots, k_\lambda \in K$ in order to ensure that for the linear combination $\alpha = k_1\alpha_1 + \ldots + k_\lambda\alpha_\lambda$ no negative powers of π_j occur at any of the P_j. But then α has no induced pole and so $\alpha \in K$, by 4.2. Suppose now that $\alpha_1, \ldots, \alpha_\lambda$ are linearly independent over K, then the dimension of the $\alpha = k_1\alpha_1 + \ldots + k_\lambda\alpha_\lambda$ for which no negative power of π_j occur at any of the P_j cannot be less than $\lambda - \delta$. But since $\alpha \in K$, this dimension is at most 1, $\lambda - \delta \leq 1$, $\lambda \leq \delta + 1$. This proves 4.3.

Let $\beta_1, \ldots, \beta_n$ be a basis of A over $K(\alpha)$ where $\alpha \in A - K$. Suppose that, in the first place, β_1 has a pole for an induced divisor P for which α does not have a pole, $V_P\,\alpha \geq 0$, $V_P\,\beta < 0$. Let V' be the restriction of V_P to $K(\alpha)$. Since $V_P\,\alpha \geq 0$, V' is not the valuation of $K(\alpha)$ at "infinity", V' is defined by a prime polynomial $p(t) \in K[t]$. Then $V'(p(\alpha)) = V_P(p(\alpha)) > 0$ so that we obtain a β'_1 with $V_P\beta'_1 > 0$ if we multiply β by a sufficiently great power of $p(\alpha)$. We apply the same procedure for all other induced divisors P for which β_1 has, and α does not have a pole, and we then do the same also for $\beta_2, \ldots, \beta_n$ in turn. In this way, we finally obtain a basis of A over $K(\alpha)$ none of whose elements has a pole for an induced divisor for which α does not have a pole. We denote the elements of this basis, without fear of confusion, again by $\beta_1, \ldots, \beta_n$. Since all the induced poles of $\beta_1, \ldots, \beta_n$ are now among the induced poles of α, $\beta_1, \ldots, \beta_n$ are induced multiples of some positive power Q_i^μ of Q_i where Q_i is, as before, obtained from the denominator Q of $(\alpha) = R/Q$ by excluding the prime divisors which do not belong to S. Now let m be an integer greater than μ and consider the set of elements $\beta_j\alpha^k$, $j = 1, \ldots, n$, $k = 0, \ldots, m - \mu - 1$. Their number is $n(m - \mu)$, they are linearly independent over K, and they are all induced multiples of Q_i^m. Hence, by 4.3

$$n(m - \mu) \leq l_i(Q_i^m) \leq d(Q_i^m) + 1 = d(Q_i) + 1$$

and so

4.4. $m(n - d(Q_i)) \leq n\mu + 1$.

If $n - d(Q_i)$ were positive then, by choosing m sufficiently large we could make the left-hand side of 4.4 greater than its right-hand side. Hence, $n \leq d(Q_i)$. But we also have $d(Q_i) \leq d(Q)$ and since $d(Q) = n$, we conclude that $d(Q_i) = n$. This completes the proof of 4.1.

5. Conclusion. We conclude with some further discussion of the circumstances under which the theory of the present paper applies. Let K be an algebraic number field and let $^*K$ be a non-standard model of K, as before. Let $f(x, y)$ be an absolutely irreducible polynomial with coefficients in K and let Γ be the irreducible curve which is given by $f(x, y) = 0$. By a K-point we mean a point (α, β) with coefficients in K, with a similar definition for $^*K$. A point of $^*\Gamma$ is non-standard if not both of its coordinates are standard.

5.1. THEOREM. *$^*\Gamma$ contains a non-standard $^*K$-point if and only if the number of K-points on Γ is infinite.*

Proof. Suppose $^*\Gamma$ contains a non-standard $^*K$-point, (α, β). The assertion "Γ contains a K-point (x, y)" is then true in the non-standard model, where "Γ" denotes $^*\Gamma$ and "K" denotes $^*K$. It therefore holds also in the standard model, for some $x = \alpha_1, y = \beta_1, \alpha_1, \beta_1 \in K$. Next, the assertion "$\Gamma$ contains a K-point (x, y) which is different from (α_1, β_1)" holds in the non-standard model and therefore also in the standard model, for some $x = \alpha_2, y = \beta_2$, $\alpha_2, \beta_2 \in K$, $(\alpha_1, \beta_1) \neq (\alpha_2, \beta_2)$. Next, the assertion "$\Gamma$ contains a K-point (x, y) which is different from (α_1, β_1) and from (α_2, β_2)" holds in the non-standard and, hence also in the standard model, for some (α_3, β_3) which is distinct from (α_1, β_1) and from (α_2, β_2). Continuing in this way, we see that Γ contains an infinite sequence $(\alpha_1, \beta_1), (\alpha_2, \beta_2), (\alpha_3, \beta_3), \ldots$ of distinct K-points. This shows that the condition is sufficient.

To show that this condition is necessary, range all elements of K in a sequence $\{\eta_n\}$, without repetitions. Then it is true in K that "for every positive integer n, there exists a point (α, β) on Γ such that for some $m > n$ either $\alpha = \eta_m$ or $\beta = \eta_m$". But the statement in quotes must still be true in $^*K$. Choosing n infinite, we obtain a non-standard point (α, β) on $^*\Gamma$.

The question whether there can be an infinite number of rational points on a curve of genus greater than 1 is the subject of a famous conjecture of Mordell's.

Suppose now that the number of K-points of Γ–which is given by $f(x, y) = 0$, $f(x, y) \in K[x, y]$ and absolutely irreducible–is infinite. Then there exists a non-standard $^*K$-point (α, β) on $^*\Gamma$. Let ξ be an indeterminate over K and let η be algebraic over $K(\xi)$ such that $f(\xi, \eta) = 0$. Then $K(\xi, \eta)$ is the algebraic function field which belongs to Γ.

We wish to show that $K(\alpha, \beta)$ is isomorphic to $K(\xi, \eta)$ under a map $\alpha \to \xi$. However, this is true only subject to the trivial restriction that Γ *is not a straight line parallel to one of the coordinate axes.*

Let $f(x, y) = \sum f_j(x)y^j$ where $f_j(x) \in K[x]$. At least one of the $f_j(x)$ cannot be a constant, otherwise Γ (being irreducible) would reduce to a straight line parallel to the x-axis. Suppose α is algebraic over K. Then $f_j(\alpha) = 0$ for all j, otherwise β would be algebraic over K also, contrary to the assumption that (α, β) is a non-standard point. But then Γ reduces to straight lines, and hence to a single straight line, parallel to the y-axis, which is again contrary to assumption. Thus, α is transcendental over K and we have a natural isomorphism ψ: $K(\xi) \to K(\alpha)$ which reduces to the identity on K, such that $\xi \overset{\psi}{\to} \alpha$. Since $f(\xi, \eta) = 0$ and $f(\alpha, \beta) = 0$, ψ can be extended to an isomorphism $K(\xi, \eta) \to K(\alpha, \beta)$ for which $\eta \to \beta$. This shows that $K(\alpha, \beta)$ can be identified with the algebraic function field which belongs to Γ.

References

Chevalley, C., 1951, Introduction to the Theory of Algebraic Functions of one variable, *Mathematical Surveys VI.*

Robinson, A., 1966, *Non-standard Analysis*, Studies in Logic and the Foundations of Mathematics (North-Holland, Amsterdam, second printing 1969).

Van der Waerden, B. L., 1967, *Algebra* (5th ed. of Moderne Algebra), 2nd part (Berlin-Heidelberg-New York).

Received 22 March 1971

A NONSTANDARD ANALYSIS APPROACH TO FOURIER ANALYSIS

W. A. J. LUXEMBURG[1])

California Institute of Technology

1. Introduction. Some of the results of the present paper were originally prepared for a course in nonstandard analysis as an illustration of how the techniques of nonstandard analysis can be successfully used in the theory of Fourier series. Since these techniques may be of broader interest I venture to submit them here in an extended version.

The basic idea which will be explored below is that nonstandard analysis provides us with a very useful tool to discretize certain parts of Fourier analysis. For instance, we will show that certain results of the theory of Fourier series such as Parseval's formula and the Hausdorff–Young inequalities can be directly obtained from their discrete analogues. The interesting feature of such a derivation, in the case of Parseval's formula, is that its validity can be shown without having to establish first that the trigonometric system is complete. That fact will now become an easy consequence of Parseval's formula.

The basic idea on which our method rests and which involves infinitely small as well as infinitely large numbers can be explained in the following way. But before we shall do this we would like to advise the interested reader who is not too familiar with the techniques and terminology of nonstandard analysis to consult Robinson [1966] on this subject or the lecture notes Luxemburg [1962a] or the forthcoming paper Luxemburg [1972b]. An excellent source of information concerning the theory of Fourier series is the recent book Katznelson [1968].

Let R denote as usual the field of real numbers. In addition, we shall consider a nonstandard model of the properties of R as far as they can be expressed formally in a higher order language chosen in advance. As usual we shall denote the field of nonstandard reals by $^*R$ and the standard part

[1]) Work on this paper was supported in part by NSF Grant GP 23392.

operation by "st". The ring of integers of R will be denoted by Z and the corresponding ring in $^*R$ by $^*Z$. The subset of Z of the natural numbers $\{1, 2, \ldots, n, \ldots\}$ will be denoted by N and the set of nonstandard natural numbers by $^*N$. The symbol $^*N\backslash N$ will be used to denote the set of infinitely large natural numbers. The circle group $R/2\pi Z$, that is, the additive group of real numbers mod. 2π will be denoted by T. The corresponding group in $^*R$ by $^*T = {}^*R/2\pi{}^*Z$. There is an obvious identification between the (internal) functions on $T(^*T)$ and 2π periodic (internal) functions on $R(^*R)$. This as far as notation is concerned. Next we need to recall a few facts from the theory of harmonic analysis on groups.

Let G be a commutative group written additively the unit element of which is denoted by 0. We recall that a character γ of G is a mapping of G into the multiplicative group of complex numbers of absolute value one such that $|(x, \gamma)| = |\gamma(x)| = 1$, $(x + y, \gamma) = (x, \gamma)(y, \gamma)$ and $(0, \gamma) = 1$ for all $x, y \in G$. The dual group Γ of G is the commutative group of the characters of G in the case that G is discrete and the group of all continuous characters in the case that G is a topological group. As is well-known the character group of the compact group T is isomorphic to the discrete group Z and the character group of the discrete group Z is isomorphic to the compact group T. The internal groups $^*T$ and $^*Z$ are related in the same way relative to the concept of an internal character.

If the commutative group G is of finite order say n, then there exist exactly n different characters on G and the dual group Γ is now isomorphic to G. In particular, if m is a natural number and $G = Z(m)$ denotes the additive group of integers mod. m, then G has m distinct characters $\{\gamma_0, \ldots, \gamma_{m-1}\}$ given by the formulas

$$(l, \gamma_k) = \gamma_k(l) = \exp\left(\frac{2\pi i}{m} kl\right),$$

where $l \in G$, $k = 0, 1, 2, \ldots, m - 1$ and "exp" denotes the exponential function, and so the character group of G can be represented by the additive group $T(2\pi m) = \{0, 2\pi/m, \ldots, 2\pi(m - 1)/m\}$, mod. 2π. It is clear that the Fourier analysis of $T(2\pi m)$ will render in a sense a discretization of the Fourier analysis of T. However, the discrete group $T(2\pi m)$ is only a poor approximation of T. Using a nonstandard model of R we can push this idea beyond the finite approximation into a more sophisticated form as follows. Let $\omega \in {}^*N\backslash N$ be an infinitely large natural number and let $^*Z(\omega)$ denote the additive group of integers mod. ω. Then $^*Z(\omega)$ is a star-finite group of the model of order ω. Hence, its internal character group can be represented by the additive group $^*T(2\pi\omega) = \{0, 2\pi/\omega, \ldots, 2\pi(\omega - 1)/\omega\}$, mod. 2π, and $^*T(2\pi\omega)$ and $^*Z(\omega)$ are internally isomorphic. Furthermore, if $\gamma \in {}^*T(2\pi\omega)$, then there is an element $k \in {}^*Z(\omega)$ such that $(l, \gamma) = \exp(2\pi ikl/\omega)$ for all $l \in {}^*Z(\omega)$. The ω-circle group $^*T(2\pi\omega)$ provides an excellent approximation to T, and it is also star-finite as far as its properties are concerned which can be formulated in the language in which we have formulated the properties of the theory of R. In fact, by taking ω sufficiently large we will get an ω-circle group $^*T(2\pi\omega)$ with the property that its standard part equals T. It is now our purpose to show in the following sections in which sense the trivial theory of Fourier analysis of the star-finite circle group $^*T(2\pi\omega)$ can be used to obtain results about the Fourier analysis of the circle group T and its dual group Z. For this purpose it is of importance that the reader should be thoroughly familiar with the theory of harmonic analysis on finite commutative groups. This theory is of course in essence trivial. But for the sake of completeness and to make the paper more readable we will denote the following section to some aspects of this subject.

2. Harmonic analysis of finite commutative groups. Let G be a finite commutative group of order $n + 1$ $(n \geq 1)$ written *additively*. The elements of G will be denoted by $x_0, x_1, \ldots, x_n$, respectively, whereby $x_0 = 0$ will denote the *unit element* of G. A general element or a variable ranging over the elements of G may also be denoted by $x, y, z, \ldots$.

In the theory of abstract harmonic analysis the *group algebra* of G plays a fundamental role. We will introduce the group algebra of G, denoted by $L(G)$, as the $(n + 1)$-dimensional vector space over the field of complex numbers C of all the complex valued functions on G in which an operation of *multiplication* is defined by means of the *convolution operation*, denoted by $*$, between elements $f, g \in L(G)$ and which can be defined as follows:

$$2.1.\quad (f*g)(x) = \sum_{i=0}^{n} f(x - x_i)\, g(x_i) = \sum_{i=0}^{n} f(x_i)\, g(x - x_i), \quad x \in G.$$

Since G is commutative it follows immediately that with the operation of convolution $L(G)$ is an $(n + 1)$*-dimensional commutative linear algebra over* C.

For each $x_i \in G (i = 0, 1, 2, \ldots, n)$ we shall denote by e_i that element of $L(G)$ which satisfies the relation $e_i(x_j) = \delta_{ij}$ for all $j = 0, 1, 2, \ldots, n$, where δ denotes the Kronecker delta. The system $\{e_0, e_1, \ldots, e_n\}$ of elements of $L(G)$ in fact forms a basis of the vector space $L(G)$, and the element e_0 is the multiplicative unit of $L(G)$. Furthermore, the mapping $x_i \to e_i$ of G into

$L(G)$ is an isomorphic mapping of the group G into the multiplicative structure of $L(G)$. Indeed, it is easy to see that $e_i * e_j = e_k$ if and only if $x_i + x_j = x_k$ holds in G.

The regular representation of $L(G)$ in the algebra of linear transformations of $L(G)$ into $L(G)$ plays an important role in the harmonic analysis of G. It is defined by assigning to each element $f \in L(G)$ the linear transformation T_f on $L(G)$ determined as follows:

2.2. *For each $f \in L(G)$ we set $T_f(g) = f * g = g * f$ for every $g \in L(G)$.*

It is obvious that T_f is a linear transformation of $L(G)$ into $L(G)$ and that the mapping $f \to T_f$ is a representation of the linear algebra $L(G)$ into the algebra of all linear transformations of $L(G)$ into $L(G)$.

$L(G)$ can also be identified with the $(n + 1)$-dimensional complex Hilbert space in which the distance is the Euclidean distance, denoted by $\|f - g\|_2$, and which is determined by the inner product between elements $f, g \in L(G)$ defined as usual by the formulas

2.3. (i) $\langle f, g\rangle = \sum_{i=0}^{n} f(x_i)\,\overline{g(x_i)}$, and

(ii) $\|f\|_2 = (\langle f, f\rangle)^{\frac{1}{2}}$.

The algebra $L(G)$ is also an *involution* algebra under the involution operation $\tilde{f}$, $f \in L(G)$ defined by the formula.

2.4. $\tilde{f}(x) = \overline{f(-x)}$ *for all $x \in G$, where the bar stands for the operation of taking complex conjugates. In particular, for all $i = 0, 1, 2, \ldots, n$, $\tilde{e}_i = e_j$ if and only if $x_i + x_j = 0$.*

From $\langle T_f g, h\rangle = \sum_x (\sum_y f(x - y)g(y))\,\overline{h(x)} = \sum_y g(y)\,\overline{\sum_x \tilde{f}(y - x)h(x)} = \langle g, T_{\tilde{f}} h\rangle$ it follows that the adjoint transformation T_f^* of T_f satisfies $T_f^* = T_{\tilde{f}}$. Since the family $\{T_f : f \in L(G)\}$ of linear transformation is commutative we obtain immediately the following result.

2.5. THEOREM. *The regular representation $f \to T_f$ of $L(G)$ into the algebra of all linear transformations of $L(G)$ into $L(G)$ is a representation of $L(G)$ into a $*$-algebra of normal linear transformation on $L(G)$. In particular, the representation $x_i \to T_{e_i}$ of the group G into the algebra of all linear transformations on $L(G)$ is a unitary representation of G.*

Proof. From $T_{\tilde{f}} = T_f^*$ and $T_f T_{\tilde{f}} = T_{\tilde{f}} T_f$, $f \in L(G)$ it follows that the linear transformations T_f are normal. By observing that e_0 is the unit element of $L(G)$ we conclude that $T_{e_0} = I$ is the identity transformation and that $T_{\bar{e}_i} = (T_{e_i})^{-1}$. Hence, the linear transformation T_{e_i} are unitary transformations, that is, which leave the metric invariant. This completes the proof.

The characters of G can now be introduced in the following manner.

2.6. THEOREM. *There exist exactly $n + 1$ different characters of G which form a complete set of $n + 1$ orthogonal eigenvectors of the commutative family of normal linear transformations $\{T_f : f \in G\}$.*

Proof. Since the family $\{T_f\}$ of normal linear transformations is commutative it follows from a well-known theorem of matrix theory that there exists an orthogonal basis $\{u_0, u_1, \ldots, u_n\}$ in $L(G)$ which form a complete set of common eigenvectors of the family $\{T_f\}$. For each $x_i \in G$ we have by definition that $(T_{e_i} u_j)(x) = u_j(x - x_i)$ for all $x \in G$. Since u_j is an eigenvector of T_{e_i} it follows that there exists a complex number λ_i such that $u_j(x - x_i) = \lambda_i u_j(x)$ for all $x, x_i \in G$. Now $u_j(0) = 0$ would imply that $u_j(x) = 0$ for all $x \in G$ which contradicts the fact that u_j is an eigenvector. Hence, $u_j(0) \neq 0$ for all $j = 0, 1, 2, \ldots, n$, and so the eigenvalue λ_i satisfies $\lambda_i = u_j(-x_i)/u_j(0)$ for all $j = 0, 1, 2, \ldots, n$. Furthermore, $u_j(x - x_i) = u_j(x)\, u_j(-x_i)/u_j(0)$ holds for all $j = 0, 1, 2, \ldots, n$ and $x, x_i \in G$. From this we conclude that if we set $(x, \gamma_j) = u_j(x)/u_j(0)$ for each j and $x \in G$, then γ_j is a non-zero element of $L(G)$ satisfying the relation $(0, \gamma_j) = 1$, $(x + y, \gamma_j) = (x, \gamma_j)(y, \gamma_j)$ for all $x, y \in G$, and so $|(x, \gamma_j)| = 1$ and $(-x, \gamma_j) = \overline{(x, \gamma_j)}$ for all $x \in G$. Hence, γ_j is a character of G, and so G has at least $n + 1$ different characters γ_j $(j = 0, 1, 2, \ldots, n)$ which form an orthogonal basis of $L(G)$.

In order to complete the proof we shall show that if γ is a character of G such that $\gamma \neq \gamma_i$, then γ is orthogonal to γ_i. If $\gamma \neq \gamma_i$, then there exists an element $y \in G$ such that $(y, \gamma) \neq (y, \gamma_i)$, or equivalently, $\overline{(y, \gamma_i)}(y, \gamma) \neq 1$. From $\langle \gamma_i, \gamma \rangle = \sum_x (x, \gamma_i)\overline{(x, \gamma)} = \sum_x (x - y, \gamma_i)\overline{(x - y, \gamma)} = \sum_x (x, \gamma_i) \cdot \overline{(y, \gamma_i)}\,\overline{(x, \gamma)}(y, \gamma) = \overline{(y, \gamma_i)}(y, \gamma)\langle \gamma, \gamma_i \rangle$ and $\overline{(y, \gamma_i)}(y, \gamma) \neq 1$ it follows that γ is orthogonal to γ_i and the proof is finished.

From the orthogonality of the eigenvectors we obtain immediately the well-known *orthogonality relations* for the characters of G.

2.7. *(Orthogonality Relations.) For all $i, j = 0, 1, 2, \ldots, n$ we have*

$$\langle \gamma_i, \gamma_j \rangle = (n + 1)\delta_{ij},$$

that is, the matrix $U = ((x_i, \gamma_j)/\sqrt{n+1})$, $i, j = 0, 1, 2, \ldots, n+1$ *is a unitary matrix, and so we have also the orthogonality relations*

$$\sum_{k=0}^{n} (x_i, \gamma_k)\overline{(x_j, \gamma_k)} = (n+1)\,\delta_{ij}$$

for all $i, j = 0, 1, 2, \ldots, n$.

The set of all characters of G will be denoted by Γ and it can be made into a group by defining $\gamma_1 + \gamma_2$ between elements of Γ to be the character satisfying $(x, \gamma_1 + \gamma_2) = (x, \gamma_1)(x, \gamma_2)$. That this operation of addition is a group operation can be readily verified. The characters of the group Γ can be identified with the original group G. Indeed, for a fixed $x \in G$ and variable $\gamma \in \Gamma$, (x, γ) is a character on Γ, and so the elements of G determine a complete set of $n + 1$ characters of Γ. Thus we have obtained the following result.

2.8. THEOREM. *The set of characters of the commutative group G of order* $n + 1$ *under the operation of pointwise multiplication, written additively, forms a group* Γ *of order* $n + 1$, *the character group of G. The character group of* Γ *is isomorphic to G under the natural isomorphism* $x \to (x, \gamma)(\gamma \in \Gamma)$ *of G onto the character group of* Γ.

It is of some interest to observe that the orthogonality relations

$$\sum_{k=0}^{n} (x_i, \gamma_k)\overline{(x_j, \gamma_k)} = \sqrt{n+1}\,\delta_{ij} \quad (i, j = 0, 1, 2, \ldots, n)$$

are also an immediate consequence of the first part of 2.7 and the fact that G is isomorphic to the character group of Γ under the isomorphism $x \to (x, \gamma)$ $(\gamma \in \Gamma)$ of G onto the character group of Γ.

The result contained in 2.7 can be improved. In fact, we have the following theorem.

2.9. THEOREM. *The character group* Γ *of a finite commutative group G is isomorphic to G.*

Proof. The proof of this result depends on the so-called main theorem for finite commutative groups which states that every finite commutative group is a direct product of cyclic groups of prime order > 1. Hence, there exists a basis $\{a_1, \ldots, a_r\}$ in G of elements of prime order $p_1, \ldots, p_r$, respectively such that every $x \in G$ can be written uniquely in the form

$$x = \sum_{i=1}^{r} n_i a_i,$$

where the n_i are natural numbers satisfying $1 \leq n_i \leq p_i$ $(i = 1, 2, ..., r)$. It is obvious that the primes $p_1, ..., p_r$ need not be different and that $p_1 p_2 \cdots p_r$ is the order of G. If γ is a character of G, then $(x, \gamma) = (a_1, \gamma)^{n_1}, ..., (a_r, \gamma)^{n_r}$, and so γ is entirely determined by the values it takes on the basis elements $a_1, ..., a_r$. For each $l = 1, 2, ..., r$, $p_i a_l - 0$ implies that $(a_i, \gamma)^{p_i} = 1$, and so, $(a_i, \gamma) = \exp(2\pi i q_i/p_i)$ with $1 \leq q_i \leq p_i$. The character γ will now be denoted by $\gamma = \gamma(q_1, ..., q_r)$. It is clear that the r-tuple $(q_1, ..., q_r)$ determines γ uniquely. Furthermore, the total number of characters equals $p_1 \cdots p_r$ which is equal to the order of the group and is a result contained in 2.6. The isomorphism between G and Γ can now be defined as follows. To each $x \in G$, $x = n_1 a_1 + ... + n_r a_r$, $1 \leq n_i \leq p_i$, $i = 1, 2, ..., r$, we assign the character $\gamma = \gamma(n_1, ..., n_r)$. The easy verification that this mapping is a group isomorphism is now left to the reader.

For each $x \in G$ and for each $f \in L(G)$ we define the *translate* of f by

2.10. $f_x(y) = f(y - x), \quad y \in G.$

Now it is easy to see that for each $x_i \in G$ we have $f_{x_i} = e_i * f$, and so, we obtain immediately that a linear subspace I of $L(G)$ is *translation invariant* if and only if I is an *ideal* in $L(G)$. Observe that if γ is a character of G, then for each $x \in G$, $\gamma_x = \overline{(x, \gamma)}\gamma$, and so, the one-dimensional linear subspace spanned by a character is translation invariant, and, in fact is a one-dimensional ideal. Conversely, every one-dimensional ideal of $L(G)$ is spanned by a character. Since, by 2.6, the characters are eigenvectors of the transformations T_f it follows that the unitary representation $x_i \to T_{e_i}$ of G is the direct sum of $(n + 1)$ *irreducible unitary transformations* given by the restrictions of the unitary transformations T_{e_i} to the one-dimensional invariant ideals spanned by the characters. As is well-known the traces of these irreducible unitary representations form a complete set of characters of G.

We shall now discuss the Fourier analysis of the group G. We begin with the following definition.

2.11. DEFINITION *(Fourier Coefficients). For each $f \in L(G)$ the complex numbers $\hat{f}(\gamma) = (1/n)\langle f, \gamma \rangle = (1/n)\sum_x f(x)\overline{(x, \gamma)}$, $\gamma \in \Gamma$ will be called the Fourier coefficients of f.*

2.12. *It follows immediately that if $f, g \in L(G)$, then*

(i) $\widehat{f+g} = \hat{f} + \hat{g}$;

(ii) *for any complex number α,* $\widehat{\alpha f} = \alpha\hat{f}$;

(iii) $\hat{\tilde{f}} = \bar{\hat{f}}$. *In particular, if* $f = \tilde{f}$, *that is, if* f *is Hermitian, then* $\hat{f}$ *is real;*
(iv) $\hat{f}_y = \overline{(y, \gamma)}\hat{f}$;
(v) $\widehat{f * g} = (n + 1)\hat{f} \cdot \hat{g}$;
(vi) $\max_\gamma |\hat{f}(\gamma)| \leq (1/(n + 1)) \sum_x |f(x)|$.

A simple computation shows that the following *inversion formula* holds.

2.13. THEOREM *(Inversion Formula). For each* $f \in L(G)$ *and for each* $x \in G$ *we have*

$$f(x) = \sum_{j=0}^{n} \hat{f}(\gamma_j)(x, \gamma_j) = \frac{1}{n+1} \sum_{i=0}^{n} \sum_{j=0}^{n} f(x_i)(x - x_i, \gamma_j).$$

Proof.
$$(n + 1) \sum_{j=0}^{n} \hat{f}(\gamma_j)(x, \gamma_j) = \left(\sum_{j=0}^{n} \sum_{i=0}^{n} f(x_i)(-x_i, \gamma_j) \right) (x, \gamma_j)$$
$$= \sum_{i=0}^{n} f(x_i) \sum_{j=0}^{n} (x, \gamma_j)\overline{(x_i, \gamma_j)} = f(x)$$

for all $x \in G$, and the proof is finished.

Incidentally, observe that the inversion formula implies that if $\hat{f}$ is real, then f is Hermitian, that is $f = \tilde{f}$.

Since the Fourier coefficients are $1/(n + 1)$-times the projections of f in the direction of the elements of the orthogonal basis $\gamma_0, \ldots, \gamma_n$, we obtain immediately from the $(n + 1)$-dimensional form of the theorem of Pythagoras the well-known Parseval's formulas.

2.14. THEOREM *(Parseval's Formula). Let* $f, g \in L(G)$. *Then* $(1/(n + 1)) \cdot \langle \hat{f}, \hat{g} \rangle = \langle f, g \rangle$. *In particular,* $(1/\sqrt{n+1}) \|f\|_2 = \|\hat{f}\|_2$.

As usual for each $f \in L(G)$ the norm $(\sum_x |f(x)|^p)^{1/p}$ will be called the Minkowski *p-norm* $(1 \leq p < \infty)$ of f and it will be denoted by $\|f\|_p$.

The Hausdorff–Young inequalities follow immediately from the following more general result about unitary transformations which is due to Riesz [1923] (see also Katznelson [1968] Chap. IV).

2.15. THEOREM *(F. Riesz). If* $U = (u_{ij})$ $(i, j = 0, 1, 2, \ldots, n)$ *is an* $(n + 1)$

$\times (n+1)$ *unitary matrix and if* $M = \max(|u_{ij}| : i, j = 0, 1, 2, \ldots, n)$, *then for* $1 < p \leq 2$, $1/p + 1/q = 1$, *we have for each* $f \in L(G)$

$$\|Uf\|_q \leq M^{(2-p)/p} \|f\|_p, \quad \textit{and}$$

$$\|f\|_q \leq M^{(2-p)/p} \|U^*f\|_p.$$

If we apply the above result of Riesz to the unitary matrix $U = ((x_i, \gamma_j)/\sqrt{n+1})$ $(i, j = 0, 1, 2, \ldots, n)$, and observing that, in this case $M = 1/\sqrt{n+1}$, $Uf = \sqrt{n+1}\,\hat{f}$ (inversion formula) and $U^*f = (1/\sqrt{n+1})f$ (definition of the Fourier coefficients) we obtain the following discrete analogue of the Hausdorff–Young Theorem.

2.16. Theorem *(Hausdorff–Young Inequalities). If* $1 \leq p \leq 2$ *and* $1/p + 1/q = 1$, *then for each* $f \in L(G)$ *we have*

$$\|\hat{f}\|_q \leq (1/(n+1))^{1/p} \|f\|_p, \quad \textit{and}$$

$$(1/(n+1))^{1/q} \|f\|_q \leq \|\hat{f}\|_p.$$

All of the theory of harmonic analysis of finite commutative groups as described in this section hold under an appropriate interpretation for the star-finite commutative groups. In the next section we shall introduce the special star-finite circle group $^*T(2\pi\omega)$. In the last two sections we will then show in what sense the properties of $^*T(2\pi\omega)$ can be reduced to properties of the circle group $^*T$.

3. The star-finite groups $^*Z(\omega)$ **and** $^*T(2\pi\omega)$. We refer to section 1 for the definition of the star-finite groups $^*Z(\omega)$ and $^*T(2\pi\omega)$. For the sake of convenience we will assume that ω is odd, that is, $\omega = 2\omega_0 + 1$, where ω_0 is a fixed infinitely large natural number. The star-finite group $^*T(2\pi\omega)$ has ω-elements which can be represented by the points $x_n = 2\pi n/\omega$, $n = 0, \pm 1, \pm 2, \ldots, \pm \omega_0$ in the interval $[-\pi, +\pi]$; and its arithmetic is addition mod. 2π. From the results of the preceding section it follows that $^*T(2\pi\omega)$ has exactly ω-characters $\{\gamma_k : k = 0, \pm 1, \pm 2, \ldots, \pm \omega_0\}$ which are given by the formulas

3.1. $$(n, \gamma_k) = \exp\left(\frac{2\pi i}{\omega} nk\right), \quad k, n = 0, \pm 1, \ldots, \pm \omega_0.$$

The character group of $^*T(2\pi\omega)$ will be denoted by $^*Z(\omega)$ and its elements can be represented by the set of integers $\{\gamma_k = k : k = 0, \pm 1, \pm 2, \ldots, \pm \omega_0\}$ and its arithmetic is addition mod. ω.

We recall that by taking ω sufficiently large, namely that every finite natural number is a divisor of ω, we obtain that $^*T(2\pi\omega)$ approximates the standard circle group very closely in the sense that *the set of standard parts of the elements of* $^*T(2\pi\omega)$ *is* T, *that is*, $\mathrm{st}(^*T(2\pi\omega)) = T$.

The group algebra of $^*T(2\pi\omega)$ will be denoted by $^*L(\omega)$ and it is the set of all *internal* mappings of $^*T(2\pi\omega)$ in the field $^*C$ of nonstandard complex numbers with the pointwise operation of addition and the operation of convolution as multiplication.

The standard linear space C^z of all doubly infinite sequences $\xi = \{\xi(n): n \in Z\}$ of complex numbers can be imbedded in a one-to-one way into $^*L(\omega)$ by assigning to ξ the sequence $^*\xi_\omega = \{^*\xi(n) : n = 0, \pm 1, \ldots, \pm \omega_0\}$, where $^*\xi$ denotes as usual the nonstandard extension of ξ. The reader does well to observe that the embedding $\xi \to {}^*\xi_\omega$ of C^z into $^*L(\omega)$ is *external*. If $\xi \in l^p(Z)(1 \leq p \leq \infty)$, that is,

$$\|\xi\|_p = \left(\sum_{n=-\infty}^{+\infty} |\xi(n)|^p \right)^{1/p} < \infty$$

if $1 \leq p < \infty$ and $\|\xi\|_\infty = \max(|\xi(n)| : n \in Z) < \infty$, then $\|^*\xi - {}^*\xi_\omega\|_p =_1 0$ (we remind the reader that $a =_1 b$ *for two numbers* a, b *means that* $a - b$ *is infinitely small*) if $1 \leq p < \infty$, and so, in particular, $\|^*\xi\|_p < \infty$ implies that $\|^*\xi_\omega\|_p$ is finite.

We recall that an element $f \in {}^*L(\omega)$ is called *p-near-standard* $(1 \leq p \leq \infty)$ whenever there exists an element $\xi \in l^p(Z)$ such that $\|f - {}^*\xi_\omega\|_p =_1 0$.

We need the following simple lemma which is a slight extension of Theorem 7.22 of Robinson [1966].

3.2. Lemma. *An element* $f \in {}^*L(\omega)$ *is p-near-standard* $(1 \leq p < \infty)$ *if and only if* $\|f\|_p$ *is finite and*

$$\sum_{n \leqslant |k| \leqslant \omega_0} |f(k)|^p =_1 0$$

for all infinitely large $n \in {}^*N \backslash N$.

Proof. We have only to show that the conditions are sufficient. From the hypothesis that $\|f\|_p$ is finite it follows that $f(n)$ is finite for all $n \in {}^*Z$. Let $\xi(n) = \mathrm{st}(f(n))$ if $n \in Z$ is a finite integer. We shall then show that f is p-near-standard to ξ. First observe that for all $n \in N$ we have that $\sum_{|k| \leqslant n} |^*\xi(k) - f(k)|^p =_1 0$. Hence, from the internal definition principle (see Luxemburg

[1972]) it follows immediately that there exists an infinitely large natural number $\nu < \omega_0$ such that

$$\sum_{|k| \leq \nu} |{}^*\xi(k) - f(k)|^p =_1 0.$$

Since $\xi \in l^p(Z)$ implies

$$\sum_{\nu \leq |k| \leq \omega_0} |{}^*\xi(k)|^p =_1 0,$$

it follows finally that

$$\|{}^*\xi_\omega - f\|_p \leq \left(\sum_{|k| \leq \nu} |{}^*\xi_\omega(k) - f(k)|^p\right)^{1/p} + \left(\sum_{\nu \leq |k| \leq \omega} |{}^*\xi_\omega(k)|^p\right)^{1/p} + $$
$$+ \left(\sum_{\nu \leq |k| \leq \omega_0} |f(k)|^p\right)^{1/p} =_1 0,$$

and the proof is finished.

3.3. Corollary. *Let* $1 \leq p < \infty$ *and let* $f \in {}^*L(\omega)$. *Then* f *is* p*-near-standard implies that* f *is* p'*-near-standard for all* $p \leq p' < \infty$.

Proof. From Jensen's inequality we deduce immediately that the little l^p-norm $(1 \leq p < \infty)$ is a decreasing function in p. Hence, if f is p-near-standard and $p \leq p' < \infty$, then $\|f\|_{p'} \leq \|f\|_p$ and

$$\left[\sum_{n \leq |k| \leq \omega_0} |f(k)|^{p'}\right]^{1/p'} \leq \left[\sum_{n \leq |k| \leq \omega_0} |f(k)|^{p}\right]^{1/p},$$

and so, by Lemma 3.2, f is also a p'-near-standard element, which finishes the proof.

We shall now leave it to the reader to see how the formulas of section 2 for finite commutative groups can be translated into the corresponding formulas for star-finite groups. In the next section we shall use them freely for ${}^*T(2\pi\omega)$.

4. The Fourier coefficients of continuous functions. Let $f \in C(T)$ be a continuous, in general, complex valued function defined on the circle group T. The purpose of the present section is to indicate the properties of the sequence of Fourier coefficients of the restriction of ${}^*f \in {}^*(C(T))$ to the ω-circle group ${}^*T(2\pi\omega)$ and its relation to the sequence of Fourier coefficients of f itself.

As usual the Fourier coefficient $\hat{f}(n)(n \in Z)$ of f are given by the formulas

4.1. $\hat{f}(n) = \frac{1}{2\pi} \int_{-\pi}^{+\pi} f(x) e^{-inx} \, dx, \quad n \in Z,$

and its Fourier series by the formal expression

4.2. $f(x) \sim \sum_{n=-\infty}^{+\infty} \hat{f}(n) e^{inx}, \quad x \in T.$

The nonstandard extension $*f$ of f on $*T$ has the sequence of Fourier coefficients $\{*\hat{f}(n) : n \in *Z\}$ which is the nonstandard extension of the sequence $\{\hat{f}(n) : n \in Z\}$. In symbols

4.3. $*\{\hat{f}(n) : n \in Z\} = \{*\hat{f}(n) : n \in *Z\}.$

Furthermore, every internal continuous function $F \in *(C(T))$ on $*T$ has a sequence of Fourier coefficients $\hat{F}(n)$, $n \in *Z$, which can be given by the formulas

4.4. $\hat{F}(n) = \frac{1}{2\pi} \int_{-\pi}^{+\pi} F(x) e^{-inx} \, dx, \quad n \in *Z,$

and its Fourier series by the formal expressions

4.5. $F(x) \sim \sum (\hat{F}(n) \, e^{inx} : n \in *Z), \quad x \in *T.$

For each $f \in C(T)$ we shall denote by f_ω the restriction of $*f$ defined on $*T$ to the ω-circle group $*T(2\pi\omega)$. The Fourier coefficients $\hat{f}_\omega(n)$, $n \in *Z$, of f_ω are given by the formulas

4.6. $$\hat{f}_\omega(n) = \frac{1}{\omega} \sum_{|k| \leqslant \omega_0} *f(x_k)(-x_k, \gamma_n)$$

$$= \frac{1}{\omega} \sum_{|k| \leqslant \omega_0} *f\left(\frac{2\pi}{\omega} k\right) \exp\left(-\frac{2\pi i}{\omega} kn\right) = \frac{1}{\omega} \langle f, \gamma_n \rangle, \quad n \in *Z.$$

It is obvious that the internal sequence $\{\hat{f}_\omega(n) : n \in *Z\}$ is ω-periodic.

From the inversion formula 2.13 for finite groups we obtain immediately that

4.7. $$*f\left(\frac{2\pi k}{\omega}\right) = \sum_{|n| \leqslant \omega_0} \hat{f}_\omega(n) \exp\left(\frac{2\pi i k}{\omega} n\right) \quad \text{for all } |k| \leq \omega_0.$$

Since $\mathrm{st}(*T(2\pi\omega)) = T$ it follows that for every $x \in T$ there exists at least one $k = k_x$ satisfying $|k_x| \leq \omega_0$ and $\mathrm{st}(2\pi k_x/\omega) = x$. Hence, we obtain the formula

4.8. *For all* $x \in T$,

$$f(x) = \mathrm{st}\left(\sum_{|n| \leqslant \omega_0} \hat{f}_\omega(n) \exp\left(\frac{2\pi i k_x}{\omega} n\right)\right).$$

From Parseval's formula 2.14 we deduce the following formulas.

For $f, g \in C(T)$

4.9. $$\frac{1}{\omega} \sum_{|k| \leqslant \omega_0} \left|{}^*f\left(\frac{2\pi}{\omega} k\right)\right|^2 = \sum_{|n| \leqslant \omega_0} |\hat{f}_\omega(n)|^2, \quad \text{and}$$

$$\frac{1}{\omega} \sum_{|k| \leqslant \omega_0} {}^*f\left(\frac{2\pi}{\omega} k\right) \overline{{}^*g\left(\frac{2\pi}{\omega} k\right)} = \sum_{|n| \leqslant \omega_0} \hat{f}_\omega(n)\overline{\hat{g}_\omega(n)}.$$

The Hausdorff–Young inequalities 2.16 take on the following form for ${}^*T(2\pi\omega)$ and $f \in C(T)$.

(Hausdorff–Young Inequalities.) Let $1 \leq p \leq 2$ *and* $1/p + 1/q = 1$

4.10. $$\left(\sum_{|n| \leqslant \omega} |\hat{f}_\omega(n)|^q\right)^{1/q} \leq \left(\frac{1}{\omega} \sum_{|k| \leqslant \omega_0} \left|{}^*f\left(\frac{2\pi k}{\omega}\right)\right|^p\right)^{1/p},$$

4.11. $$\left(\frac{1}{\omega} \sum_{|k| \leqslant \omega_0} \left|{}^*f\left(\frac{2\pi}{\omega} k\right)\right|^q\right)^{1/q} \leq \left(\sum_{|n| \leqslant \omega_0} |\hat{f}_\omega(n)|^p\right)^{1/p}.$$

In order to use the above formulas successfully to obtain some useful results about the Fourier coefficients and the Fourier series of $f \in C(T)$ we have to study first the relationship between the sequence $\{\hat{f}(n) : n \in Z\}$ of Fourier coefficients of f and the ω-periodic sequence $\{\hat{f}_\omega(n) : n \in {}^*Z\}$ of Fourier coefficients of f_ω.

Before we begin with our first result in that direction we need to warn the reader that, since ω denotes an infinitely large natural number, the modulus of continuity of a function f in this paper will be denoted by m_f rather than by the usual notation ω_f.

From 4.6 written in the form

$$\hat{f}_\omega(n) = \frac{1}{2\pi}\left(\frac{2\pi}{\omega} \sum_{|k| \leqslant \omega_0} {}^*f\left(\frac{2\pi k}{\omega}\right) \exp\left(-\frac{2\pi i k}{\omega} n\right)\right),$$

and by observing that the expression on the right-hand side between the brackets for every finite $n \in Z$ is a Riemann sum of the continuous function $f(x)\exp(-inx)$, $x \in T$, we obtain immediately the following result.

4.12. THEOREM. *If* $f \in C(T)$, *then* $\hat{f}(n) =_1 \hat{f}_\omega(n)$ *for all finite* $n \in Z$. *More precisely, for all* $|n| \leq \omega_0$ *we have*

$$|\widehat{{}^*f}(n) - \hat{f}_\omega(n)| \leq m_{*f}\left(\frac{2\pi}{\omega}\right) + 2\max(|{}^*f(x)| : x \in {}^*T)\sin\left(\frac{n\pi}{\omega}\right).$$

In particular, $\widehat{{}^*f}(n) =_1 \hat{f}_\omega(n)$ *for all* $|n| \leq \omega_0$ *satisfying* $\sin(n\pi/\omega) =_1 0$.

Proof. We only need to indicate how to prove the inequality contained in the theorem. But that inequality is an easy consequence of the fact that $m_{gh}(\delta) \leq (\max|g|)m_h(\delta) + (\max|h|)m_g(\delta)$ when applied to $f(x)\exp(-inx)$, $x \in T$, with $\delta = 2\pi/\omega$. The details are left to the reader.

In order to study the relationship between $\hat{f}$ and $\hat{f}_\omega$ more closely we shall introduce an auxiliary internal function F_ω by means of the following definition.

4.13. *For each* $f \in C(T)$ *we shall denote by* F_ω *the internal step function on* $^*T$ *satisfying*

$$F_\omega(t) = {}^*f\left(\frac{2\pi}{\omega}k\right) \text{ whenever } -\frac{\pi}{\omega} < t - \frac{2\pi}{\omega}k \leq \frac{\pi}{\omega},$$

where $k = 0, \pm 1, \ldots, \pm\omega_0$.

From the internal definition principle it follows immediately that F_ω is indeed an internal function. The function F_ω is a step function as well and at its points of discontinuity its jump is infinitesimal (f is continuous), and, in fact, these jumps are in absolute value less than $m_{*f}(2\pi/\omega)$. More precisely, we have

4.14. *For all* $t \in {}^*T$ *we have*

$$|F_\omega(t) - {}^*f(t)| \leq m_{*f}\left(\frac{\pi}{\omega}\right) =_1 0.$$

For the sequence $\hat{F}_\omega$ of the Fourier coefficients of F_ω we have the following result

4.15. LEMMA. *For each* $f \in C(T)$ *and for each* $n \in {}^*Z$ *we have*

$$\hat{F}_\omega(n) = \frac{1}{2\pi}\int_{-\pi}^{+\pi} F_\omega(t)e^{-int}\,dt = \left(\sin\left(\frac{n\pi}{\omega}\right)\Big/\left(\frac{n\pi}{\omega}\right)\right)\hat{f}_\omega(n).$$

Proof. From $\hat{F}_\omega(n) = \frac{1}{2\pi}\sum_{|k|\leq\omega_0} {}^*f\left(\frac{2\pi}{\omega}k\right)\int_{(2\pi k-\pi)/\omega}^{(2\pi k+\pi)/\omega} e^{-int}\,dt$

it follows that

$$\widehat{F_\omega}(n) = \frac{1}{n\pi}\sum_{|k|\leq\omega_0} {}^*f\left(\frac{2\pi}{\omega}k\right)\exp\left(-\frac{2\pi}{\omega}ikn\right)\sin\left(\frac{n\pi}{\omega}\right).$$

Hence, the required result follows.

Observe now that if $t_1, t_2 \in {}^*T$ and $|t_1 - t_2| < \delta$, then $|F_\omega(t_1) - F_\omega(t_2)| \leq |F_\omega(t_1) - {}^*f(t_1)| + |F_\omega(t_2) - {}^*f(t_2)| + |{}^*f(t_1) - {}^*f(t_2)|$ implies, by 4.14, that

4.16. *for all* $0 < \delta \in {}^*R$, *we have* $m_{F_\omega}(\delta) \leq 2m_{*f}(\pi/\omega) + m_{*f}(\delta)$.

Furthermore,

$$\hat{F}_\omega(n) = \frac{1}{2\pi}\int_{-\pi}^{+\pi} F_\omega(t)e^{-int}\,dt = -\frac{1}{2\pi}\int_{-\pi}^{+\pi} F_\omega\left(t+\frac{\pi}{n}\right)e^{-int}\,dt$$

implies

4.17. *for all* $0 \neq n \in {}^*Z$ *we have* $|\hat{F}_\omega(n)| \leq \frac{1}{2}\, m_{F_\omega}(\pi/|n|)$.

Combining 4.16 and 4.17 we obtain the following special case of the Riemann–Lebesgue Lemma for the ω-circle group ${}^*T(2\pi\omega)$.

4.18. THEOREM *(Riemann–Lebesgue Lemma). For each* $f \in C(T)$ *and for all* $0 \neq |n| \leq \omega_0$, *we have*

$$|\hat{f}_\omega(n)| \leq \tfrac{1}{2}\pi\left(m_{*f}\left(\frac{\pi}{\omega}\right) + \tfrac{1}{2}m_{*f}\left(\frac{\pi}{|n|}\right)\right).$$

In particular, $\hat{f}_\omega(n) =_1 0$ *for all infinitely large* $|n| \leq \omega_0$.

Proof. By 4.14, $\hat{f}_\omega(n) = ((n\pi/\omega)/\sin(n\pi/\omega))\ \hat{F}_\omega(n)$. Hence, using 4.15 and 4.16 we obtain that

$$|\hat{f}_\omega(n)| \leq \left|\left(\frac{n\pi}{\omega}\right)\Big/\sin\left(\frac{n\pi}{\omega}\right)\right|\left(m_{*f}\left(\frac{\pi}{\omega}\right) + \tfrac{1}{2}m_{*f}\left(\frac{\pi}{|n|}\right)\right)$$

for all $0 \neq |n| \leq \omega_0$. Since $|n| \leq \omega_0$ implies that $|n\pi/\omega| \leq \frac{1}{2}\pi$ it follows that $|n\pi/\omega|/|\sin(n\pi/\omega)| \leq \frac{1}{2}\pi$. Finally observe that f is continuous on T implies that $m_{*f}(\pi/|n|) =_1 0$ for all infinitely large n, and so the required result follows.

Remark. It may not be without interest to point out that Theorem 4.18 expressing that $f_\omega(n) =_1 0$ for all infinitely large $|n| \leq \omega_0$ for the Fourier coefficients of $f_\omega \in L(\omega)$ is by no means trivial. The result may of course fail for an arbitrary element of ${}^*L(\omega)$.

The following result about $\{\hat{f}_\omega\}$ is also worth observing, and is needed below.

4.19. THEOREM. *For each $f \in C(T)$ and each l, $1 \leq l \in N$, we have*

$$4 \sum_{|n| \leqslant \omega_0} |\hat{f}_\omega(n)|^2 \sin^2\left(\frac{\pi l n}{\omega}\right) =$$

$$\frac{1}{\omega} \sum_{|k| \leqslant \omega_0} \left|{}^*f\left(\frac{2\pi}{\omega}(k + l)\right) - {}^*f\left(\frac{2\pi}{\omega}k\right)\right|^2.$$

In particular, for $l = 1$ we obtain

$$\sum_{|k| \leqslant \omega_0} \left|{}^*f\left(\frac{2\pi}{\omega}(k + 1)\right) - {}^*f\left(\frac{2\pi}{\omega}k\right)\right|^2 = 4\pi^2\left(\frac{1}{\omega} \sum_{|n| \leqslant \omega_0} n^2|F_\omega(n)|^2\right).$$

Proof. Observe that if $1 \leq l \in N$, then

$$\hat{f}_\omega(n) = \frac{1}{\omega}\langle f_\omega, \gamma_n\rangle = \frac{1}{\omega} \sum_{|k| \leqslant \omega_0} {}^*f\left(\frac{2\pi}{\omega}(k + l)\right) \exp\left(-\frac{2\pi i(k + l)n}{\omega}\right),$$

and so,

$$\hat{f}_\omega(n)\left(\exp\left(\frac{2\pi i}{\omega}ln\right) - 1\right) =$$

$$\frac{1}{\omega} \sum_{|k| \leqslant \omega_0}\left({}^*f\left(\frac{2\pi}{\omega}(k + l)\right) - {}^*f\left(\frac{2\pi}{\omega}k\right)\right) \exp\left(-\frac{2\pi i}{\omega}kn\right).$$

The first part of the theorem then follows by applying Parseval's formula 2.14 for finite commutative groups. The second part follows by applying 4.15 to the first formula for the case $l = 1$. This completes the proof of the theorem.

Concerning the sequence $\{\hat{f}_\omega\}$ we have shown so far that if n is finite, then $\hat{f}_\omega(n) =_1 \hat{f}(n)$ and $\hat{f}_\omega(n)$ is infinitely small for all infinitely large n, satisfying $|n| \leq \omega_0$. This suggests that the sequence $\{\hat{f}_\omega\}$ may be a near-standard sequence. The affirmative answer is contained in the following theorem, which may be looked at as being the principle result of this section.

4.20. THEOREM. *For each $f \in C(T)$ the sequence $\{\hat{f}_\omega(n):|n| \leq \omega_0\}$ of the Fourier coefficients of f is p-near-standard for all $p \geq 2$, and its near-standard part in the Euclidean space $^*L(\omega)$ is the sequence $\{\hat{f}(n):n \in Z\}$ of the Fourier coefficients of f.*

Proof. According to Corollary 3.3 we have only to show that the sequence $\{\hat{f}_\omega\}$ is a 2-near-standard sequence of $^*L(\omega)$. First we observe that if $g \in C(T)$ satisfies a Lipschitz condition, that is, $|g(x) - g(y)| \leq M|x - y|$ for all $x, y \in T$, then, by 4.17, we have that $|\hat{g}_\omega(n)| \leq M\pi/2|n|$ for all $0 \neq |n| \leq \omega_0$. Hence, by 3.2, $\{\hat{g}_\omega\}$ is 2-near-standard. For each $f \in C(T)$ and for each $0 < \varepsilon \in R$ there exists a function $g \in C(T)$ satisfying a Lipschitz condition such that $|f(x) - g(x)| < \varepsilon$ for all $x \in T$. Using Parseval's formula 2.15 for finite groups we obtain if $v < \omega_0$ and infinitely large

4.21.

$$\begin{aligned}
\Big(\sum_{v\leq|n|\leq\omega_0} |\hat{f}_\omega(n)|^2\Big)^{\frac{1}{2}} &\leq \Big(\sum_{v\leq|n|\leq\omega_0} |\hat{g}_\omega(n)|^2\Big)^{\frac{1}{2}} + \Big(\sum_{v\leq|n|\leq\omega_0} |\hat{f}_\omega(n) - \hat{g}_\omega(n)|^2\Big)^{\frac{1}{2}} \\
&\leq \Big(\sum_{v\leq|n|\leq\omega_0} |\hat{g}_\omega(n)|^2\Big)^{\frac{1}{2}} + \Big(\sum_{|n|\leq\omega_0} |\hat{f}_\omega(n) - \hat{g}_\omega(n)|^2\Big)^{\frac{1}{2}} \\
&= \Big(\sum_{v\leq|n|\leq\omega_0} |\hat{g}_\omega(n)|^2\Big)^{\frac{1}{2}} + \left(\frac{1}{\omega}\sum_{|k|\leq\omega} \left|{}^*f\left(\frac{2\pi}{\omega}k\right) - {}^*g\left(\frac{2\pi}{\omega}k\right)\right|^2\right)^{\frac{1}{2}} \\
&\leq \Big(\sum_{v\leq|n|\leq\omega_0} |g_\omega(n)|^2\Big)^{\frac{1}{2}} + \varepsilon \leq 2\varepsilon.
\end{aligned}$$

The last inequality follows from the fact that since $\{\hat{g}_\omega\}$ is 2-near-standard $(\sum_{v\leq|n|\leq\omega_0}|\hat{g}_\omega(n)|^2)^{\frac{1}{2}}$ is infinitesimal. Since $0 < \varepsilon \in R$ is arbitrary it follows from 4.21 that $(\sum_{v\leq|n|\leq\omega_0}|f_\omega(n)|^2)^{\frac{1}{2}}$ is infinitesimal, and so the sequence

$\{\hat{f}_\omega\}$ is p-near-standard for all $p \geq 2$. The fact that its standard part is $\{\hat{f}\}$ follows from 4.12, and the proof is finished.

Remark. Theorem 4.20 is best possible in the sense that there exists a continuous function $f \in C(T)$ such that $\{\hat{f}_\omega\}$ is not p-near-standard for any $1 \leq p < 2$. Indeed, it is well-known that $f(x) = \sum_{n=2}^{\infty} \exp(in \log n + ixn)/\sqrt{n}(\log n)^{\frac{3}{2}}$, $x \in T$, is an element of $C(T)$ with the property that $\|\hat{f}\|_p = \infty$ for all $1 < p < 2$ (see Katznelson [1968] p. 99), and so for this function f the sequence $\{f_\omega\}$ *can not be p-near-standard for any* $1 \leq p < 2$.

In view of this remark it is natural to ask the following question which lacks an answer.

PROBLEM. For each $1 \leq p < 2$, what are the necessary and sufficient conditions for a function $f \in C(T)$ in order that the sequence $\{\hat{f}_\omega(n) : |n| \leqslant \omega_0\}$ is p-near-standard?

It is obvious that the condition $\|\hat{f}\|_p < \infty$ is necessary. It seems unlikely that this condition is also sufficient.

5. Applications to Fourier series. For a proper understanding of the significance of the way we shall obtain in this section some results of the theory of Fourier series it is important to realize that, except for the results of the theory of harmonic analysis on finite commutative groups and the simple result that every continuous function on a bounded and closed interval can be uniformly approximated by functions satisfying a Lipschitz condition, no results from the theory of Fourier series of T were used to obtain the results of the preceding sections.

Out of the many applications one can make of the results of the preceding section, we have selected as our main applications to prove Parseval's formula and the Hausdorff–Young inequalities. Since the space $L^2(T)$ is complete and $C(T)$ is dense in $L^2(T)$ we may restrict the discussion to continuous functions only.

Usually Parseval's formula is obtained from Bessel's inequality for orthogonal systems and the completeness on T of the trigonometric system. Our approach will be to use Parseval's formula for finite commutative groups in conjunction with the important result that the sequence $\{\hat{f}_\omega\}$ is 2-near-standard. The details are as follows.

5.1. THEOREM *(Parseval's Formula). If* $f, g \in C(T)$, *then*

$$\frac{1}{2\pi}\int_{-\pi}^{+\pi} f(x)\overline{g(x)}\,dx = \sum_{n=-\infty}^{+\infty} \hat{f}(n)\overline{\hat{g}(n)}, \quad and$$

$$\frac{1}{2\pi}\int_{-\pi}^{+\pi} |f(x)|^2\,dx = \sum_{n=-\infty}^{+\infty} |\hat{f}(n)|^2.$$

Proof. From the formulas 4.19 we obtain

$$5.2. \quad \sum_{|n|\leqslant\omega_0} \hat{f}_\omega(n)\overline{\hat{g}_\omega(n)} = \frac{1}{2\pi}\left(\frac{2\pi}{\omega}\sum_{|k|\leqslant\omega_0} {}^*f\left(\frac{2\pi}{\omega}k\right){}^*g\left(\frac{2\pi}{\omega}k\right)\right).$$

From 4.20 it follows immediately, using Schwarz' inequality, that the left-hand side of 5.2 is 1-near-standard to $\sum_{n=-\infty}^{\infty} f(n)g(n)$. Furthermore, the standard part of the right-hand side of 5.2 obviously is equal to $(1/2\pi)\int_{-\pi}^{+\pi} f(x)g(x)dx$, and so, by taking standard parts in 5.2, the required result follows.

As an immediate corollary from the way Parseval's formula is obtained we obtain the following well-known and fundamental result.

5.3. THEOREM. *The trigonometric system* $\{e^{inx}: n \in Z,\ x \in T\}$ *is complete in* $L^1(T)$.

Proof. It is well-known that the completeness in $L^1(T)$ is an immediate consequence of the completeness of the system in $C(T)$. The latter now follows trivially from Parseval's formula.

Remark. If $F \in {}^*(C(T))$ is an internal bounded function defined on ${}^*T$ which is a near-standard element of ${}^*(C(T))$, that is, there exists a *unique* continuous function $f \in C(T)$ such that $\max(|F(t) - {}^*f(t)| : t \in {}^*T) =_1 0$, then the sequence of Fourier coefficients $\{\hat{F}(n): n \in {}^*Z\}$ of F is p-near-standard for all $p \geq 2$ to the sequence $\{\hat{f}\}$ of Fourier coefficients of f. Indeed, if we apply Parseval's formula to the internal function $F - {}^*f$, we obtain

$$\sum_{n\in{}^*Z} |\hat{F}(n) - \widehat{{}^*f}(n)|^2 = \frac{1}{2\pi}\int_{-\pi}^{+\pi} |F(t) - {}^*f(t)|^2\,dt =_1 0.$$

In particular, if we apply this result to the function F_ω as defined in 4.13 we obtain the result that $\sum_{n\in{}^*Z} |\hat{F}_\omega(n) - \widehat{{}^*f}(n)|^2 =_1 0$.

We shall now turn our attention to the famous Hausdorff–Young inequalities. Again, there is no loss in generality to restrict the discussion to continuous functions. The general result follows immediately by using the completeness of the $L^p(T)$-spaces.

5.4. THEOREM *(Hausdorff–Young Inequalities). For each $f \in C(T)$ and for each real number p satisfying $1 < p \leq 2$ and q satisfying $1/p + 1/q = 1$ we have*

$$\text{(i)}\ \left(\sum_{n=-\infty}^{+\infty} |\hat{f}(n)|^q \right)^{1/q} \leq \left(\frac{1}{2\pi} \int_{-\pi}^{+\pi} |f(x)|^p \,\mathrm{d}x \right)^{1/p}$$

$$\text{(ii)}\ \left(\frac{1}{2\pi} \int_{-\pi}^{+\pi} |f(x)|^q \,\mathrm{d}x \right)^{1/q} \leq \left(\sum_{n=-\infty}^{+\infty} |\hat{f}(n)|^p \right)^{1/p}.$$

Proof. Using the fact that, if $1 < p \leq 2$, then $q \geq 2$, and Theorem 4.20 the inequality (i) is obtained by taking the standard parts on both sides of the inequality 4.10.

In order to obtain (ii) we need to apply first 4.11 to the standard partial sums $s_m(x) = \sum_{|l| \leq m} \hat{f}(l)\exp(\mathrm{i}lx)$, $x \in T$, of the Fourier series of f, where $m \in N$. Since $s_{m,\omega}(n) = 0$ for all $m < |n| \leq \omega_0$, we can then take the standard part on both sides of the inequality 4.11 applied to $(s_m)_\omega$. Hence,

$$5.5.\quad \left(\frac{1}{2\pi} \int_{0}^{2\pi} |s_m(x)|^q \,\mathrm{d}x \right)^{1/q} \leq \left(\sum_{n=-\infty}^{+\infty} |f(n)|^p \right)^{1/p},$$

and so we obtain that $\|s_m\|_q$ is uniformly bounded in m. From this we conclude immediately that $\|s_m - f\|_q \to 0$ as $m \to \infty$ (see Katznelson [1968] p. 47), and so, finally, by letting m tend to infinity in 5.5, the inequality (ii) of the theorem appears, and the proof is finished.

We shall conclude this section with an application of the formulas contained in 4.19 which may be of interest in itself.

5.6. THEOREM. *Assume that $f \in C(T)$ satisfies the following two conditions*

$$\text{(i)}\ \sum_{n=-\infty}^{+\infty} |n|\, |\hat{f}(n)|^2 < \infty,$$

(ii) $m_f(\delta) = \mathrm{o}(\sqrt{\delta})$ *as* $0 < \delta$ *tends to zero.*

Then

$$\lim_{n\to\infty} \sum_{k=0}^{n-1} \left| f\left(\frac{2\pi}{n}(k+1)\right) - f\left(\frac{2\pi}{n}k\right)\right|^2 = 0.$$

Proof. We need to show that

$$a_\omega = \left(\sum_{|k|\leqslant \omega_0} \left| {}^*f\left(\frac{2\pi}{\omega}(k+1)\right) - {}^*f\left(\frac{2\pi}{\omega}k\right)\right|^2 \right)^{\frac{1}{2}} =_1 0.$$

From 4.19 it follows that

$$a_\omega \leq 2\pi \left(\frac{1}{\omega} \sum_{|n|\leqslant \omega_0} n^2 |{}^*\hat f(n)|^2 \right)^{\frac{1}{2}} + 2\pi \left(\sum_{|n|\leqslant \omega_0} n^2 |\hat F_\omega(n) - {}^*\hat f(n)|^2 \right)^{\frac{1}{2}}.$$

We shall first show that condition (i) implies that

$$\frac{1}{\omega} \sum_{|n|\leqslant \omega_0} n^2 |^*\ (n)|^2 =_1 0.$$

To this end, observe that since $\sum_{n=-\infty}^{+\infty} |n|^2\ |\hat f(n)|^2 < \infty$,

$$\frac{1}{\omega} \sum_{|n|\leqslant \omega_0} n^2 |{}^*\hat f(n)|^2 = \frac{1}{\omega} \sum_{|n|\leqslant \sqrt{\omega_0}} n^2 |{}^*\hat f(n)|^2 + \frac{1}{\omega} \sum_{\sqrt{\omega_0}<|n|\leqslant \omega_0} n^2 |{}^*\hat f(n)|^2$$

$$\leq \frac{1}{\sqrt{\omega}} \sum_{|n|\leqslant \sqrt{\omega_0}} n |{}^*\hat f(n)|^2 + \sum_{\sqrt{\omega_0}<|n|\leqslant \omega_0} n |{}^*\hat f(n)|^2 =_1 0.$$

Next we shall show that $m_f(\delta) = o(\sqrt{\delta})$ implies that

$$\frac{1}{\omega} \sum_{|n|\leqslant \omega_0} n^2 |\hat F_\omega(n) - {}^*\hat f(n)|^2 =_1 0.$$

For this purpose we first observe, by applying Parseval's formula for $^*T$ to the internal function $F_\omega - {}^*f$, that

$$\frac{1}{\omega} \sum_{|n|\leqslant \omega_0} n^2 |\hat F_\omega(n) - {}^*\hat f(n)|^2 \leq \omega \sum_{|n|\leqslant \omega_0} |\hat F_\omega(n) - {}^*\hat f(n)|^2$$

$$\leq \frac{\omega}{2\pi} \int_0^{2\pi} |F_\omega(t) - {}^*f(t)|^2\, \mathrm{d}t.$$

From 4.14 and condition (ii) it now follows that

$$\frac{\omega}{2\pi} \int_0^{2\pi} |F_\omega(t) - {}^*f(t)|^2\, \mathrm{d}t \leq \left(\sqrt{\omega} m_{*f}\left(\frac{\pi}{\omega}\right)\right)^2 =_1 0.$$

In exactly the same way we can show that $a_\omega =_1 0$ if ω is even. This completes the proof of the theorem.

Remark. The reader should observe that condition (i) by itself implies that the Fourier series of f converges uniformly (Tauberian Theorem). In view of Bernstein's Theorem on absolute convergence of Fourier series, namely, if $m_f(\delta) = O(\delta^{\frac{1}{2}+\varepsilon})$, $\varepsilon > 0$, then the Fourier series of f converges absolutely, it may not be without interest to determine whether (i) and (ii) together will imply that the Fourier series of f converges absolutely. The example $f(x) = \sum_{n=1}^{\infty} \exp(inx)/n \log(n+1)$, $x \in T$, shows that (i) by itself does not imply absolute convergence. But unfortunately, since f is of bounded variation, it cannot satisfy a Lipschitz condition, and so, in particular, it does not satisfy the condition (ii) of the theorem.

6. Positive definite functions. Let G be a topological commutative group. A complex valued function φ on G is said to be *positive definite* whenever the inequality

6.1. $$\sum_{i,j=1}^{m} \varphi(x_i - x_j)\, c_i \overline{c_j} \geq 0$$

holds for each set $\{x_1, \ldots, x_m\}$ of elements and for every set $\{c_1, \ldots, c_m\}$ of complex numbers.

We recall (see Katznelson [1968]) that by specializing n and the sets $\{x_1, \ldots, x_n\}$, $\{c_1, \ldots, c_n\}$ it can be shown that positive definite functions satisfy the following properties.

6.2. (i) $\varphi(x) = \overline{\varphi(-x)}$ *for all* $x \in G$;

(ii) $|\varphi(x)| \leq \varphi(0)$ *for all* $x \in G$;

(iii) $|\varphi(x) - \varphi(y)|^2 \leq 2\, \varphi(0) \operatorname{Re}(\varphi(0) - \varphi(x - y))$ *for all* $x \in G$, *where* "Re" *stands for the real part of a complex number;*

(iv) $|\varphi(0)\varphi(x+y) - \varphi(x)\varphi(y)|^2 \leq (\varphi^2(0) - |\varphi(x)|^2)^{\frac{1}{2}} (\varphi^2(0) - |\varphi(y)|^2)^{\frac{1}{2}}$ *for all* $x, y \in G$. *In particular,* $|\varphi(x+y) - \varphi(x)| \leq (\varphi^2(0) - |\varphi(y)|^2)^{\frac{1}{2}} + |\varphi(0) - \varphi(y)|$.

From 6.2 we conclude that for non-zero positive definite functions φ, $\varphi(0) > 0$ and, positive definite functions are bounded, and that a positive definite function is uniformly continuous if and only if it is continuous at the unit element of the group.

The purpose of this section is to discuss briefly the theory of positive definite functions on the circle group T via the corresponding but trivial theory for finite commutative groups. We shall begin with the following observation.

If $G = (x_0 = 0, x_1, \ldots, x_n)$ is a finite commutative group, then a function φ on G is positive definite whenever

6.3. $\sum_{i,j=0} \varphi(x_i - x_j)\, c_i \overline{c_j} \geq 0$

holds for every choice of complex numbers $c_0, c_1, \ldots, c_n$.

Every character of G is positive definite. Indeed, in that case 6.3 reduces immediately to $\sum_{i=0}^{n} |c_i(x_i, \gamma)|^2$. Hence, every positive linear combination of characters is a positive definite function. The fact that the converse holds is contained in the following theorem, which is nothing but the trivial finite commutative group version of the Bochner–Weil Theorem for positive definite functions in abstract harmonic analysis.

6.4. THEOREM. *A complex valued function φ on a finite Abelian group G is positive definite if and only if $\hat{\varphi}(\gamma) \geq 0$ for all $\gamma \in \Gamma$.*

Proof. From the definition of $\hat{\varphi}(\gamma)$ it follows that

$$\hat{\varphi}(\gamma) = \frac{1}{n+1}\langle p, \gamma\rangle = \frac{1}{n+1}\sum_{i=0}^{n} \varphi(x_i - x_j)(-x_i + x_j, \gamma),$$

and so by summing over j we obtain that

$$\hat{\varphi}(\gamma) = \frac{1}{n+1}\sum_{i,j=0}^{n} \varphi(x_i - x_j)\overline{(x_i, \gamma)}(x_j, \gamma) \geq 0.$$

In order to prove the converse we have only to observe that the inversion formula 2.13 implies that φ is a positive linear combination of characters which are positive definite, and so the required result follows.

We are now in a position to prove the following theorem about positive definite functions defined on the circle group.

6.5. THEOREM. *A continuous function $\varphi \in C(T)$ is positive definite if and only if $\hat{\varphi}(n) \geq 0$ for all $n \in Z$ and $\sum_{n=-\infty}^{\infty} \hat{\varphi}(n) < \infty$.*

Proof. Since φ is positive definite on T it follows immediately that $^*\varphi$ is positive definite on $^*T$. Hence, φ_ω is a positive definite function on the ω-circle group $^*T(2\pi\omega)$ for all infinitely large ω. Then, by Theorem 6.4, $\hat{\varphi}_\omega(n) \geq 0$ for all $n \in {}^*Z$. Furthermore, $\varphi(0) = \sum_{|n| \leqslant \omega_0} \hat{\varphi}_\omega(n)$ is finite. Since, by 4.12, $\hat{\varphi}(n) = \mathrm{st}(\hat{\varphi}_\omega(n))$ for all finite $n \in Z$ it follows that $\hat{\varphi}(n) \geq 0$

for all $n \in Z$. We shall now show that $\sum_{n=-\infty}^{+\infty} \hat{\varphi}(n)$ is convergent. To this end, we first observe that, by Parseval's formula 5.1, for each $f \in C(T)$ we have

$$\frac{1}{\omega} \sum_{|k| \leqslant \omega_0} {}^*\overline{f\left(\frac{2\pi}{\omega} k\right)} {}^*\varphi\left(\frac{2\pi}{\omega} k\right) = \sum_{|n| \leqslant \omega_0} \hat{\varphi}_\omega(n) \overline{\hat{f}_\omega(n)},$$

and so by taking standard parts on both sides and using the fact that $\sum_{|n| \leqslant \omega_0} \hat{\varphi}_\omega(n)$ is finite we obtain the inequality.

$$6.6 \quad \left| \frac{1}{2\pi} \int_0^{2\pi} \overline{f(x)} \varphi(x) \, \mathrm{d}x \right| \leq \operatorname{st}\left(\sum_{|n| \leqslant \omega_0} \hat{\varphi}_\omega(n) \right) \cdot \max_{n \in Z} |\hat{f}(n)|.$$

From 6.6 and $\hat{\varphi}_\omega(n) \geq 0$ for all $n \in {}^*Z$ it follows that the linear functional $T_\varphi(\hat{f}) = (1/2\pi) \int_0^{2\pi} \varphi(x)\overline{f(x)} \, \mathrm{d}x$, $f \in C(T)$, is a bounded and positive linear functional on the normed space of sequences of Fourier coefficients with the maximum norm. Hence, by the Hahn–Banach extension theorem, T_φ can be extended to a bounded and positive linear functional on $c_0(Z)$. We conclude that there exists an element $\mu \in l^1(Z)$ such that $\mu(n) \geq 0$ for all $n \in Z$ and

$$\frac{1}{2\pi} \int_0^{2\pi} \varphi(x)\overline{f(x)} \, \mathrm{d}x = \sum_{n=-\infty}^{+\infty} \mu(n) \hat{f}(-n) = \frac{1}{2\pi} \int_0^{2\pi} \sum_{n=-\infty}^{+\infty} \mu(n) \, \mathrm{e}^{inx} \overline{f(x)} \, \mathrm{d}x,$$

and hence, $\hat{\varphi}(n) = \mu(n)$ for all $n \in Z$, and the proof is finished.

Since the groups ${}^*T(2\pi\omega)$ and ${}^*Z(\omega)$ are isomorphic an entirely similar argument gives the following characterization of positive definite functions on Z. This result is due to Herglotz (see Katznelson [1968]) and is the first result of this nature which appeared in the literature. It was later that Bochner recognized the fundamental role which the concept of positive definite function plays in harmonic analysis.

6.7. THEOREM *(G. Herglotz). A function φ defined on the additive group of integers is positive definite if and only if there exists a positive linear functional μ on $C(T)$ such that*

$$\varphi(n) = \frac{1}{2\pi} \int_0^{2\pi} \mathrm{e}^{inx} \, \mathrm{d}\mu(x)$$

for all $n \in Z$.

Remark. It is not without interest to observe that on the circle group T the linear space spanned by the set of all continuous positive definite functions is the linear subspace $A(T)$ of $C(T)$ of all the continuous functions whose Fourier series converges absolutely.

Incidentally, it is much easier to show that a function $f \in C(T)$ is positive definite if and only if $\hat{f}(n) \geq 0$ for all $n \in Z$.

References

Katznelson, Y., 1968, *An Introduction to Harmonic Analysis* (New York).

Luxemburg, W. A. J., 1962a, *Non-Standard Analysis*, Lectures on Robinson's Theory of Infinitely Large and Infinitely Small Numbers (Pasadena, rev. ed. 1964).

Luxemburg, W. A. J., 1972b, What is Nonstandard Analysis? *Am. Math. Monthly*, to appear.

Luxemburg, W. A. J. (editor), 1969, *Application of Model Theory to Algebra, Analysis and Probability Theory* (New York).

Riesz, F., 1923, Über eine Verallgemeinerung der Parsevalschen Formel, *Math. Zeitschr.* 18, pp. 117–124.

Robinson, A., 1966, *Non-Standard Analysis* (North-Holland, Amsterdam).

Received 15 July 1971

A REMARK ON THE CANTOR–LEBESGUE LEMMA

W. A. J. LUXEMBURG[1])
California Institute of Technology

1. Introduction. One of the many applications of nonstandard methods given by Robinson in his book on Non-standard Analysis is a new and more straightforward proof of the famous Cantor–Lebesgue Lemma (see Hardy and Rogosinski [1950] p. 84 and Robinson [1966] Theorem 5.24, p. 132), which states that if

$$\lim_{n\to\infty} (a_n \cos nx + b_n \sin nx) = 0$$

for all x in a set of positive measure, then $\lim_{n\to\infty} a_n = \lim_{n\to\infty} b_n = 0$.

Independently and at about the same time the present author also found a nonstandard proof of the Cantor–Lebesgue lemma. Although the author's proof strongly resembles Robinson's proof it differs from it in the sense that it is based on a convenient nonstandard formulation of a property of points of density one of sets measurable in the sense of Lebesgue. The purpose of the present paper is to present the essentials of a nonstandard formulation of Lebesgue's theory of points of density of measurable sets and to show how it can be applied to obtain a generalization of the Cantor–Lebesgue Lemma.

2. Points of density and dispersion. For terminology and notation concerning nonstandard analysis not explained in the present paper we refer the reader to Robinson [1966] and Luxemburg [1972].

Let e be a Lebesgue measurable subset of the real line R. For the sake of convenience the characteristic function of e will also be denoted by the same letter e. For each measurable subset $e \subset R$ we set $E(x) = \int_c^x e(t)\mathrm{d}t$, where $x, c \in R$ and c is kept fixed. Points of density one of e and points of dispersion of e can be characterized as follows (see Saks [1948] Chap. IV, section 10, p. 128).

[1]) This work was supported in part by NSF Grant GP 23392.

2.1. *A point $x \in R$ is a point of density one of a measurable subset $e \subset R$ if and only if E is differentiable at x and its derivative $E'(x) = 1$. A point $x \in R$ is a point of dispersion of e if and only if $E'(x) = 0$.*

The reader should observe that a point x is a point of dispersion of a measurable set e if and only if it is a point of density one of the complement of e. In view of this fact we shall concentrate our attention to points of density one.

The set of points of density one of a measurable subset $e \subset R$ will be denoted by e_1. Concerning the set e_1 we have the following result (see Saks [1948]).

2.2. *For every measurable subset $e \subset R$ the set e_1 is measurable and $\mu(e \backslash e_1) + \mu(e_1 \backslash e) = 0$.*

Consider now a nonstandard model of R. The field of nonstandard reals in the model will be denoted as usual by $^*R$, the set of infinitesimals of $^*R$ by M_1 and the set of finite elements of $^*R$ by M_0. The set of natural numbers $\{1, 2, \ldots, n, \ldots\}$ of R will be denoted by N and in $^*R$ by $^*N$. If $a, b \in {}^*R$, then $a =_1 b$ means that $a - b$ is an infinitesimal.

Our method in obtaining Cantor–Lebesgue type theorems is based on following property of points of density one in $^*R$.

2.3. THEOREM. *Let e be a measurable subset of R of positive measure and let $x_0 \in e_1$ be a point of density one of e. Then for each infinitely large number $\gamma \in {}^*R \backslash R$ and for each non-zero finite standard real number $a \in M_0$ there exists a non-zero infinitesimal h $(0 \neq h \in M_1)$ such that $\gamma h =_1 a$ and $x_0 \pm h \in {}^*e_1 \cap {}^*e$.*

Proof. There is no loss in generality to assume that γ and a of the theorem satisfy $0 < a$ and $0 < \gamma$. Let k be an infinitesimal such that $0 < k < a$ and let $x_0 \in e_1$. Then from $0 < a/\gamma \in M_1$ and 2.1 it follows that

$$2.4. \quad \text{(i)}\ \frac{\gamma}{k}\left({}^*E\left(x_0 + \frac{a}{\gamma}\right) - {}^*E\left(x_0 + \frac{a-k}{\gamma}\right)\right) =_1 1, \quad \text{and}$$

$$\text{(ii)}\ \frac{\gamma}{k}\left({}^*E\left(x_0 - \frac{a}{\gamma}\right) - {}^*E\left(x_0 - \frac{a-k}{\gamma}\right)\right) =_1 1.$$

Hence, by adding the expressions 2.4 (i) and 2.4 (ii) and dividing by 2 we obtain

2.5. $$\frac{\gamma}{2k}\left({}^*E\left(x_0+\frac{a}{\gamma}\right)-{}^*E\left(x_0+\frac{a-k}{\gamma}\right)+{}^*E\left(x_0-\frac{a}{\gamma}\right)\right.$$
$$\left.-{}^*E\left(x_0-\frac{a-k}{\gamma}\right)\right)=_1 1.$$

It follows from 2.5 that there is an infinitesimal $h \neq 0$ such that $x_0 \pm h \in e_1 \cap e$ and $a - k \leq h\gamma \leq a$. For otherwise the expression in $^*E$ in 2.5 would be at most $\frac{1}{2}$, contradicting 2.5, and the proof is finished.

An interesting class of real functions of a real variable, the so-called *approximate continuous functions*, was introduced by A. Denjoy (see Saks [1948] p. 131). We shall recall the definition. A measurable real function f defined on an open interval I *is called approximately continuous at a point* $x_0 \in I$ *whenever for every* $\varepsilon > 0$ *the point* x_0 *is a point of density one of the set* $\{x: |f(x) - f(x_0)| < \varepsilon\}$. It was shown by A. Denjoy that approximately continuous functions on R are of Baire class 1 and have the Darboux property. Furthermore, Denjoy showed that if f is a real measurable function defined on a measurable set e, then f is *almost everywhere approximately continuous* on e. In the case that f is also *bounded, then f is approximately continuous at a point $x \in e$ if and only if the function* $F(x) = \int_c^x f(t)\mathrm{d}t$ *is differentiable at x and its derivative $F'(x)$ at x satisfies* $F'(x) = f(x)$.

From the last result we conclude that if e is the characteristic function of a measurable subset e of R, then e *is approximately continuous at x if and only if x is a point of density one of e.*

In view of Theorem 2.3, the reader will have no difficulty in proving the following theorem.

2.6. THEOREM. *Let f be a real measurable function defined on R. Then for each infinitely large $\gamma \in {}^*R\backslash R$ and for each non-zero finite number $a(0 \neq a \in M_0)$ there exists for almost all $x \in R$ an infinitesimal $h = h_f(x, \gamma, a)$ such that $h \neq 0$, $h\gamma =_1 a$ and $^*f(x_0 \pm h) =_1 f(x_0)$.*

3. A generalization of the Cantor–Lebesgue Lemma. Before we introduce a more general Cantor–Lebesgue Lemma we shall first present a proof of the Cantor–Lebesgue Lemma based on Theorem 2.3.

3.1. THEOREM *(Cantor–Lebesgue Lemma). If* $A_n(x) = a_n \cos nx + b_n \sin nx = \rho_n \cos(nx + \mu_n)$, *where* $\rho_n = \sqrt{\{a_n^2 + b_n^2\}}$, *satisfies* $\lim_{n\to\infty} A_n(x) = 0$

for all x in a set e of positive measure, then $\lim_{n\to\infty} \rho_n = 0$. *If we only assume that* A_n *is uniformly bounded in n in a set of positive measure e, then the sequence* $\{\rho_n\}$ *is bounded.*

Proof. We shall first prove the limit theorem. From Egoroff's theorem it follows that there is no loss in generality to assume that $\lim_{n\to\infty} A_n(x) = 0$ uniformly in e. Hence, $A_\omega(z) =_1 0$ for all $z \in {}^*e$ and for all infinitely large natural numbers $\omega \in {}^*N\backslash N$. Let $x_0 \in e_1 \cap e$ be a point of density one of e and let $\omega \in {}^*N\backslash N$. If $\cos(\omega x_0 + {}^*\mu_\omega) \neq 0$, then ${}^*\rho_\omega =_1 0$. If, on the other hand, $\cos(\omega x_0 + {}^*\mu_\omega) =_1 0$, then by 2.3, there exists an infinitesimal $h \neq 0$ such that $x_0 \pm h \in {}^*e$ and $h\omega =_1 \frac{1}{2}\pi$. Hence, $1 =_1 {}^*\rho_\omega \cos(\omega(x_0 + h) + {}^*\mu_\omega) =_1 {}^*\rho_\omega \sin(\omega x_0 + {}^*\mu_\omega) =_1 {}^*\rho_\omega$, since $\cos(\omega x_0 + {}^*\mu_\omega) =_1 0$ implies that $\sin(\omega x_0 + {}^*\mu_\omega) =_1 1$. We conclude that ${}^*\rho_\omega =_1 0$ for all $\omega \in {}^*N\backslash N$ which is equivalent to $\lim_{n\to\infty} \rho_n = 0$, and finishes the proof of the first part of the theorem.

For the second part assume that $|A_n(x)| \leq M$ for all $n \in N$ and for all $x \in e$. In order to show that $\{\rho_n\}$ is bounded we have only to show that ${}^*\rho_\omega$ is finite for all $\omega \in {}^*N\backslash N$. To this end, let $x_0 \in e_1 \cap e$ and let $\omega \in {}^*N\backslash N$. If $\cos(\omega x_0 + {}^*\mu_\omega) =_1 0$, then as above there exists an $0 \neq h \in M_1$ such that $\cos(\omega(x_0 + h) + {}^*\mu_\omega) =_1 1$. From this we conclude that ${}^*\rho_\omega$ is finite for all $\omega \in {}^*N\backslash N$ and the proof is finished.

From the various other applications one can make of Theorem 2.3 we have chosen to prove the following Cantor–Lebesgue Lemma type theorem.

3.2. THEOREM. *Let f be a real periodic function of period one which is continuous everywhere and which has the property that its set of zeros has measure zero. Let* $\{\alpha_n\}$ $(n \in N)$ *be a sequence of real numbers such that* $\lim_{n\to\infty} \alpha_n = +\infty$ *and assume that* $\{\beta_n\}$ $(n \in N)$ *is an arbitrary sequence of real numbers. Then we have the following two results.*

(i) *If* $\{\rho_n\}$ $(n \in N)$ *is a sequence of real numbers such that*

$$\lim_{n\to\infty} \rho_n f(\alpha_n x + \beta_n) = 0$$

in a measurable set e of positive measure, then $\lim_{n\to\infty} \rho_n = 0$.

(ii) *If* $\{\rho_n\}$ $(n \in N)$ *is a sequence of real numbers such that*

$$|\rho_n f(\alpha_n x + \beta_n)| \leq M$$

for all $n \in N$ *and for all x in a measurable set e of positive measure, then the sequence* $\{\rho_n\}$ $(n \in N)$ *is bounded.*

Proof. We shall only prove (i) since the proof of (ii) is similar and is, in fact, a little easier.

As in the proof of the Cantor–Lebesgue Lemma there is no loss in generality to assume that $\lim_{n\to\infty} \rho_n f(\alpha_n x + \beta_n) = 0$ uniformly in $x \in e$. Hence, $^*\rho_\omega {}^*f({}^*\alpha_\omega x + {}^*\beta_\omega) =_1 0$ for all $\omega \in {}^*N\backslash N$ and for all $x \in {}^*e$. Let $x_0 \in e \cap e_1$ be a point in e of density one and let $\omega \in {}^*N\backslash N$. If ${}^*f({}^*\alpha_\omega x_0 + {}^*\beta_\omega) =_1 0$, then since the set of zeros of f has measure zero and e has positive measure it follows that there is a point $y \in e$ such that $|f(y)| > 0$. Let $a \in M_0$ be such that ${}^*\alpha_\omega x_0 + {}^*\beta_\omega - [{}^*\alpha_\omega x_0 + {}^*\beta_\omega] + a = y$. Since $\lim_{n\to\infty} \alpha_n = +\infty$ it follows that ${}^*\alpha_\omega$ is infinitely large, and so, by taking $\gamma = {}^*\alpha_\omega$ in Theorem 2.3 we obtain that there exists an infinitesimal $h \neq 0$ such that ${}^*\alpha_\omega h =_1 a$ and $x_0 + h \in {}^*e \cap {}^*e_1$. Hence, $0 =_1 {}^*\rho_\omega {}^*f({}^*\alpha_\omega(x_\omega + h) + {}^*\beta_\omega) = {}^*\rho_\omega {}^*f(y + k)$, where $k \in M_1$. Since $|f(y)| > 0$ and f is continuous at y we have that ${}^*f(y + k) \neq_1 0$, and so ${}^*\rho_\omega {}^*f(y + k) =_1 0$ implies that ${}^*\rho_\omega =_1 0$ for all $\omega \in {}^*N\backslash N$ which finishes the proof.

Remark. If we take $f(x) = \cos 2\pi x$ $(x \in R)$ and $\alpha_n = n/2\pi$ $(n \in N)$, then we obtain the Cantor–Lebesgue Lemma.

From the above proof of Theorem 3.2 it follows that it is sufficient to assume that f is continuous almost everywhere.

We shall now show that the *conditions of the theorem are best possible.* Let C be the Cantor set of the interval $0 \leq x \leq 1$, and let $f(x) = \max(|x - y| : y \in C)$ $0 \leq x \leq 1$ and extended periodically mod. 1. Then f is continuous and its set of zeros has measure zero. Since $3^n x - [3^n x] \in C$ for all $n \in N$ and for all $x \in C$ we have, by taking $\rho_n = n$, for all $n \in N$ that $\lim_{n\to\infty} \rho_n f(3^n x) = 0$ for all $x \in C$ but $\lim_{n\to\infty} \rho_n = +\infty$, which shows that the hypothesis $\mu(e) > 0$ in (i) and (ii) of the theorem cannot be dropped. On the other hand, if $f(x) = 0$ for $0 \leq x \leq \frac{1}{2}$ and $f(x) = (1 - 2x)(1 - x)$ for $\frac{1}{2} \leq x \leq 1$ and $f(x + 1) = f(x)$ for all other values of x, then f is continuous and its set of zeros in $0 \leq x \leq 1$ has measure $\frac{1}{2}$. If $\rho_n = n$ $(n \in N)$, then, by observing that $f(2^n x) = 0$ for all $0 \leq x \leq \frac{1}{2}$, we obtain that $\lim_{n\to\infty} \rho_n f(2^n x) = 0$ for all x in the set of positive measure $0 \leq x \leq \frac{1}{2}$ but the sequence $\{\rho_n\}$ is not even bounded, which shows that the condition that f may vanish only on a set of measure zero cannot be dropped in (i) and (ii) of the theorem.

In conclusion we may point out that Theorem 2.3 can also be used to obtain a more straight forward proof of Kuttner's Theorem (see Hardy and Rogosinski [1950] p. 82) in the theory of trigonometric series.

References

Hardy, G. H. and Rogosinski, W. W., 1950, *Fourier Series*, Cambridge tracts in Mathematics and Mathematical Physics 38 (Cambridge, second ed.).

Luxemburg, W. A. J., 1972, What is Nonstandard Analysis? *Amer. Math. Monthly*, to appear.

Robinson, A., 1966, *Non-Standard Analysis* (North-Holland, Amsterdam).

Saks, S., 1948, *Theory of the Integral* (New York, second rev. ed.).

Received 15 July 1971

UNIFORM CONTINUITY AND RATES OF GROWTH OF MEROMORPHIC FUNCTIONS[1])

K. D. STROYAN
California Institute of Technology
and The University of Wisconsin

1. Introduction. The purpose of this note is to show that several theories of the rate of growth of meromorphic functions can be treated in a unified fashion. Introducing appropriate metrics we see that they all amount to a study of uniform continuity (or uniform equicontinuity). In the case of Julia–Milloux's Theorem and Gavrilov's W_p classes (5.6) the introduction of the metric is new.

The connection between these theories and the classical Picard Theorem is made through Theorem 3.1 via the mechanism of S-continuity. (This generalizes a result of Robinson [1966] who introduced S-continuity.) In standard terms this relates exceptional values and non-uniformity, but the use of nonstandard analysis and S-continuity results in considerable simplification because non-uniformity and sequences of Milloux circles are reflected in a single S-discontinuity at a remote point. In part, this also extends Robinson's treatment of the holomorphic Julia–Milloux Theorem to the meromorphic case.

The nonstandard approach can greatly simplify a number of proofs of known results, particularily in the extensive theory of normal meromorphic functions (4.8). We offer a few simple examples. The original motivation for this work was the study of normal functions, unfortunately a search of the literature revealed that most of our early applications were done during the 1960's by various authors.

Some remarks about our setting are in order. Smooth convex metrics are emphasized because then we have a mean value theorem with which to measure S-continuity. (In this generality even this simple result seems to be

[1]) This note appeared as one chapter of the author's doctoral dissertation, Applications of Model Theory to Complex Analysis, at the California Institute of Technology written under W. A. J. Luxemburg.

new.) A more general discussion (without magnification operators) in terms of uniform continuity or S-continuity is possible.

The domains of functions are viewed as Riemann surfaces for the sake of simplicity. Even in the case of a planar region we wish to emphasize a preferred metric and not be confused with others. This is important since different metrics have different infinitesimals and infinite galaxies. Moreover, some care is needed to apply Theorem 3.1 at remote points, for example, in the plane metric near the boundary of the unit disk the infinitesimals are cut off by the unit circle, whereas Theorem 3.1 applies with respect to the hyperbolic metric. We feel therefore that even in the case of studying boundary behavior of a function defined on the unit disk it is easier to think in terms of a Riemann surface. We hope that this will not cause confusion; the primary examples are the punctured plane, the plane, the unit disk and hyperbolic surfaces (the punctured disk in specific).

We shall use a leisurely elementary style. In effect the point is that some of the known work is more elementary than it might appear because of complicated sequential arguments which our approach avoids.

2. A Mean Value Theorem in metric spaces. A metric space (X, d) is said to be convex if for each $A, B \in X$, there exists $C \in X$, different from A and B, for which $d(A, B) = d(A, C) + d(C, B)$. When a metric space is complete and convex any two points can be connected by a *segment*, that is, an isometric image of the interval $[0, d(A, B)]$. (The segment need not be unique, of course.) In what follows (X, d) will be a *complete convex metric space*.

We give an adaptation to metric spaces of a proof of W. A. J. Luxemburg for a Mean Value Theorem in Euclidean n-space. We begin with a lemma following a theorem of P. Levy.

Let (Y, Δ) be an arbitrary metric space. Let $A, B \in X$ and let $[A, B]$ be a segment between A and B.

2.1. LEMMA. *If $f:(X, d) \to (Y, \Delta)$ is continuous, then for each natural number $n \geq 3$ there exist points A_n, $B_n \in (A, B)$ such that*

$$(1)\quad d(A, A_n) < d(B_n, A),$$

$$(2)\quad d(A_n, B_n) = d(A, B)/n,$$

$$(3)\quad \frac{\Delta(f(A), f(B))}{d(A, B)} \leq \frac{\Delta(f(A_n), f(B_n))}{d(A_n, B_n)}.$$

Proof. Let $\psi:[0, d(A, B)] \to [A, B]$ be the isomorphism from the interval in R onto $[A, B]$ in X. Normalize to

$$\varphi(t) = \psi(d(A, B) \cdot t), \quad t \in [0, 1].$$

Define

$$g(t) = \Delta\left(f\left(\varphi\left(t + \frac{1}{n}\right)\right), f(\varphi(t))\right)$$

for fixed but arbitrary $n \geq 3$. Then by the triangle inequality

$$\Delta(f(A), f(B)) \leq \sum_{k=0}^{n-1} g\left(\frac{k}{n}\right)$$

and

$$\frac{\Delta(f(A), f(B))}{d(A, B)} \leq \frac{1}{n} \sum_{k=0}^{n-1} \frac{g(k/n)}{d(A, B)/n}.$$

Since the terms in the sum are non-negative, either

$$\text{(1) for every } k, \quad \frac{\Delta(f(A), f(B))}{d(A, B)} = \frac{g(k/n)}{d(A, B)/n}$$

or

$$\text{(2) for some } k_0, \quad \frac{\Delta(f(A), f(B))}{d(A, B)} < \frac{g(k_0/n)}{d(A, B)/n}.$$

In case (1) pick $k_0 \neq 0$ or $n - 1$ or in case (2) when $k_0 \neq 0$ or $n - 1$ we take $A_n = \varphi(k_0/n)$ and $B_n = \varphi(k_0 + 1/n)$.

In case (2) when $k_0 = 0$ or $n - 1$ we do the following. By continuity of $g(t)$ we may move t away from the appropriate endpoint while still maintaining the strict inequality in the expression (2). In this case take $A_n = \varphi(t)$ and $B_n = \varphi(t + 1/n)$.

This proves the lemma.

The *magnification* or metric derivative of a function $f:X \to Y$ can be described as follows. Let C be a standard point of $^*X$ whose monad is non-degenerate (i.e., a non-isolated point). Provided that for every pair of points A and B within an infinitesimal of C, $\Delta(f(A), f(C))/d(A, C)$ is finite and infinitesimally close to $\Delta(f(B), f(C))/d(B, C)$ we say the *magnification of f at C* is

$$M(\Delta/d)f(C) = Mf(C) = \operatorname{st}\left(\frac{\Delta(f(A), f(C))}{d(A, C)}\right)$$

where st denotes the standard part homomorphism. In other words, as long as the standard part exists and is independent of the particular A within an infinitesimal of C, this expression is the magnification.

We describe the operator $M(\Delta/d)$ in the standard model by applying this definition at each standard point. As an operator $M(\Delta/d)$ can be extended to the nonstandard model, though the above description does not apply for internal functions. We leave the limit definition to the reader since we shall not have any need of it.

2.2. A MEAN VALUE THEOREM. *Let (X, d) be a complete convex metric space, let (Y, Δ) be a metric space, and let $f: X \to Y$ have a magnification everywhere on X. Then for every segment $[A, B]$ in X, there exists $C \in (A, B)$ such that*

$$\frac{\Delta(f(A), f(B))}{d(A, B)} \leq M(\Delta/d)f(C).$$

Proof. f is continuous since $d(x, y) \approx 0$ implies $\Delta(f(x), f(y)) \approx 0$. Thus we may apply the lemma as follows.

Pick A_3, $B_3 \in (A, B)$ satisfying the conditions of the lemma, next pick A_4, $B_4 \in (A_3, B_3)$ and proceed by induction.

Take the nonstandard extension of the sequences $(A_n)_{n \in N}$ and $(B_n)_{n \in N}$. Let ω be an infinite $*$-natural number and let $C = \text{st}_d(A_\omega) = \text{st}_d(B_\omega)$, the standard point C such that $C \overset{d}{=} A_\omega \overset{d}{=} B_\omega$. (A segment is an isometric image of a real compact interval.)

Now we conclude by examining the following inequality.

$$\frac{\Delta(f(A), f(B))}{d(A, B)} \leq \frac{\Delta(f(A_\omega), f(B_\omega))}{d(A_\omega, B_\omega)}$$

$$\leq \frac{d(A_\omega, C)[\Delta(f(A_\omega), f(C)) + \delta]}{d(A_\omega, B_\omega)d(A_\omega, C)} + \frac{d(C, B_\omega)[\Delta(f(C), f(B_\omega)) + \varepsilon]}{d(A_\omega, B_\omega)d(C, B_\omega)}$$

$$\leq M(\Delta/d)f(C) + \xi$$

where δ, ε and ξ are infinitesimal.

We use continuity to see that $\Delta(f(A_\omega), f(C)) \approx \Delta(f(A_\omega), f(B_\omega))$, that is, that δ and ε are infinitesimal. We use property (1) of the lemma and convexity to combine $d(A_\omega, C) + d(C, B_\omega) = d(A_\omega, B_\omega)$.

This completes the proof of the theorem.

Remarks. A non-convex example where the theorem fails is provided by $f(x) = x$ on the interval $[0, 1]$ where the chordal metric of stereographic projection is taken in the domain space and the spherical arc length is taken in the range. Then $M(s/\chi)f(x) = 1$ and $s(f(0), f(1))/\chi\ (0, 1) = \frac{1}{2}\pi/(2/\sqrt{2}) = \frac{1}{4}\pi\sqrt{2} > 1$.

As the following example shows, a minimal growth condition is not possible. $f(x) = |x|$ on $[-1, 1]$ has magnification 1 even at zero whereas $f(\pm 1) = 1$ so nowhere is the magnification below the divided difference.

Applications to meromorphic functions follow.

2.3. Some examples of complete convex metric spaces are:

1. A Banach space with the metric $\|x - y\|$.
2. The unit disk with the hyperbolic metric.
3. The Riemann sphere with the great circle arc length metric (or any manifold with global geodesics).
4. The complex plane with zero removed and $|\log(x/y)|$ (principal value $-\pi < \arg(z) \leq \pi$) as a metric.

The following result is an application of Theorem 2.2. See section 3 for the definition of S-continuity and Robinson [1966] for more details.

2.4. Corollary. *If $f:(X, d) \to (Y, \Delta)$ is an internal map whose magnification exists and is finite at each point of the internal complete convex metric space (X, d), then f is uniformily S-continuous on X.*

Proof. The set of bounds, $B = \{r \in {}^*R^+ : |Mf(x)| < r \text{ for every } x \in X\}$ is an internal set since it is described by an internal statement. Since B contains all infinite positive nonstandard reals it must contain a finite uniform bound for the magnification of f. Now apply 2.2.

While we are on the subject of uniform continuity we give a result (which we use in 6.1 below) that we hope gives the reader who is unfamiliar with nonstandard analysis an idea of the meaning of infinitesimals around a remote point. Sequences without limits in X, but which tend together, play a role analogous to infinitesimals around a remote point.

2.5 Theorem. *Let $f:(X, d) \to (Y, \Delta)$ be a continuous standard function. The following are equivalent:*

(1) *f is uniformly continuous on X.*

(2) *$^*f$ is S-continuous on the remote points of $^*X$, and hence everywhere on $^*X$.*

(3) *Every pair of sequences $(x_n : n \in N)$, $(y_n : n \in N)$ which satisfy $d(x_n, y_n) \to 0$ also satisfy $\Delta(f(x_n), f(y_n)) \to 0$. In particular when Y is compact, if f is not uniformly continuous there are sequences $(z_n : n \in N)$, $(w_n : n \in N)$ such that $d(z_n, w_n) \to 0$, $f(z_n) \to a$, and $f(w_n) \to b \neq a$.*

Proof. The equivalence of (1) and (2) follows from a more general result of Robinson [1966], but the fact that (1) implies (2) also follows automatically from interpreting the definition of uniform continuity in the nonstandard model and applying it at a remote point.

That (2) implies (3) follows easily from the nonstandard interpretation of $d(z_n, y_n) \to 0$, namely, that when $\omega \in {}^{\#}N$, $d(x_\omega, y_\omega) \approx 0$. By S-continuity $\Delta(f(x_\omega), f(y_\omega)) \approx 0$ and (3) follows.

We can conclude by showing that if f is not uniformly continuous (3) does not hold. There exists $\varepsilon > 0$ such that for every n there are points x_n and y_n with $d(x_n, y_n) < 1/n$ and $\Delta(f(x_n), f(y_n)) > \varepsilon$, by the negation of uniform continuity.

3. Continuous $*$-meromorphic functions. In this section we give a basic lemma on S-continuity for internal or $*$-meromorphic functions. Since the theorem is local in nature and since we wish to consider different metrics even on familiar regions like the punctured plane and the unit disk it seems best to think in terms of coordinate patches on a Riemann surface. If Mer (Ω) denotes the standard space of meromorphic functions on a standard Riemann surface Ω, then *Mer is a function defined on $*$-Riemann surfaces. No harm seems likely if we extend *Mer to external subsets of a surface by requiring that this means there is a $*$-region containing the set and a function $*$-meromorphic in that region.

Let Ω be a $*$-Riemann surface with a topologically compatible $*$-metric d. We will say $f \in {}^*\text{Mer}\ (\Omega)$ is S-continuous in d provided it is S-continuous in the sense of Robinson [1966] as a map from (Ω, d) to $({}^*S, s)$, the $*$-Riemann sphere with the great circle metric. At $a \in \Omega$ this means that for every standard $\varepsilon > 0$ $(\varepsilon \in \hat{R}^+)$ there exists a standard $\delta > 0$ such that $d(z, a) < \delta$ implies $s(f(z), f(a)) < \varepsilon$, or equivalently that $z \overset{d}{=} a$ implies $f(z) \overset{s}{=} f(a)$. Where the notation denotes the respective infinitesimal relations.

Now let (Ω, d) be a standard Riemann surface. Robinson [1966] has shown that the near-standard $*$-meromorphic functions on $^*\Omega$ (with respect to uniform convergence on compact subsets) are those which are S-continuous on the near-standard points of $^*\Omega$, ns$(^*\Omega)$. (This can also be shown by writing down the monad of the uniformity of compact convergence in $*\mathrm{Mer}(\Omega) \times *\mathrm{Mer}(\Omega)$, namely, $(f, g) \in \mu(u_K)$ if and only if $f(z) \overset{s}{=} g(z)$ for all $z \in \mathrm{ns}(*\Omega)$. We use the fact that Ω is locally compact.) The standard part of a function can be taken pointwise (with respect to s) and $(d/dz)(\mathrm{st}(f)) = \mathrm{st}(df/dz)$.

Now that we see the basic importance of S-continuity for $*$-meromorphic functions, we give the following local theorem. We state the result in terms of the plane metric, $p(x, y) = |x - y|$, of a coordinate disk. For this reason some care is necessary in applications at remote points or when several metrics are involved.

Let f be an internal meromorphic function defined on the monad of zero and hence in some finite disk of the complex plane. Continuity refers to the plane metric p as above. Magnification refers to $M(s/p)$.

3.1. THEOREM. *The following are equivalent*:

(1) *f is S-continuous at zero.*

(2) *There exist three values $\alpha, \beta, \gamma \in *S$, finitely separated in the spherical metric, which f does not attain in the infinitesimals, $\mathfrak{o}$.*

(3) *The magnification of f, $Mf(z)$, is finite on the infinitesimals, $\mathfrak{o}$.*

Proof. The equivalence of (1) and (2) follows from a theorem of Robinson [1966, Theorem 6.3.1] and the following lemma:

The near standard transformations of the $*$-Möbius transformations are those specified by taking three finitely separated points on $*S$ onto three other finitely separated points on $*S$.

One way to see this is by first observing that the *infinitesimal group* is described by taking three finitely separated values to their respective standard parts on S. Direct computation: $\alpha, \beta, \gamma \in *S$ and $\alpha, \gamma \in *C$, then when $a \overset{s}{=} \alpha$, etc.

$$[w, a; b, c] = [z, \alpha; \beta, \gamma] \text{ implies}$$

$$\frac{w - a}{w - c} = \varkappa \frac{z - \alpha}{z - \gamma}, \text{ where } \varkappa \approx 1.$$

Then

$$w = [(a - \varkappa c)z + (\varkappa\alpha c - a\gamma)]/[(1 - \varkappa)z + (\varkappa\alpha - \gamma)]$$

so that $w = [(1 + \delta)z + \varepsilon]/(\eta z + 1)$, where $\delta, \varepsilon, \eta$ are infinitesimal.

A transformation of this last type changes finite values only by an infinitesimal and leaves infinite values infinite so it is within an infinitesimal of the identity. Conversely, an infinitesimal transformation moves each point at most an s-infinitesimal. The pre-images of 0, 1, ∞ will therefore uniquely determine the transformation.

One may now apply Robinson's theorem to the mapping $g = w \circ f$ where w is the $*$-Möbius transformation taking α, β, γ of (2) into 0, 1, ∞.

Next we show that (1) implies (3). Assume $f(0) = 0$, otherwise work with $w \circ f$ where w is a $*$-Möbius rotation of the sphere taking $f(0)$ to zero which is justified since $M(s/p)f \equiv M(s/p)w \circ f$. [E.g., $w(z) = (z + f(0))/(1 - f(0)z)$.] By continuity and the fact that f is defined on a standard disk around a, we know $|f|$ is smaller than 1 on a disk of standard positive radius, r, about a. Thus, integrating around $|z| = \frac{3}{4} r$,

$$|f'(b)| = |(1/2\,\pi i) \int (f(z)/(z - b)^2)dz| \leq 1/(\tfrac{1}{2}r)^2, \quad \text{for } b \approx 0,$$

and $M(s/p)f(b)$ is finite on $\mathfrak{o}$ since $Mf(b) = |f'(b)|/(1 + |f(b)|^2)$. For $z \approx b$,

$$Mf(b) \approx |f(z) - f(b)|/(|z - b| \sqrt{1 + |f(z)|^2}\, \sqrt{1 + |f(b)|^2}).$$

The magnification $M(s/p)$ is usually denoted by ρ and is called the *spherical derivative*. This shows (1) implies (3).

We conclude by remarking that since the segment from 0 to b in $\mathfrak{o}$ is internal, the set

$$\{K : \rho f(z) < K, \quad z \text{ on the segment}\}$$

is internal and contains all infinite numbers, so $\rho f(z)$ is finitely bounded. By Theorem 2.2,

$$s(f(b), f(a)) \leq K_0 |b - a| \approx 0,$$

so f is S-continuous and (3) implies (1).

We wish to deal with applications of this theorem at remote points of a given metric. In these cases it is necessary that the d-infinitesimals "look" like the monad of zero in $^*C$. The precise reformulation of 3.1 follows.

3.2. We begin with an example of the difficulties one may encounter (which also shows why we view domains as Riemann surfaces). Take the right half-plane $\{z \in C : \mathrm{Re}(z) > 0\}$ with the plane metric $|x - y|$ and consider the function $\exp(1/z)$ in the part of the monad of zero which lies in the right half plane. The function omits the entire unit disk and still fails to be S-continuous.

We take Ω a $*$-Riemann surface, d a $*$-metric on Ω and $b \in \Omega$. $^*U$ is the $*$-unit disk, $\{z \in {}^*C : |z| < 1\}$.

3.3. DEFINITION. *We say b is the center of an S-disk of* Ω *with respect to d provided there exists an internal conformal* $(1-1)$ *mapping* φ: $^*U \to \Omega$ *satisfying*:

(1) $\varphi(0) = b$,

(2) $\varphi(\mathfrak{o}) = \mathfrak{o}_d(b)$,

(3) $M(d/p)\varphi(z)$ *exists, is finite and non-infinitesimal for z in the monad of zero.*

3.4. COROLLARY. *The conditions of Theorem* 3.1 *apply at the center* $b \in \Omega$ *of an S-disk with respect to d where S-continuity in* 3.1(1) *and the magnification in* 3.1(3) *are taken with respect to d.*

Proof. $f(\varphi(z))$ is S-continuous at zero if and only if $f(w)$ is d – S-continuous at b and $M(s/p)f \circ \varphi(z) = M(d/p)\varphi(z) \cdot M(s/d)f(w)$. (Existence of the latter magnification is imposed by 3.3(3).)

4. Invariant normal families. The purpose of this section is to unify several theories of the rate of growth of meromorphic functions whose definitions involve normal families constructed from given functions. These theories are discussed and applications of the basic theorem are given at the end of the section. We feel that for a number of applications S-continuity applied directly is simpler than introducing normal families and this is justified by Corollary 4.3.

We shall discuss a basic setting which is less general than is possible, but which encompasses the three classical cases given in the applications. One generalization is mentioned in 4.5. We feel that a number of results have been unnecessarily obscured in the classical theories and we feel that S-continuity can reveal their true simplicity.

4.1. Our basic setting is as follows. Ω is a *Riemann surface* with a topologically compatible convex *metric d*. We assume that d is asymptotic to the plane metric of a coordinate disk D at its center $a \in D \subseteq \Omega$. In terms of magnification operators this means $M(d/p)\mathrm{id}(a) = 1$, where id denotes the identity function and p the plane metric of D. W is a *group of conformal d-isometries* of Ω onto itself such that for every $b \in \Omega$ there exists a $w \in W$ with $w(a) = b$. As a result of this, d is a smooth metric, $M(d/d)w(z) = 1$, for every $w \in W$ and $z \in \Omega$, and the magnification of a meromorphic function $M(s/d)f(z)$ exists at each point of Ω (since d is asymptotic to p at a).

Let F be a subfamily of $\mathrm{Mer}(\Omega)$. We say F is *W-invariant* provided $F \circ W = \{f \circ w : f \in F \text{ and } w \in W\} = F$. When W consists of all conformal automorphisms of Ω, we say F is *conformally invariant*. If F is an arbitrary family, $F \circ W$ is invariant by the group property of W.

4.2. THEOREM. *The following are equivalent for a W-invariant family F:*
(1) *F is a normal family.*
(2) *$M(s/d)f(z)$ is a finite for every $z \in {}^*\Omega$ and every $f \in {}^*F$.*
(3) *$M(s/d)f(z) < K$ (a standard constant) for every $z \in \Omega$ and $f \in F$.*
(4) *Every $f \in {}^*F$ is S-continuous on all of ${}^*\Omega$ and hence uniformly S-continuous in the metric d.*

Proof. ($1 \Rightarrow 2$). Take $f \in {}^*F$ and $z \in {}^*\Omega$. Let $w(a) = z$, $w \in {}^*W$. $\rho g(a) \equiv M(s/p)g(a) = M(s/d)g(a)$ is finite for every $g \in {}^*F$ by Robinson's characterization of normal families (Robinson [1966] Theorem 6.4.1) and Theorem 3.1. $M(s/d)f(z) = [M(s/d)f(z)] \cdot [M(d/d)w(a)] = M(s/d)f \circ w(a)$, so (2) holds.

($2 \Rightarrow 3$). Since the set of bounds of $Mf(z)$ where $f \in {}^*F$ and $z \in {}^*\Omega$ is internal and contains all the infinite positive numbers there is a standard bound K. Condition (3) holds since its $*$-transform holds (with this K) in the nonstandard model.

($3 \Rightarrow 4$). Apply Corollary 2.4.

($4 \Rightarrow 1$). S-continuity on the near standard points implies that F is a normal family by Robinson [1966, Theorem 6.4.1]. (The topological compatibility of d enters as $\text{st}(x) = \text{st}(y)$ if and only if $d(x, y) \approx 0$, for $x, y \in \text{ns}({}^*\Omega)$.)

4.3. COROLLARY. *When $F = \{f_1, \ldots, f_k\} \circ W$ the conditions of the theorem are equivalent to (standard) uniform continuity of the f_k on all of Ω.*

In the setting of 4.8 this is apparently due to Lappan [1965].

4.4. *Remark*. Condition (3) is a generalization of results of Yosida, Noshiro and Lehto-Virtanen.

4.5. One generalization of this idea is to take W to be conformal mappings defined only on D and such that for every $b \in \Omega$ there is a $w \in W$ with $w(a) = b$. M. F. Behrens has obtained some results in this case where Ω is a disk with holes removed. W consists of dilation of a fixed disk translated within Ω. A function f for which $f \circ W$ is normal is termed *regular* and our condition (3) states that $\text{dist}(z, b\ \Omega)\rho f(z)$ is bounded.

Examples

4.6. *Julia exceptional functions*. Take $\Omega = C\backslash\{0\}$, the punctured plane, $W = \{bz : b \in \Omega\}$, $d(x, y) = |\log(x/y)|$ where $-\pi < \arg \leq \pi$ and $a = 1$. Ostrowski [1926] discovered that Julia's Theorem fails for meromorphic functions, e.g., take $f(z) = \prod(z - 2^n)/(z + 2^n)$, then $f \circ W$ is normal.

Marty [1931] characterized Julia exceptional functions as those for which $|z|\rho f(z)$ is bounded. (ρ denotes the spherical derivative, $M(s/p)$, see the proof of 3.1.) This is condition (3) since $M(s/d)f(z) = M(p/d)w(1)\rho f(z) = |z|\rho f(z)$ where $w(1) = z$. This is because when $x \approx 1$, $M(p/d)w(1) \approx |z|\ |x - 1|/|\log x| \approx |z|$, and the far sides are standard numbers, hence equal.

4.7. *Yosida's Theory* [1934]. Take $\Omega = C$, the complex plane, $W = \{z + b : b \in \Omega\}$, $d(x, y) = |x - y|$ and $a = 0$. (Doubly periodic functions arise in this context with Ω as the universal covering surface of the torus.) Yosida obtained condition (3) as *necessary and sufficient for normality of* $f \circ W$ *in the form* $\rho f(z) < K$. (We showed in the proof of 3.1 that $M(s/d)f(z) = \rho f(z) = |f'(z)|/(1 + |f(z)|^2)$.)

Yosida also observed that results similar to Julia–Milloux's Theorem hold in case normality fails. His results follow from our work in section 5 below.

Yosida also connects this growth requirement with the Nevanlinna characteristic by integrating $\rho f(z)$ in the Ahlfors–Shimizu formula.

4.8. *Normal meromorphic functions*. (Noshiro [1938], Lehto and Virtanen [1957].) Let $\Omega = U = \{z \in C : |z| < 1\}$, the unit disk, $W = \{\exp(i\theta) \times [(z - \alpha)/(\bar{\alpha}z - 1)] : \theta \in R, |\alpha| < 1\}$, all conformal automorphisms of U, $a = 0$ and $d(x, y) = \eta(x, y)$, the hyperbolic metric ($= \frac{1}{2}\log[(|x - y| + |\bar{y}x - 1|)/(|x - y| - |\bar{y}z - 1|)]$). A meromorphic function is called normal if $f \circ W$ is a normal family.

When G is a hyperbolic surface so U is its universal covering surface, a meromorphic function on G is normal provided $\hat{f} = f \circ P$ is normal on U where P is the projection of U onto G. This definition is extrinsic to G but conditions (2), (3) and (4) apply directly by projecting the metric. The S-continuity approach on G could be applied directly.

Noshiro [1938] gave condition (3) in the form $(1 - z\bar{z})\rho f(z) < K$. We know

$$M(s/\eta)f(z) = M(s/\eta)f \circ w(0) = [M(p/\eta)w(0)]\rho f(z) = (1 - z\bar{z})\rho f(z),$$

where $w(0) = z$. This is because

$$M(p/\eta)w(0) \approx \frac{|((x + z)/(\bar{z}x - 1)) - z|}{\eta(x, 0)} = \frac{x + z - z(\bar{z}x - 1)}{(\bar{z}x - 1)\eta(x, 0)}$$

$$\approx (1 - z\bar{z})\frac{|x|}{\eta(x, 0)} \approx (1 - z\bar{z}),$$

where $x \approx 0$. Since the far sides are standard and within an infinitesimal they are equal. (The hyperbolic metric is asymptotic to the plane metric at zero, so $(|x|/\eta(x, 0)) \approx 1$.)

Applications of a classical nature to the theory of normal functions are possible and the author has given a number of simplified proofs of known results using the nonstandard theory of the metric space (U, η). We give a few examples of this nature which involve a minimum of function theory.

If $\alpha \in {}^*U$, the *η-galaxy* around α is the set of points a finite distance from α, $G(\alpha) = \{z \in {}^*U : \eta(z, \alpha) \in \mathcal{O}\}$.

We begin with an observation of Noshiro [1938] which the reader can easily generalize to other settings (see Yosida [1934]).

4.9. *If $\varphi(t)$, $0 \leq t < 1$, is a continuous curve in U with $|\varphi(t)| \to 1$, and if the normal function f satisfies $f(\varphi(t)) \to b$ as $t \to 1$, then $f \circ W$ has the constant function b as a limit.*

Let $a \approx 1$ and $\alpha = \varphi(a)$ be fixed. Take $w(z) = [(z + \alpha)/(\bar{\alpha}z - 1)]$. The function $f \circ w$ is S-continuous on $\mathrm{ns}({}^*U)$ by 4.2, hence $\mathrm{st}(f \circ w)$ is meromorphic. Since $f(\varphi(t)) \to b$, whenever $t \approx 1$ we have $f(\varphi(t)) \stackrel{s}{=} b$, therefore $\mathrm{st}(f \circ w) = b$ on the points which map onto the points $\varphi(t)$ which lie in $G(\alpha)$. This means $\mathrm{st}(f \circ w)$ is constant on a set with a (non-trivial) adherent point, hence identically constant. Also, $f \circ w \approx b$ on all of $\mathrm{ns}({}^*U) = G(0)$ and f is near constant on $G(\alpha)$. In fact we see that a *necessary and sufficient condition that $f \circ W$ has a constant limit is that f is near constant on a galaxy of ${}^*U$.*

4.10. Nonstandardizing the work of Hoffman [1962], M. F. Behrens [1971] has shown that by identifying infinitesimally near-by points of infinite galaxies which contain points of interpolating sequences the galaxies correspond to non-trivial Gleason parts of $H^\infty(U)$. Moreover, the pseudo-hyperbolic metric $|(x - y)/(\bar{y}x - 1)|$ is infinitesimally close to the parts metric. Now since a normal function is S-continuous on the galaxies, identifying points infinitesimally near-by and taking the standard part of the function gives us a standard function, continuous in the parts metric, defined on the Gleason part. This proves a recent result of Brown and Gauthier [1971] that *normal functions can be extended to non-trivial parts.*

Many other applications could be given, but we refer the reader to the forthcoming monograph of A. J. Lohwater for more on normal functions. The bibliographies of Noshiro [1960] and Collingwood and Lohwater [1966] contain many other interesting references to normal functions.

5. Milloux circles and points of discontinuity. Milloux's theory of "cercles de remplissage" has seen recent interest with generalization in several directions (Lehto [1959], Lange [1960], Gavrilov [1968a and b] and Gauthier [1969, 1971]). Robinson [1966] "nonstandardized" the classical theory obtaining a new lemma for the existence of such circles. Robinson's lemma does not generalize directly to meromorphic functions because the $*$-sphere has only one S-component. The main idea of replacing sequences of circles with the monad of a discontinuity does extend to a very general setting as we show in this section.

Several of the known results in the various settings reduce to the equivalence of 3.1(2) and 3.1(3) at a discontinuity for an appropriately chosen metric. Our method simplifies the previous approaches to the theory and we hope also shows how nonstandard analysis can be useful when complicated quantification arises. This approach also shows that "Julia-sets" and "Milloux-sets" amount to the same thing since they both reduce to a discontinuity.

In a metric space (X, d) we shall use the notation

$$D_d(B;\varepsilon) = \{x \in X : \exists\, b \in B \quad \text{and} \quad d(x,b) < \varepsilon\}$$

where $B \subseteq X$. We also use the $*$-transform in $^*X$. Also

$$\mathfrak{D}_d(B) = \{x \in {}^*X : \exists\, b \in B \quad \text{and} \quad d(x,b) \approx 0\},$$

shall denote the *infinitesimal neighborhood* of B.

5.1. DEFINITIONS.

We say $A \subseteq \Omega$ is a d-Julia-set for f if for every (standard) positive ε,

$$f(D_d(A;\varepsilon)) \supseteq S \backslash \{\alpha, \beta\},$$

for two values $\alpha, \beta \in S$, the sphere. (J-set.)

We say A is a d-Milloux-set for f if for every positive r, δ, ε, there exist $\xi_1, \xi_2 \in S$ *and* $y \in A$ *such that* $d(a, y) > r$ *and*

$$f(D_d(y; \delta)) \supseteq S \backslash D_s(\{\xi_1, \xi_2\}; \varepsilon).$$

(M-set.)

The connection between discontinuities and standard J- and M-sets is as follows.

5.2. THEOREM. *Let b be the center of an S-disk on* Ω *with respect to d. If b is an S-discontinuity in the metric d for a standard meromorphic function f defined on* Ω *and if* $b \in \mathfrak{o}_d(^*A)$, *then A is a* J-*set. If b is in an infinite galaxy, then A is an* M-set.

Proof. We may apply 3.4 at the discontinuity to see that

$$f(\mathfrak{o}_d(b)) \supseteq {}^*S \backslash \mathfrak{o}_s(\{\alpha, \beta\})$$

for at most two standard $\alpha, \beta \in S$.

We know that the set of standard points in ${}^*f({}^*[D_d(A; \varepsilon)]$ is $f(D_d(A; \varepsilon))$. When ε is standard $\mathfrak{o}_d(b) \subseteq {}^*D_d(A; \varepsilon) = D_d({}^*A; \varepsilon)$ and therefore A is a J-set.

If b is infinite the standard set B given below satisfies ${}^*B \supseteq \mathcal{O}^+ \times ({}^*R \backslash \mathfrak{o}) \times ({}^*R \backslash \mathfrak{o})$, that is the first component can be any finite positive real number and the next two any non-infinitesimal. Then ${}^\circ({}^*B) = B = R^+ \times R^+ \times R^+$ and A is an M-set.

$$\begin{aligned} {}^*B = \{(r, \delta, \varepsilon) : r, \delta, \varepsilon > 0 \quad &\text{and} \quad \exists \xi_1, \xi_2 \in {}^*S \quad \text{and} \quad \exists y \in {}^*A \\ \text{st } d(y, a) > r \quad &\text{and} \quad f({}^*D_d(y; \delta)) \supseteq {}^*S \backslash D_s(\xi_1, \xi_2; \varepsilon)\}. \end{aligned}$$

(If r is finite and δ and ε non-infinitesimal we take $y \in \mathfrak{o}_d(b) \cap {}^*A$ and apply the reasoning in the first part of the proof.)

5.3. *Remarks.* When we begin with a given remote *S*-discontinuity of a standard function we may obtain a standard sequence which is a J-set or M-set by applying 2.5. (This avoids the somewhat more delicate problem of approximation of a particular point by a standard sequence.) When $\omega \in {}^\# N$, x_ω of the sequence in 2.5(3) is a (remote) *S*-discontinuity.

If d is finite exactly on $\text{ns}({}^*\Omega)$, as is the case in 4.6, 4.7 and 4.8 for example, then J-sets and M-sets coincide for standard functions since they are necessarily continuous on $\text{ns}({}^*\Omega)$.

J-sets and M-sets have infinite discontinuities in their non-standard extensions, so their non-existence in the Examples 4.6, 4.7 and 4.8 is equivalent to normality.

Next we extend a result of Marty–Lehto to this setting. If $A \subseteq \Omega$, let

$$\limsup_{z \in A} h(z) = \inf[\sup(h(z) : z \in A \quad \text{and} \quad d(z, a) > r) : r > 0],$$

for real valued functions $h(z)$, where $a \in \Omega$ is fixed.

We shall also assume from now on that if $d(z, a) > r_0$ $(z \in {}^*\Omega)$ for some fixed finite r_0, then z is the center of an *S-disk*.

5.4. THEOREM. *If* $\limsup_{z \in A} M(s/d)f(z) = \infty$, *then* ${}^*A$ *contains an infinite S-discontinuity of* f, *or* A *is an* M-*set.*

Proof. The $*$-transform of lim sup says there is an infinite point $z \in {}^*A$ for which $M(s/d)f(z)$ is infinite. Since we have assumed $\mathfrak{d}_d(z)$ is an infinitesimal disk we may apply 3.4 which says then that z is a point of discontinuity.

As applications we now consider some of the known results.

5.5. *Julia–Milloux theorem for meromorphic functions.* Apply 5.2 to the setting of Example 4.6. Observe that since $x \overset{d}{=} y$ in that metric if and only if $|x - y| < \delta|y|$ for some infinitesimal δ, we may substitute the J- and M-set conditions for standard disks $|x - y| < \delta|y|$ which is the classical form. Thus we have the classical result that *if* $\limsup |z_n| \; \rho f(z_n) = \infty$ *then the sequence* (z_n) *is an* M-*set for* f.

We have already remarked that $|z| \; \rho f(z)$ can fail to be infinite in 4.6.

5.6. *Gavrilov's classes* $W_p (p \geq 1)$ (Gavrilov [1968a, b]). Ω is a punctured disk around ∞. The metric is given locally by the differential form $|dz|/|z|^{2-p}$, $p \geq 1$. $M(s/d)f(z) = |z|^{2-p} \; \rho f(z)$. W_p is the class of uniformly continuous meromorphic functions, which was introduced by the requirement that $\limsup |z|^{2-p} \; \rho f(z) < \infty$. By examining infinitesimals, d-disks may be replaced by $|x - y| < \varepsilon|y|^{2-p}$. The theorem of Gavrilov which follows is immediate.

If $|z_n|^{2-p} \; \rho f(z_n) = \infty$, *for a holomorphic function* f *defined in a neighborhood of* ∞, *then for every* $r > 0$ *and* $\varepsilon > 0$ *there exists a point* z_n *such that in the disk* $|z - z_n| < \varepsilon|z_n|^{2-p}$, f *takes on every value in the circle* $|w| < r$ *with the exception of a set of diameter less than* $2/r$.

5.7. Lehto and Virtanen [1957] proved that no meromorphic function can be normal (in the sense of Example 4.8) in the neighborhood of an isolated essential singularity. We put the hyperbolic metric on a disk punctured at ∞ and find $M(s/\eta)f(z) = |z| \log|z| \, \rho f(z)$ must be infinite near ∞. Hence there are the corresponding J- and M-sets in the hyperbolic metric around any sequence on which lim sup $M(s/\eta)f(z) = \infty$. We contrast this with the case of 5.5 where functions can fail to have these sets (see 4.6 above).

5.8. *Functions in the unit disk.* The study of M-sets (in the context of 4.8) for the unit disk originated in Lange [1960] and has had many contributors. We give one very simple example (which follows from more refined work of Bagemihl and Seidel [1960]; also see Collingwood and Lohwater's [1966] bibliography) to indicate the "flavor" of the theory.

Let Γ and Λ be boundary paths in U and suppose $f \to \alpha$ along Γ. If $M(s/\eta)f$ is finite on a finite neighborhood of $^*\Gamma$, $^*D_\eta(\Gamma; \varepsilon)$, $\varepsilon \in \hat{R}^+$, then f is near α on any sub-neighborhood of an infinite point of $^*\Gamma$. From this we see that if Λ lies in such a neighborhood of Γ, either $f \to \alpha$ along Λ or $^*D_\eta(\Gamma; \varepsilon)$ is an M-set. Hence, *if Γ and Λ are finitely separated boundary curves and $f \to \alpha$ on Γ, then either $f \to \alpha$ on Λ or every mutual neighborhood of the curves is an* M-*set. In particular, if f is normal, $f \to \alpha$ along Λ.*

6. A note on two cluster set theorems of Gauthier. In Gauthier [1968] a standard version of the following definition is given. U is the unit disk with η the hyperbolic metric. I is the set of η-infinite points of $^*U$, (or the set $\{z : |z| \approx 1\}$). Two standard sets A_1 and $A_2 \subseteq U$ are equivalent if $\mathfrak{o}_\eta(I \cap {}^*A_1) = \mathfrak{o}_\eta(I \cap {}^*A_2)$.

We have immediately:

6.1. THEOREM. *Let $f : U \to S$ be a continuous function. Then f is uniformly continuous on U if and only if for every pair of equivalent subsets of U, $A_1 \sim A_2$, the cluster sets $C(f;\, A_1)$ and $C(f;\, A_2)$ are equal.*

The theorem is strictly standard, the proof is nonstandard.

Proof. ($\Rightarrow$): The nonstandard characterization of the cluster set is: $C(f;\, A_1) = \mathrm{st}_s(f(I \cap {}^*A_1)) = \mathrm{st}_s(f(\mathfrak{o}_\eta(I \cap {}^*A_1))) = \mathrm{st}_s(f(\mathfrak{o}_\eta(I \cap {}^*A_2))) = C(f;\, A_2)$. The step $\mathrm{st}(f(I \cap *A_j)) = \mathrm{st}(f(\mathfrak{o}(I \cap *A_j)))$ $(j = 1, 2)$ requires uniform continuity.

($\Leftarrow$): If f is not uniformly continuous there exist sequences $(x_n)_{n \in N}$ and $(y_n)_{n \in N}$ with $\eta(x_n, y_n) \to 0$ and $\eta(0, x_n) \to \infty$, $\eta(0, y_n) \to \infty$ while $f(x_n) \to \alpha \neq \beta \leftarrow f(y_n)$. In this case $\{x_n : n \in N\} \sim \{y_n\}$, but $C(f;\, \{x_n\}) \neq C(f;\, \{y_n\})$.

6.2. A corollary which contains Gauthier's Theorem 2 is: *A meromorphic* *function f is normal on U if and only if $C(f; A_1) = C(f; A_2)$ for every pair of equivalent subsets of U.*

In order to establish his results Gauthier introduced the following cluster set in standard terms,

$$\hat{C}(f; A) = \text{st}_s f(I \cap \mathfrak{v}_\eta(^*A)).$$

Of course, if $A_1 \sim A_2$ we have $\hat{C}(f; A_1) = \hat{C}(f; A_2)$. Now if $f: U \to S$ is S-continuous on $^*A$ we have $\hat{C}(f; A) = C(f; A)$ and in light of 5.1 above, when f is meromorphic, either A is an M-set or $\hat{C}(f; A) = C(f; A)$. This sharpens his Corollary 1 and Theorem 1.

References

Bagemihl, F. and Seidel, W., 1960, Behavior of Meromorphic Functions on Boundary Paths, with Applications to Normal Functions, *Arch. Math.* 11, pp. 263–269.

Behrens, M. F., 1971, untitled preprint, to appear.

Brown, L. and Gauthier, P., 1971, oral communication, to appear.

Collingwood, E. F. and Lohwater, A. J., 1966, *The Theory of Cluster Sets*, Cambridge Tracts in Math. and Phys. 56 (Cambridge at The Univ. Press, London).

Gauthier, P., 1968, The Non-Plessner Points for the Schwarz Triangle Functions, *Ann. Acad. Sci. Fenn.* AI 422, pp. 1–6.

Gauthier, P., 1969, "Cercles de Remplissage" and Asymptotic Behavior, *Can. J. Math.* 21, pp. 447–455.

Gauthier, P., 1971, "Cercles de Remplissage" and Asymptotic Behavior along Circuitous Paths, preprint, *Can. J. Math.*, to appear.

Gavrilov, V. I., 1968a, The Behavior of a Meromorphic Function in the Neighborhood of an Essentially Singular Point, *AMS Transl.* (2) 71, pp. 181–201.

Gavrilov, V. I., 1968b, Some Classes of Meromorphic Functions Characterized by their Spherical Derivative, *Izv. Akad. Nauk SSSR Ser. Mat.* 32, pp. 687–693.

Hoffman, K., 1967, Bounded Analytic Functions and Gleason Parts, *Ann. Math.* 86, pp. 74–111.

Lange, L. H., 1960, Sur les cercles de remplissage non-euclidiens, *Ann. Sci. Ecole. Norm. Sup.* (3) 77, pp. 257–280.

Lappan, P., 1965, Some Results on Harmonic Normal Functions, *Math. Zeitschr.* 90, pp. 155–159.

Lehto, O., 1959, The Spherical Derivative of Meromorphic Functions in the Neighborhood of an Isolated Singularity, *Comm. Math. Helv.* 33, pp. 196–205.

Lehto, O. and Virtanen, K. I., 1957, Boundary Behavior and Normal Meromorphic Functions, *Acta Math.* 97, pp. 47–65.

Marty, F., 1931, Recherches sur la répartition des valeurs d'une fonction méromorphe, *Ann. Fac. Sci. Univ. Toulouse* III 23, pp. 183–261.

Noshiro, K., 1938, Contributions to the Theory of Meromorphic Functions in the Unit Circle, *J. Fac. Sci. Hokkaido Univ.* 7, pp. 149–159.

Noshiro, K., 1960, *Cluster Sets*, Ergebnisse d. Math. new series 28 (Springer-Verlag, Berlin).

Ostrowski, A., 1926, Über Folgen analytischer Funktionen und einige Verschärfungen des Picardschen Satzes, *Math. Zeit.* 24, pp. 215–258.
Robinson, A., 1966, *Non-Standard Analysis*, Studies in Logic (North-Holland, Amsterdam).
Yosida, K., 1934, On a Class of Meromorphic Functions, *Proc. Phys.-Math. Soc. Japan* 3, ser 16, pp. 227–235.

Received 15 July 1971

A NON-STANDARD REPRESENTATION OF MEASURABLE SPACES, L_∞, AND L_∞^*

Peter A. LOEB[1])
University of Illinois

In this paper, we apply the methods of non-standard analysis developed by Abraham Robinson [1966] to measure theory. We show that there are linear mappings from an arbitrary, real L_∞ space and its dual L_∞^* into Euclidean ω-space, E^ω, where ω is an infinite integer. Finite valued, finitely additive measures on the underlying measurable space are also mapped onto elements of E^ω, and integrals are infinitesimally close to the corresponding inner products in E^ω. Yosida and Hewitt's [1952] representation of L_∞^* is an immediate consequence of these results. We also describe non-standard representations of multiplicative linear functionals on L_∞ and bounded Radon–Nikodym derivatives[2]).

In general, we use Robinson's [1966] notation. If we have an enlargement of a structure that contains the set R of real numbers, then $^*R$ denotes the set of non-standard real numbers and $^*N$, the set of non-standard natural numbers. A set S is called *finite if there is an internal bijection from an initial segment of $^*N$ onto S; a *finite set has all of the "formal" properties of a finite set. Given b and c in $^*R$, we write $b \simeq c$ if $b - c$ is in the monad of 0; when b is finite, we write $^\circ b$ for the unique, standard real number in the monad of b.

1. The partition P and bounded measurable functions. Let X be a fixed set and $\mathscr{M}$ a fixed σ-algebra of subsets of X. We shall assume that both X and $\mathscr{M}$ are infinite sets. By a finite $\mathscr{M}$-partition of X, we mean a finite collection $\{B_i \in \mathscr{M} : 1 \leq i \leq n\}$ of non-empty sets with $X = \bigcup_{i=1}^n B_i$ and $B_i \cap B_j = \emptyset$ if $i \neq j$. We let $\mathscr{P}$ denote the collection of all finite $\mathscr{M}$-partitions of X.

If P_1 and P_2 are elements of $\mathscr{P}$, we say that P_2 is finer than P_1 and we

1) This work was supported by NSF Grant 14785.

2) For other applications of non-standard analysis to measure theory, see Robinson [1964] and Bernstein and Wattenberg (Luxemburg [1969]).

write $P_1 \leq P_2$ if for each $C \in P_1$, $C = \cup \{B \in P_2 : B \subset C\}$. This partial ordering in $\mathscr{P}$ is a concurrent relation in the sense of Robinson [1966]. That is, if $\{P_j\}$ is a finite subset of $\mathscr{P}$, there is a $P_0 \in P$ with $P_j \leq P_0$ for each j.

We now take a fixed enlargement of a structure that contains X and the extended real numbers. (See Robinson [1966] or Machover and Hirschfeld [1969]). Since the relation "$\leq$" is concurrent, we have the following result:

1.1. THEOREM. *There is a partition* $P \in {}^*\mathscr{P}$ *such that* ${}^*P_0 \leq P$ *for any* $P_0 \in \mathscr{P}$. *That is,* $P \subset {}^*\mathscr{M}$ *has the following properties:*

(i) *There is an infinite integer* $\omega_P \in {}^*N$ *and an internal bijection from* $I = \{i \in {}^*N : 1 \leq i \leq \omega_P\}$ *onto P. Thus we may write* $P = \{A_i : i \in I\}$.

(ii) *If i and j are in I and* $i \neq j$, *then* $A_i \neq \emptyset$ *and* $A_i \cap A_j = \emptyset$.

(iii) ${}^*X = \bigcup_{i \in I} A_i$.

(iv) *For each* $B \in \mathscr{M}$, *let* $I_B = \{i \in I : A_i \subset {}^*B\}$. *Then* I_B *is *finite, and* ${}^*B = \bigcup_{i \in I_B} A_i$.

We shall hereafter let $P = \{A_i : i \in I\}$ be a fixed partition of ${}^*X$ with the above properties (i) through (iv). In particular, if $B \in \mathscr{M}$ then $I_B = \{i \in I : A_i \subset {}^*B\}$. Note that the cardinality of P and, therefore, ${}^*N$ can be arbitrarily large. For example, if X has cardinality $\aleph$ and $\mathscr{M}$ is the power set of X, then for each $x \in X$, $\{x\} \in P$, whence both P and ${}^*N$ have cardinality $\geq \aleph$.

DEFINITION. *Let Q be the set of functions from X to* $R \cup \{+\infty, -\infty\}$, *M, the* $\mathscr{M}$*-measurable functions in Q and* MB, *the bounded functions in M. For each* $f \in Q$ *and non-empty* $C \in \mathscr{M}$, *let*

$$D(f, C) = \sup_{x \in C} f(x) - \inf_{x \in C} f(x).$$

We easily list the properties of the extension ${}^*D$ of the function D, for these properties are formally the same as the properties of D. We use ${}^*D$ to show that the extensions of functions in MB are essentially constant on each set $A_i \in P$. In what follows, R^+ will denote the non-negative real numbers.

1.2. PROPOSITION. *Given* $g \in {}^*Q$ *and* $A \neq \emptyset$ *in* ${}^*\mathscr{M}$, *we have* ${}^*D(g, A) \in {}^*R^+ \cup \{+\infty\}$. *For any x and y in A,* $|g(x) - g(y)| \leq {}^*D(g, A)$ *and for any* $\delta > 0$ *in* ${}^*R$, *there are points x and y in A with*

$$|g(x) - g(y)| > {}^*D(g, A) - \delta.$$

If $A' \in {}^*\mathscr{M}$, $A' \neq \emptyset$, *and* $A' \subset A$, *then* $D(g, A') \leq D(g, A)$.

1.3. THEOREM. *A bounded function $f \in Q$ is measurable iff there is a $\delta \simeq 0$ in $^*R^+$ such that $^*D(^*f, A_i) \leq \delta$ for all $i \in I$.*

Proof. Since I is *finite, there is a maximum number δ in the set $\{^*D(^*f, A_i): i \in I\}$. Now $f \in$ MB iff $\forall\, \varepsilon > 0$ in R, there is a standard partition $P_\varepsilon \in \mathscr{P}$ such that $D(f, B) \leq \varepsilon$ for each $B \in P_\varepsilon$. But $^*P_\varepsilon \leq P$, $D(f, B) = {}^*D(^*f, {}^*B)$ for each $B \in P_\varepsilon$, and $^*D(^*f, A_i) \leq {}^*D(^*f, {}^*B)$ for each $i \in I_B$. Therefore, $\delta \leq \varepsilon\ \forall\, \varepsilon > 0$ in R, i.e. $\delta \simeq 0$, iff $f \in$ MB.

Note that Theorem 1.3 has an obvious generalization when MB is replaced by a family of $\mathscr{M}$-measurable functions each of which has its range in a compact subset of some uniform space. In particular, we can replace MB with bounded, complex-valued measurable functions. We shall, however, limit this discussion to the real case.

DEFINITION. *Let E be the set of all internal mappings from the index set I into $^*R$. We write x_i instead of $x(i)$ for $x \in E$ and $i \in I$. Let "$\cong$" denote the external equivalence relation in E defined by setting $x \cong y$ when $x_i \simeq y_i$ for all $i \in I$. Let c_P be a fixed mapping of I into $^*X$ so that for each $i \in I$, $c_P(i) \in A_i$, and let T denote the mapping of* MB *into E defined by setting $T(f)(i) = {}^*f(c_P(i))$ for each $f \in$* MB *and $i \in I$.*

Note that the set E has all of the "formal" properties of Euclidean n-space. The fact that the choice function c_P exists follows from the fact a choice function exists for every standard partition in $\mathscr{P}$. Moreover, it follows from Theorem 1.3 that if $\hat{c}_P$ is any other choice function with respect to P, and $\hat{T}$ is the corresponding map of MB into E, then for each $f \in$ MB, $T(f) \cong \hat{T}(f)$. Finally, we note the following properties of T:

1.4. PROPOSITION. *Given f, g in* MB *and α, β in R, $T(\alpha f + \beta g) = \alpha T(f) + \beta T(g)$, $T(fg) = T(f)T(g)$, where $(T(f)T(g))(i) = (T(f)(i)) \cdot (T(g)(i))$, and $T(f) \not\cong T(g)$ if $f \neq g$.*

Proof. The first two statements are clear, and the third follows from the fact that if $f \neq g$, then $\exists B \in \mathscr{M}$ and $\varepsilon > 0$ in R with $|f(x) - g(x)| \geq \varepsilon$ for each $x \in B$. Thus $|T(f)(i) - T(g)(i)| \geq \varepsilon$ for each $i \in I_B$.

2. Measures. We now consider the relationship between measures on $(X, \mathscr{M})$ and the partition P. Most of our results deal with finitely additive, totally finite measures. Recall that a function $\mu: \mathscr{M} \to R$ is finitely additive if whenever B_1 and B_2 are disjoint elements of $\mathscr{M}$ we have $\mu(B_1 \cup B_2) = \mu(B_1) + \mu(B_2)$; in particular, $\mu(\emptyset) = 0$.

DEFINITION. *Let $\Phi(X, \mathscr{M})$, or simply Φ, denote the set of all finitely additive real-valued functions μ on $\mathscr{M}$ such that* $\sup_{B\in M} |\mu(B)| < +\infty$. *Let U be the mapping of Φ into E defined by setting $U(\mu)(i) = {}^*\mu(A_i)$ for each $\mu \in \Phi$ and $i \in I$. If $e \in E$ and both $\sum_{i\in I} (e_i \vee 0)$ and $\sum_{i\in I} (-e_i \vee 0)$ are finite in ${}^*R$, let $\varphi(e)$ be that element of Φ such that for each $B \in \mathscr{M}$, $\varphi(e)(B) = {}^\circ\sum_{i\in I_B} e_i$.*

Note that we are writing $\sum$ instead of ${}^*\sum$ for the extension of the summation operator. We now show that for $\mu \in \Phi$, $\varphi(U(\mu)) = \mu$; we shall see that in general it is not true that $U(\varphi(e)) \cong e$.

2.1. PROPOSITION. *Given μ, ν in Φ and α, β in R, we have $U(\alpha\mu + \beta\nu) = \alpha U(\mu) + \beta U(\nu)$. Moreover, $\varphi(U(\mu))$ is defined and equals μ.*

Proof. The first statement is clear. Let $b = \sup_{B\in\mathscr{M}} |\mu(B)|$. For each $A \in {}^*\mathscr{M}$, $|{}^*\mu(A)| \leq b$, and so $\sum_{i\in I} (U(\mu)(i) \vee 0) \leq b$ and $\sum_{i\in I} (-U(\mu)(i) \vee 0) \leq b$. For any $B \in \mathscr{M}$, $\varphi(U(\mu))(B) \simeq \sum_{i\in I_B} U(\mu)(i) = \sum_{i\in I_B} {}^*\mu(A_i) = {}^*\mu({}^*B) = \mu(B)$, since ${}^*\mu$ is *finitely additive. The numbers $\mu(B)$ and $\varphi(U(\mu)(B))$ are both standard and therefore equal.

In R and ${}^*R$, we use the usual lattice operations $\vee$ and $\wedge$, where for $a, b \in {}^*R$, $a \vee b = \max(a, b)$ and $a \wedge b = \min(a, b)$. In E the operations $\vee$ and $\wedge$ are defined by setting $(x \vee y)(i) = x(i) \vee y(i)$ and $(x \wedge y)(i) = x(i) \wedge y(i)$ for any x and y in E and $i \in I$. These operations are related to the lattice operations $\vee$ and $\wedge$ in Φ. Recall that for any pair μ and ν in Φ and any $B \in \mathscr{M}$,

$$\mu \vee \nu(B) = \sup_{\substack{C\subset B \\ C\in\mathscr{M}}} (\mu(C) + \nu(B - C)).$$

Also, $\mu \wedge \nu = -(-\mu \vee -\nu)$, $\mu^+ = \mu \vee 0$, $\mu^- = -\mu \vee 0$ and $|\mu| = \mu^+ + \mu^-$. We write ${}^*\mu^+$ for $({}^*\mu)^+ = {}^*(\mu^+)$, and we write ${}^*\mu^-$ for $({}^*\mu)^- = {}^*(\mu^-)$. Note that $|{}^*\mu| = {}^*|\mu|$.

2.2. PROPOSITION. *Let μ and ν be in Φ. Then*

(i) $U(\mu \vee \nu)(i) \geq U(\mu)(i) \vee U(\nu)(i)$ *for each* $i \in I$;

(ii) $\sum_{i\in I} [U(\mu \vee \nu)(i) - U(\mu) \vee U(\nu)(i)] = \mu \vee \nu(X) - \sum_{i\in I} U(\mu) \vee U(\nu)(i) \simeq 0$;

(iii) $U(\mu \vee \nu) \cong U(\mu) \vee U(\nu)$;

(iv) $\mu \vee \nu = \varphi(U(\mu) \vee U(\nu))$; *and*

(v) $\sum_{i \in I} |U(\mu)(i)| = |\mu|(X) - \delta$, *where* $\delta \geq 0$, $\delta \simeq 0$.

Similar results hold for the operation $\wedge$.

Proof. (i) is a consequence of the fact that for any $B \in \mathscr{M}$, $\mu \vee \nu(B) \geq \mu(B) \vee \nu(B)$ in R. For any $\varepsilon > 0$ in R, $\exists B \in \mathscr{M}$ with $\mu \vee \nu(X) - [(\mu(B) \vee \nu(B)) + (\mu(X - B) \vee \nu(X - B))] < \varepsilon$. But P is finer than the partition $\{B, X - B\}$ and ε is any positive element of R, thus (ii) and (iii) follow. One obtains (iv) from (ii) by replacing X with an arbitrary $C \in \mathscr{M}$ and I with I_C. Again by (ii) we have

$$\begin{aligned}\sum_{i \in I} |U(i)| &= \sum_{i \in I} (U(\mu)(i) \vee 0) + \sum_{i \in I} (-U(\mu)(i) \vee 0) \\ &= \sum_{i \in I} [{}^*\mu^+(A_i) + {}^*\mu^-(A_i)] - \delta \\ &= |\mu|(X) - \delta\end{aligned}$$

where $\delta \geq 0$ and $\delta \simeq 0$.

DEFINITION. *Given* Φ, *we let* Φ^+ *denote the set of non-negative elements of* Φ, Φ_c, *the set of countably additive elements of* Φ, *and* Φ_p, *the set of purely finitely additive elements of* Φ. *Also, we set* $\Phi_c^+ = \Phi_c \cap \Phi^+$ *and* $\Phi_p^+ = \Phi_p \cap \Phi^+$.

Recall that $\mu \in \Phi_c$ iff for any sequence $\{B_i\} \subset \mathscr{M}$ with $B_1 \supset B_2 \supset B_3 \supset \ldots$ and $\cap B_i = \emptyset$, we have $\lim_i \mu(B_i) = 0$. Also recall that $\nu \in \Phi_p^+$ if $\nu \wedge \mu = 0$ for every $\mu \in \Phi_c^+$, and $\nu \in \Phi_p$ iff ν^+ and ν^- are in Φ_p^+.

The sets Φ_c and Φ_p are closed under addition, real scalar multiplication and the operations $\vee$ and $\wedge$; moreover, $\Phi = \Phi_p \oplus \Phi_c$ (Yosida and Hewitt [1952] pp. 48–52).

DEFINITION. *For each* $\mu \in \Phi_c^+$, $\nu \in \Phi_p^+$, $\varepsilon > 0$ *in* R *and* $B \in \mathscr{M}$ *we say that the triple* (μ, ν, ε) *stands in relation* S *to* B *when* $\mu(B) < \varepsilon$ *and* $\nu(X - B) = 0$.

Theorem 1.19 of Yosida and Hewitt [1952] states that for each triple (μ, ν, ε) in $\Phi_c^+ \times \Phi_p^+ \times (R^+ - \{0\})$ there is a $B \in \mathscr{M}$ with (μ, ν, ε) S B. This theorem of Yosida and Hewitt has the following generalization:

2.3. THEOREM. *There is a set* $K \in {}^*\mathscr{M}$ *such that for all* $\mu \in \Phi_c$, $|{}^*\mu|(K) \simeq 0$ *and for all* $\nu \in \Phi_p$, $|{}^*\nu|({}^*X - K) = 0$.

Proof. The relation S is concurrent, for if $\{(\mu_j, \nu_j, \varepsilon_j)\}$ is a finite set in the domain of S and $(\sum_j \mu_j, \sum_j \nu_j, \min_j \varepsilon_j)$ S B, then for each j, $(\mu_j, \nu_j, \varepsilon_j)$ S B. Thus $\exists K \in {}^*\mathcal{M}$ such that for each $\nu \in \Phi_p^+$, ${}^*\nu({}^*X - K) = 0$, and for each $\mu \in \Phi_c^+$ and $\varepsilon > 0$ in R, ${}^*\mu(K) < \varepsilon$, whence ${}^*\mu(K) \simeq 0$.

By taking a refinement of P, we may assume that there is a set $K \in {}^*\mathcal{M}$ such that K has the properties described in Theorem 2.3 and $K = \cup \{A_i \in P: A_i \subset K\}$. Now if $\mu = \mu_c + \mu_p$ is the decomposition of an element μ in $\Phi = \Phi_c \oplus \Phi_p$, then when $A_i \subset {}^*X - K$, $U(\mu)(i) = U(\mu_c)(i)$ and when $A_i \subset K$, $U(\mu)(i) \simeq U(\mu_p)(i)$.

We next show that with respect to P, there is a "maximum" null set for each $\mu \in \Phi^+$, and we extend the Hahn decomposition theorem for countably additive signed measures. Recall that for $\mu \in \Phi$ and $B \in \mathcal{M}$, B is a μ-positive (μ-negative) set if for each $C \in \mathcal{M}$ with $C \subset B$ we have $\mu(C) \geq 0$ ($\mu(C) \leq 0$); B is a μ-null set if it is both μ-positive and μ-negative.

2.4. THEOREM. *Let μ be an arbitrary, finitely additive signed measure on $(X, \mathcal{M})$. Let $A_+ = \cup \{A_i \in P: {}^*\mu(A_i) > 0\}$, $A_- = \cup \{A_i \in P: {}^*\mu(A_i) < 0\}$, and $A_0 = \cup \{A_i \in P: {}^*\mu(A_i) = 0\}$. Then ${}^*\mu(A_0) = 0$, and for each standard μ-null set B, ${}^*B \subset A_0$. If there exists a μ-positive set B_+ and a μ-negative set B_- in $\mathcal{M}$ with $X = B_+ \cup B_-$ and $B_+ \cap B_- = \emptyset$, then $A_+ \subset {}^*B_+$, $A_- \subset {}^*B_-$, each $A_i \in P$ is either a ${}^*\mu$-positive set or a ${}^*\mu$-negative set, and A_0 is a ${}^*\mu$-null set.*

Proof. Since A_0 is the *finite union of sets A_i with ${}^*\mu(A_i) = 0$, ${}^*\mu(A_0) = 0$. If B is a μ-null set, then for each $i \in I_B$, ${}^*\mu(A_i) = 0$, so ${}^*B = \bigcup_{i \in I_B} A_i \subset A_0$. For a μ-positive set B_+ and a μ-negative set B_- forming a partition of X, we have ${}^*X = {}^*B_+ \cup {}^*B_-$ and ${}^*B_+ \cap {}^*B_- = \emptyset$. If ${}^*\mu(A_i) > 0$, then $A_i \not\subset {}^*B_-$, and thus $A_+ \subset {}^*B_+$. Similarly, $A_- \subset {}^*B_-$.

2.5. COROLLARY. *If μ is countably additive, every $A_i \in P$ is either a ${}^*\mu$-positive or a ${}^*\mu$-negative set.*

Example 1: Let X be the real line, $\mathcal{M}$ the Lebesgue measurable subset of X, and μ, Lebesgue measure on $(X, \mathcal{M})$. For each $x \in X$, $\{x\} \in P$ and $\mu(\{x\}) = 0$, whence the null set $A_0 = \cup \{A_i \in P: {}^*\mu(A_i) = 0\}$ contains every standard real number.

Example 2: If $X = N$ and $\mathcal{M}$ is the power set of N, then $\{n\} \in P$ for each $n \in N$. Let ω be the first element of the non-empty internal set $\{n \in {}^*N: \{n\} \notin P\}$, and assume that $A_i = \{i\}$ for $i < \omega$. Let $e \in E$ be defined by setting $e_i = 2^{-i}$

for $1 \leq i \leq \omega - 2$, $e_{\omega-1} = -2$, and $e_i = 0$ for $i \geq \omega$. For each $n \in N$, $\varphi(e)(\{n\}) = 2^{-n}$, but $\varphi(e)(N) = -1$. Clearly, $\varphi(e)$ has no standard Hahn decomposition. Moreover, $*\varphi(e)(\{\omega - 1\}) > 0$, so $U(\varphi(e)) \not\approx e$. Note that here for the set K of Theorem 2.3 we may take $\{n \in *N : n \geq \omega\}$.

In dealing with multiplicative linear functionals on L_∞, we shall need facts about zero-one measures in Φ.

DEFINITION. *Let* $\Phi_1 = \{\mu \in \Phi : \mu(X) = 1$ *and* $\forall B \in \mathcal{M}, \mu(B) = 0$ *or* $\mu(B) = 1\}$. *For each* $j \in I$, *let* δ^j *be the element of* e *such that* $\delta^j_i = 0$ *if* $i \neq j$ *and* $\delta^j_j = 1$.

2.6. PROPOSITION. *For each* $\mu \in \Phi_1$, $U(\mu) = \delta^j$ *for some* $j \in I$, *and for all* $j \in I$, $\varphi(\delta^j) \in \Phi_1$.

Proof. The proof is clear.

Note that for $j_1 \in I$, $U(\varphi(\delta^{j_1})) = \delta^{j_2}$ for some $j_2 \in I$, and in general, $j_1 \neq j_2$. (See Example 5 below.) Of course by Proposition 2.1, $U(\varphi(\delta^{j_2})) = \delta^{j_2}$. It follows that for each $j \in I$, $\varphi(\delta^j) \in \Phi_p$ or $\varphi(\delta^j) \in \Phi_c$. To say more, we need the notion of a free $\mathcal{M}$-measurable ultrafilter, i.e., a filter $\mathcal{F} \subset \mathcal{M}$ such that $\cap \{B : B \in \mathcal{F}\} = \emptyset$ and for each $B \in \mathcal{M}$, $B \in \mathcal{F}$ or $X - B \in \mathcal{F}$. A chain in $\mathcal{F}$ is a countable set $\{B_n\} \subset \mathcal{F}$ with $B_1 \supset B_2 \supset B_3 \ldots$. The next theorem is a restatement of the well known relation between $\mathcal{M}$-measurable ultrafilters and Φ_1.

2.7. THEOREM. *If* $\{x\} \in \mathcal{M}$ *for each* $x \in X$, *then the following statements are equivalent*:

(i) *For each* $j \in I$, $\varphi(\delta^j) \in \Phi_p$ *iff* $A_j \neq \{x\}$ *for any standard* $x \in X$.

(ii) *Every free* $\mathcal{M}$*-measurable ultrafilter contains a chain*

$$\{B_n\} \text{ with } \bigcap_{n=1}^{\infty} B_n = \emptyset.$$

Proof. (i) $\Rightarrow$ (ii): Given a free $\mathcal{M}$-measurable ultrafilter $\mathcal{F}$, define $\mu \in \Phi_1$ by setting $\mu(B) = 1$ for $B \in \mathcal{F}$ and $\mu(B) = 0$ for $B \in \mathcal{M} - \mathcal{F}$. By Proposition 2.6, $\mu = \varphi(\delta^j)$ where $j \in I$, but $A_j \neq \{x\}$ for any $x \in X$ since $\mathcal{F}$ is free. By assumption, $\mu \notin \Phi_c$, i.e., there is a sequence $B_1 \supset B_2 \supset B_3 \ldots$ in $\mathcal{M}$ with $\bigcap_{n=1}^{\infty} B_n = \emptyset$ and $\lim_n \mu(B_n) \neq 0$. It follows that $B_n \in \mathcal{F}$ for each n.

(ii) $\Rightarrow$ (i): It is well known that $\varphi(\delta^j) \in \Phi_c$ when $x \in X$ and $A_j = \{x\}$. If $A_j \neq \{x\}$ for any $x \in X$, and $\mathcal{F} = \{B \in \mathcal{M} : \varphi(\delta^j)(B) = 1\}$, then $\mathcal{F}$ is a free

$\mathscr{M}$-measurable ultrafilter. Given a chain $\{B_n\} \subset \mathscr{F}$ with $\bigcap_{n=1}^{\infty} B_n = \emptyset$, we have $\lim_n \varphi(\delta^j)(B_n) = 1$, whence $\varphi(\delta^j) \notin \Phi_c$.

Example 3. If $\mathscr{M}$ is the collection of Borel sets in the unit interval $[0,1]$, then every free $\mathscr{M}$-measurable ultrafilter contains a chain $\{B_n\}$ with $\bigcap_{n=1}^{\infty} B_n = \emptyset$.

Example 4. If $\mathscr{M}$ is the collection of countable sets and their complements in an uncountable set X, then the collection of complements of countable sets is free, but contains no chain $\{B_n\}$ with $\bigcap_{n=1}^{\infty} B_n = \emptyset$.

Example 5. Let $X, \mathscr{M}, P$ and ω be the same as in Example 2, and let $j_0 = \omega - 1$. Since $j_0 \in {}^*N - N$, it follows from Theorem 2.7 that $\varphi(\delta^{j_0}) \notin \Phi_c$. Therefore, ${}^*(\varphi(\delta^{j_0})) \notin {}^*\Phi_c$, and so $U(\varphi(\delta^{j_0})) \neq \delta^{j_0}$.

3. Integration. In this section we show that for $f \in MB$ and $\mu \in \Phi$, $\int_X f\, d\mu$ is infinitesimally close to the inner product $T(f) \cdot U(\mu)$ in E. First we have the following result:

3.1. THEOREM. *Let μ be a non-negative finitely additive measure on $(X, \mathscr{M})$, and let $f \geq 0$ be in M. For each $B \in \mathscr{M}$, the number*

$$S_B = \sum_{i \in I_B} (\inf_{x \in A_i} {}^*f(x))^*\mu(A_i)$$

is finite in ${}^*R$ if and only if the restriction of f to B is μ-integrable. In this case, $\int_B f\, d\mu \simeq S_B$.

Proof. The theorem follows from the fact that for any standard simple function $\psi \leq f$ on B, we have $\int_B \psi\, d\mu \leq S_B \leq \int_B f\, d\mu$ in ${}^*R \cup \{+\infty\}$.

3.2. THEOREM. *If $\mu \in \Phi$, $f \in$ MB, and $B \in \mathscr{M}$, then*

$$\int_B f\, du = {}^\circ\sum_{i \in I_B} {}^*f(c_P(i)) \;{}^*\mu(A_i).$$

In particular,

$$\int_X f\, d\mu = T(f) \cdot U(\mu),$$

where "·" denotes the inner product $(x, y) \to \sum_{i \in I} x_i y_i$ in E.

Proof. Since we can replace f with $f + c$ where c is a positive constant, or instead replace B with the sets where f and $-f$ are positive, we can assume that $f \geq 0$ on B. For each $i \in I_B$, we write $f(i)$ instead of ${}^*f(c_P(i))$ and $\underline{f}(i)$ instead of $\inf_{x \in A_i} {}^*f(x)$. Let $\eta = \max_{i \in I_B} (f(i) - \underline{f}(i))$; by Theorem 1.3. $\eta \simeq 0$. Let $s = \sup_{x \in X} f(x)$. Writing $\sum$ instead of $\sum_{i \in I_B}$ we now have by Proposition 2.2 and Theorem 3.1,

$$\left|\int_B f\,d\mu - \sum f(i)^*\mu(A_i)\right| = \left|\int_B f\,d\mu^+ - \int_B f\,d\mu^- - \sum f(i)^*\mu(A_i)\right|$$

$$\simeq \left|\sum \underline{f}(i)^*\mu^+(A_i) - \sum \underline{f}(i)^*\mu^-(A_i) - \sum f(i)^*\mu(A_i)\right|$$

$$= \Big|\sum \underline{f}(i)[{}^*\mu^+(A_i) - (0 \vee {}^*\mu(A_i))] + \sum \underline{f}(i)\,[-\,{}^*\mu^-(A_i) + (0 \vee -\,{}^*\mu(A_i))]$$
$$+ \sum (\underline{f}(i) - f(i))^*\mu(A_i)\Big|$$

$$\leq s \sum [{}^*\mu^+(A_i) - (0 \vee {}^*\mu(A_i))] + s \sum [{}^*\mu^-(A_i) - (0 \vee -\,{}^*\mu(A_i))]$$
$$+ \eta|\mu|(X) \simeq 0.$$

Example. It is easy to see that Theorem 3.2 does not hold for Lebesgue measure on $[0, \infty)$ when $f(x) = x^{-2}$, since one of the sets $A_i \in P$ must have infinite measure. Neither does the theorem hold for Lebesgue measure on $(0, 1]$ when $f(x) = x^{-\frac{1}{2}}$ and c_P is an arbitrary choice function.

One can transform unbounded elements of M into elements of E so that a variation of Theorem 3.2 is valid for each $\mu \in \Phi$. Fix an element $f \in M$. For each $n \in N$, let $f_n = -n \vee f \wedge n$, and for each $n \in {}^*N$ let ${}^*f_n = -n \vee {}^*f \wedge n$. If $f|f^{-1}[(-\infty, \infty)]$ is not bounded, let $J = \{n \in {}^*N : \forall i \in I, {}^*D({}^*f_n, A_i) \leq 1/n\}$; let $\omega + 1$ be the first element of ${}^*N - J$. By Theorem 1.3, $\omega \in {}^*N - N$. If $\mu \in \Phi$ and f is μ-integrable, we have for each $B \in \mathscr{M}$,

$$\int_B f\,d\mu = {}^\circ\sum_{i \in I_B} {}^*f_\omega(c_P(i))^*\mu(A_i).$$

This equality follows from the fact that for each $B \in \mathscr{M}$,

$$\int_B f\,d\mu \simeq \int_{*B} {}^*f_\omega d^*\mu = \sum_{i \in I_B} ({}^*f_\omega(c_P(i)) + \delta_i)^*\mu(A_i)$$

where $\delta_i \simeq 0$ for each $i \in I_B$, and the fact that

$$\left|\sum_{i \in I_B} \delta_i\, {}^*\mu(A_i)\right| \leq (\max |\delta_i|)|\mu|(B) \simeq 0.$$

4. The space L_∞ and its conjugate space. Let $\mathcal{N}$ be a proper subfamily of $\mathcal{M}$ such that $\mathcal{N}$ is closed under the formation of countable unions and every $\mathcal{M}$-measurable subset of an element of $\mathcal{N}$ is an element of $\mathcal{N}$. $\mathcal{N}$ may, for example, be the set of null sets for a non-negative countably additive measure on $(X, \mathcal{M})$. For each $f \in M$, set

$$\|f\|_\infty = \inf\{\alpha \in R: \{x \in X: |f(x)| > \alpha\} \in \mathcal{N}\},$$

and let $M_0 = \{f \in M: \|f\|_\infty < +\infty\}$. We say that two functions f and g in M_0 are equivalent if $\|f - g\|_\infty = 0$, and we let L_∞ denote the usual Banach space of equivalence classes in M_0 with norm $\|\cdot\|_\infty$.

DEFINITION. *Given $\mathcal{N}$, let $I_0 = \{i \in I: A_i \in {}^*\mathcal{N}\}$. For each $f \in M_0$, let $T_0(f)$ be that element of E such that $T_0(f)(i) = {}^*f(c_P(i))$ for $i \in I - I_0$ and $T_0(f)(i) = 0$ for $i \in I_0$.*

4.1. PROPOSITION. *Given $B \in \mathcal{M}$, we have $B \in \mathcal{N}$ if and only if $I_B \subset I_0$.*

Proof. If $B \in \mathcal{N}$, then $\forall A_i \subset {}^*B$, $A_i \in {}^*\mathcal{N}$, whence $I_B \subset I_0$. If $I_B \subset I_0$, then ${}^*B = \bigcup_{i \in I_B} A_i \in {}^*\mathcal{N}$. Since the statement "${}^*B \in {}^*\mathcal{N}$" is true, the statement "$B \in \mathcal{N}$" is true.

The next result shows that we may consider T_0 to be a mapping from L_∞ into E, and thus we may write $T_0(h)$ when $h \in L_\infty$.

4.2. PROPOSITION. *If f and g are in M_0, then*
(i) $T_0(f + g) = T_0(f) + T_0(g)$;
(ii) $T_0(\alpha f) = \alpha T_0(f)$ *for each* $\alpha \in R$;
(iii) $T_0(fg) = T_0(f)T_0(g)$, *where* $[T_0(f)T_0(g)](i) = T_0(f)(i)T_0(g)(i) \forall i \in I$;
(iv) $T_0(f) \cong T_0(g) \Rightarrow \|f - g\|_\infty = 0 \Rightarrow T_0(f) = T_0(g)$;
(v) $\|f\|_\infty \simeq \max_{i \in I} |T_0(f)(i)|$.

Proof. (i), (ii) and (iii) are clear. The first part of (iv) follows from the fact that if $\|f - g\|_\infty \neq 0$, then $\exists B \in \mathcal{M} - \mathcal{N}$ and an $n \in N$ with $|f(x) - g(x)| \geq 1/n$ for all $x \in B$, whence $|T_0(f)(i) - T_0(g)(i)| > 1/n$ for each $i \in I_B - I_0$. On the other hand, if $\|f - g\|_\infty = 0$, then $\exists B \in \mathcal{N}$ with $f(x) = g(x)$ for all $x \in X - B$. Since $I_B \subset I_0$, $T_0(f) = T_0(g)$. To prove (v), let $m = \max_{i \in I} |T_0(f)(i)|$ and $r = \|f\|_\infty$. Given any standard $\varepsilon > 0$ in R, $\exists C \in \mathcal{N}$ with $|f(x)| < r + \varepsilon$ on $X - C$, whence $m < r + \varepsilon$. Moreover, $\exists$ a set $D \in \mathcal{M} - \mathcal{N}$ with $|f(x)| > r - \varepsilon$ for all $x \in D$, and so for $i \in I_D - I_0$, $|T_0(f)(i)| > r - \varepsilon$. Thus $r - \varepsilon < m < r + \varepsilon$ for any $\varepsilon > 0$ in R, i.e., $m \simeq r$.

We now define a mapping of the conjugate space L_∞^* of L_∞ into E, and we use this mapping to reestablish the Yosida and Hewitt representation of L_∞^* (see Yosida and Hewitt [1952] p. 53). If f is in $^*M_0$, we write f for the equivalence class in $^*L_\infty$ that contains f. Thus if $g \in {}^*M_0$ and $^*\|f - g\|_\infty = 0$, then for each $F \in L_\infty^*$, $^*F(f) = {}^*F(g)$. If $A \in {}^*\mathcal{M}$, then χ_A denotes the characteristic function of A; i.e., $\chi_A(x) = 1$ for $x \in A$ and $\chi_A(x) = 0$ for $x \in {}^*X - A$.

DEFINITION. *Let V be the mapping of L_∞^* into E defined for each $F \in L_\infty^*$ and $i \in I$ by setting*

$$V(F)(l) = {}^*F(\chi_{A_i}).$$

For each $F \in L_\infty^*$, let μ_F be the element in Φ such that $\mu_F(B) = F(\chi_B)$ for each $B \in \mathcal{M}$.

4.3. PROPOSITION. *Let F and G be elements of L_∞^*. Then*
(i) *for each α, β in R, $V(\alpha F + \beta G) = \alpha V(F) + \beta V(G)$;*
(ii) $V(F)(i) = {}^*F(\chi_{A_i}) = 0$ *for each $i \in I_0$;*
(iii) *for each $i \in I$, $^*\mu_F(A_i) = {}^*F(\chi_{A_i})$;*
(iv) $\mu_F = \varphi(V(f))$;
(v) $U(\mu_F) = V(F)$;
(vi) $\mu_F^+ = \varphi(V(F) \vee 0)$ *and* $\mu_F^- = \varphi(-V(f) \vee 0)$.

Proof. (i), (ii) and (iii) are clear. For each $B \in \mathcal{M}$, $\mu_F(B) = F(\chi_B) = \sum_{i \in I_B} {}^*F(\chi_{A_i}) \simeq \varphi(V(F))(B)$, and thus (iv) follows. Statement (v) follows from (iii), and (vi) follows from (v) and Proposition 2.2, part iv.

4.4. THEOREM. *Let Φ_0 denote the normed vector space $\{\mu \in \Phi : \mu(B) = 0$ for all $B \in \mathcal{N}\}$ with norm defined by setting $\|\mu\| = |\mu|(X)$ for all $\mu \in \Phi_0$. For each $F \in L_\infty^*$, let $\Theta(F) = \mu_F$. Then Θ is an isometric isomorphism from the Banach space L_∞^* onto Φ_0, and for each $F \in L_\infty^*$ and $f \in L_\infty$ we have*

$$F(f) = \int_X f \, d\mu_F \simeq V(F) \cdot T_0(f).$$

Proof. Let Ψ be the linear mapping of Φ_0 into L_∞^* defined for each $v \in \Phi_0$ and $f \in L_\infty$ by setting

$$\Psi(v)(f) = \int_X f \, dv.$$

For each $v \in \Phi_0$ and $f \in L_\infty$, $|\Psi(v)(f)| \leq \|f\|_\infty \|v\|$, and $\Psi(v)(f) \simeq U(v) \cdot T_0(f)$ by Theorem 3.2.

On the other hand, if $v \neq 0$ and l is the element of *MB such that $l/A_i = {}^*v(A_i)/|{}^*v(A_i)|$ when ${}^*v(A_i) \neq 0$ and $l/A_i = 0$ when ${}^*v(A_i) = 0$, then ${}^*\|l\|_\infty = 1$ and by part v of Proposition 2.2,

$$|{}^*(\Psi(v))(l)| = \left| \int_{{}^*X} l \, d{}^*v \right| = \sum_{i \in I} |{}^*v(A_i)| \simeq |v|(X) = \|v\|.$$

It follows that for each $v \in \Phi_0$, $\|\Psi(v)\| = \|v\|$. Thus Ψ is injective; to show that Ψ is bijective and $\Theta = \Psi^{-1}$, we show that $\Psi \circ \Theta$ is the identity map on L_∞^*. Given an arbitrary $F \in L_\infty^*$ and $\varepsilon > 0$ in R, let $g \in$ MB have the property that $\|g\|_\infty = 1$ and $\|F - \Psi \circ \Theta(F)\| < |(F - \Psi \circ \Theta(F))(g)| + \frac{1}{2}\varepsilon$. Let $h = {}^*g - \sum_{i \in I} {}^*g(c_P(i)) \cdot \chi_{A_i}$. Then $\|h\|_\infty \simeq 0$, and by Theorem 3.2 and part iii of Proposition 4.3,

$$|(F - \Psi \circ \Theta(F))(g)| = \left| F(g) - \int_X g \, d\mu_F \right| \simeq |F(g) - \sum_{i \in I} {}^*g(c_P(i)){}^*F(\chi_{A_i})|$$

$$= |{}^*F(h)| \leq \|F\|{}^*\|h\|_\infty \simeq 0.$$

Therefore, $\|F - \Psi \circ \Theta(F)\| < \varepsilon, \forall \varepsilon > 0$ in R, and thus $F = \Psi \circ \Theta(F)$ for all $F \in L_\infty^*$.

As a corollary of Theorem 4.4 and Proposition 2.6, we have the following results concerning multiplicative linear functionals on L_∞. Recall that a functional $F \in L_\infty^*$ is multiplicative if for every pair $f, g \in L_\infty$, $F(f \cdot g) = F(f) \cdot F(g)$.

4.5. THEOREM. *If $F \in L_\infty^*$ and $F \neq 0$, then the following are equivalent statements:*

(i) *F is multiplicative;*
(ii) $\mu_F \in \Phi_1 \cap \Phi_0$;
(iii) *$\mu_F = \varphi(\delta^k)$ for some $k \in I - I_0$;*
(iv) *$U(\mu_F) = V(F) = \delta^j$ for some $j \in I - I_0$;*
(v) *$\exists j \in I - I_0$ so that $\forall f \in L_\infty$, $F(f) = {}^\circ({}^*f(c_P(j)))$,*

where ${}^*f(c_P(j))$ denotes the extension of any standard representative of f evaluated at $c_P(j)$.

Proof. If $B \in \mathscr{M}$ and $F(\chi_B) \neq 0$, then given (i) we have $F(\chi_B) = F(\chi_B^2) = [F(\chi_B)]^2$, i.e. $F(\chi_B) = 1$. Since $F \neq 0$, $\mu_F \neq 0$, i.e., $\exists B \in \mathscr{M}$ with $\mu_F(B) =$

$F(\chi_B) \neq 0$. Thus (i) $\Rightarrow$ (ii). By Proposition 2.6, (ii) $\Leftrightarrow$ (iii) and (iii) $\Rightarrow$ (iv). If $V(F) = \delta^j$ where $j \in I - I_0$, then by Theorem 4.4, $F(f) \simeq T_0(f) \cdot V(F) = {}^*f(c_P(j))$ for all $f \in L_\infty$. Thus (iv) $\Rightarrow$ (v); (v) $\Rightarrow$ (i) is clear.

4.6. PROPOSITION. *If i and j are in $I - I_0$ and $\delta^j = U(\varphi(\delta^i))$, then for each $f \in L_\infty$, ${}^*f(c_P(i)) \simeq {}^*f(c_P(j))$. In particular, $\forall B \in \mathcal{M}$, $A_i \subset {}^*B \Leftrightarrow A_j \subset {}^*B$.*

Proof. Fix $f \in L_\infty$. Let $\mu_F = \varphi(\delta^j)$, and let F be the corresponding functional in L_∞^*. Then $F(f) \simeq {}^*f(c_P(j))$. Let $a = {}^\circ({}^*f(c_P(j)))$, and for $\varepsilon > 0$ in R, let $B = \{x \in X : |f(x) - a| < \varepsilon\}$. Since $A_j \subset {}^*B$, $F(\chi_B) = \mu_F(B) = 1$, and so $A_i \subset {}^*B$. Therefore $|{}^*f(c_P(i)) - a| < \varepsilon$. Since ε is arbitrary, the proposition follows.

Let Ω be the set of equivalence classes in $\{c_P(i) : i \in I - I_0\}$ under the relation that sets $c_P(i)$ equivalent to $c_P(j)$ when ${}^*f(c_P(i)) \simeq {}^*f(c_P(j))$ for every $f \in L_\infty$. For each $f \in L_\infty$, let $\tau(f)$ be the function on Ω whose value at each equivalence class $\{c_P(i)\}$ is ${}^\circ({}^*f(c_P(i)))$, and let Ω have the weakest topology for which the functions in $\{\tau(f) : f \in L_\infty\}$ are continuous. Using the ideas outlined at the end of section 3, the mapping τ can be extended to equivalence classes in M, where $f \in M$ is equivalent to $g \in M$ if $\|f - g\|_\infty = 0$. For an unbounded function $f \in M$, we set $\tau(f)(\{c_P(i)\})$ equal to ${}^\circ({}^*f(c_P(i)))$ when ${}^*f(c_P(i))$ is finite in ${}^*R$, $+\infty$ when ${}^*f(c_P(i))$ is $+\infty$ or infinite in ${}^*R^+$, and $-\infty$ when ${}^*f(c_P(i))$ is $-\infty$ or infinite in ${}^*R^-$; it is easy to see that $\tau(f)$ is a continuous mapping of Ω into the extended real numbers.

We have shown that the mapping that sends each point $\{c_P(i)\}$ in Ω onto the functional corresponding to the measure $\varphi(\delta^i)$ is a bijection of Ω and the set of non-zero multiplicative linear functionals $\mathcal{F}_m$. Let $\mathcal{F}_m$ be given the relative weak * topology of L_∞^* and let $C(\mathcal{F}_m)$ be the Banach algebra of continuous real-valued functions on this compact Hausdorff space. It is well known that the mapping that sends each $f \in L_\infty$ onto the element $g \in C(\mathcal{F}_m)$ such that $g(F) = F(f)\ \forall F \in \mathcal{F}_m$ is an isometric isomorphism (see Yosida and Hewitt [1952] p. 60). It follows that Ω is a compact Hausdorff space and τ is an isometric isomorphism of L_∞ and $C(\Omega)$. Except for compactness, these facts are also consequences of our preceding results and the Stone–Weierstrass Theorem. We prove compactness with a non-standard proof of the following standard result:

4.7. THEOREM. *The set $\mathcal{F}_m$ is compact in the relative weak * topology of L_∞^*.*

Proof. Let $\{F_\alpha: \alpha \in \mathscr{A}\}$ be a net in $\mathscr{F}_m$, where $\geq$ is the partial ordering in $\mathscr{A}$, and let $\{F_\alpha: \alpha \in {}^*\mathscr{A}\}$ denote the extension of $\{F_\alpha: \alpha \in \mathscr{A}\}$. For each $\alpha \in {}^*\mathscr{A}, \exists A_i \in P$ with $F_\alpha(\chi_{A_i}) = 1$ and $F_\alpha(\chi_{A_j}) = 0$ for $j \neq i$. Since I is *finite, $\exists i_0 \in I$ so that $\forall \alpha \in {}^*\mathscr{A}\ \exists \beta \geq \alpha$ in ${}^*\mathscr{A}$ with $F_\beta(\chi_{A_{i_0}}) = 1$. Let F_0 be the standard functional corresponding to $\varphi(\delta^{i_0})$. Let f_k, $k = 1, 2, \ldots, n$ be any standard finite set in L_∞, and let ε be any standard, positive real number. We must show that $\forall \alpha \in \mathscr{A}\ \exists \beta \geq \alpha$ in $\mathscr{A}$ with $|F_\beta(f_k) - F_0(f_k)| < \varepsilon$ for $k = 1, 2, \ldots, n$. For any $\alpha \in {}^*\mathscr{A}$, however, $\exists \beta \geq \alpha$ in ${}^*\mathscr{A}$ with $F_\beta(\chi_{A_{i_0}}) = 1$, and so for $k = 1, 2, \ldots, n$,

$$|F_\beta({}^*f_k) - F_0(f_k)| \simeq \left| \int_{{}^*X} {}^*f_k \mathrm{d}\mu_{F_\beta} - {}^*f_k(c_P(i_0)) \right| < \tfrac{1}{2}\varepsilon$$

since the variation ${}^*D\ ({}^*f_k, A_{i_0})$ is infinitesimal and $\mu_{F_\beta}(A_{i_0}) = 1$. Thus, $\forall \alpha \in {}^*\mathscr{A}, \exists \beta \geq \alpha$ in ${}^*\mathscr{A}$ with $|F_\beta({}^*f_k) - F_0(f_k)| < \varepsilon$ for $k = 1, 2, \ldots, n$, whence $\forall \alpha \in \mathscr{A}, \exists \beta \geq \alpha$ in $\mathscr{A}$ with $|F_\beta(f_k) - F_0(f_k)| < \varepsilon$ for $k = 1, 2, \ldots, n$.

5. Radon–Nikodym derivatives. In this section, we characterize those elements $\rho \in E$ such that $\rho \cong T_0(f)$ for some $f \in L_\infty$, and we give an application of our results to Probability Theory. We assume now that X, $\mathscr{M}$ and $\mathscr{N}$ are given as above, and in addition that $\mathscr{N}$ is the collection of null sets for a fixed non-negative measure $\mu \in \Phi_c^+$. Of course, this assumption is satisfied if $\mathscr{N}$ is the collection of null sets for a non-negative σ-finite measure on $(X, \mathscr{M})$.

5.1. THEOREM. *Let ρ be an element of E such that*
(i) $\rho_i = 0$ *for* $i \in I_0$,
(ii) $\max_{i \in I} |\rho_i| \simeq m \in R$, *and*
(iii) $\forall\, i \in I - I_0$ *and* $\forall\, \varepsilon > 0$ *in* R, $\exists B \in \mathscr{M}$ *with* $A_i \subset {}^*B$ *and* $\rho_i - \varepsilon < \rho_j < \rho_i + \varepsilon$ *for all* $j \in I_B - I_0$. *Let $\rho U(\mu)$ be the element of E such that $\rho U(\mu)(i) = \rho_i{}^*\mu(A_i)$ for each $i \in I$. Let $\nu = \varphi(\rho U(\mu))$; then $\nu \in \Phi_c$ and ν is absolutely continuous with respect to μ, i.e., $\nu \ll \mu$. Let $f = \mathrm{d}\nu/\mathrm{d}\mu$; then $f \in L_\infty$, and*
(iv) $T_0(f)(i) \simeq \rho_i \simeq {}^*\nu(A_i)/{}^*\mu(A_i)$ *for each $i \in I - I_0$. Conversely, for any $f \in L_\infty$ with $\|f\|_\infty = m$, if $\nu \in \Phi_c$ is given by setting $\nu(B) = \int_B f\, \mathrm{d}\mu$ for each $B \in \mathscr{M}$ and $\rho = T_0(f)$, then statements* (i), (ii), (iii) *and* (iv) *hold, and* $\nu = \varphi(\rho U(\mu))$.

Proof. If $\nu = \varphi(\rho U(\mu))$, then $\forall B \in \mathscr{M}$, $|\nu(B)| \leq {}^\circ\sum_{i \in I_B} |\rho_i|{}^*\mu(A_i) \leq m\mu(B)$. Therefore, $\nu \in \varphi_c$, $\nu \ll \mu$, and $\|\mathrm{d}\nu/\mathrm{d}\mu\|_\infty \leq m$. Let $f \in \mathrm{MB}$ represent $\mathrm{d}\nu/\mathrm{d}\mu$.

To prove (iv), fix $i \in I - I_0$ and $\varepsilon > 0$ in R. Let $a = {}^\circ\rho_i$, and let B be a set in $\mathscr{M}$ with $A_i \subset {}^*B$ and $a - \varepsilon < \rho_j < a + \varepsilon$, $\forall j \in I_B - I_0$. For each set $C \in \mathscr{M}$ with $C \subset B$ we have

$$\text{(I)} \qquad (a - \varepsilon)\mu(C) \leq {}^\circ\sum_{j \in I_C} \rho_j {}^*\mu(A_j) = \nu(C) = \int_C f \, \mathrm{d}\mu \leq (a + \varepsilon)\, \mu(C).$$

It follows that $\exists Q \in \mathscr{N}$ with $(a - \varepsilon) \leq f(x) \leq (a + \varepsilon)$ on $B - Q$, whence $|{}^*f(c_P(i)) - a| \leq \varepsilon$. Replacing C with A_i, it also follows from eq. (I) that $|{}^*\nu(A_i)/{}^*\mu(A_i) - a| \leq \varepsilon$. Since ε is arbitrary, $T_0(f)(i) \simeq a \simeq \rho_i \simeq {}^*\nu(A_i)/{}^*\mu(A_i)$.

On the other hand, given any $f \in L_\infty$ such that $\|f\|_\infty = m$, $f = \mathrm{d}\nu/\mathrm{d}\mu$ for $\nu \in \Phi_c$, and $\rho = T_0(f)$, it is clear that (i), (ii) and (iii) hold. For each $B \in \mathscr{M}$, we have

$$(\inf_{x \in B} f(x))\, \mu(B) \leq \nu(B) \leq (\sup_{x \in B} f(x))\, \mu(B),$$

and so $\rho_i \simeq {}^*\nu(A_i)/{}^*\mu(A_i)$ for every $i \in I - I_0$. This establishes (iv) and more, for given any $B \in \mathscr{M}$ there is for each $i \in I_B$ a $\delta_i \simeq 0$ such that $\nu(B) = \sum_{i \in I_B} {}^*\nu(A_i) = \sum_{i \in I_B} (\rho_i + \delta_i){}^*\mu(A_i)$. But $|\sum_{i \in I_B} \delta_i {}^*\mu(A_i)| \leq (\max_{l \in I_B} |\delta_l|) \cdot \mu(B) \simeq 0$. Therefore, $\nu(B) \simeq \sum_{i \in I_B} \rho_i {}^*\mu(A_i) \simeq \varphi(\rho U(\mu))(B)$ for each $B \in \mathscr{M}$, and so $\nu = \varphi(\rho U(\mu))$.

We close with an application of these results to the Theory of Probability. Assume that $\mu(X) = 1$, and let $\mathscr{M}_1$ be a σ-algebra contained in $\mathscr{M}$. Let P_1 be the collection of all non-empty sets $C \in {}^*\mathscr{M}_1$ such that $C = \cup \{A_i \in P: A_i \subset C\}$ and such that for each $D \in {}^*\mathscr{M}_1$ with $D \subset C$, either $D = C$, $D = \emptyset$, or $D \neq \cup \{A_i \in P: A_i \subset D\}$. If $C_1 \in P_1$, $C_2 \in P_1$ and $C_1 \neq C_2$, then $C_1 \cap C_2 = \emptyset$, for given $x \in C_1 \cap C_2$, there is an $A \in P$ with $x \in A$, whence $A \subset C_1$ and $A \subset C_2$. Thus $C_1 \cap C_2 = \cup \{A_i \in P: A_i \subset C_1 \cap C_2\}$. Since either $C_1 \cap C_2 \neq C_1$ or $C_1 \cap C_2 \neq C_2$, $C_1 \cap C_2 = \emptyset$. It follows that P_1 is a *finite ${}^*\mathscr{M}_1$-measurable partition of ${}^*X$ and P_1 is finer than any standard finite $\mathscr{M}_1$-measurable partition of X.

5.2. THEOREM. *If $Y \in$ MB and $E(Y, \mathscr{M}_1)$ is the conditional expectation of Y with respect to $\mathscr{M}_1$, then for all $C \in P_1$, ${}^*D({}^*E(Y, \mathscr{M}_1), C) \simeq 0$. Moreover, given $C \in P_1$ with $\mu(C) \neq 0$ and $x \in C$,*

$${}^*E(Y, \mathscr{M}_1)(x) \simeq [\sum_{\substack{A_i \in P \\ A_i \subset C}} {}^*Y(c_P(i)){}^*\mu(A_i)]/{}^*\mu(C).$$

Proof. The fact that $^*D(^*E(Y, \mathcal{M}_1), C) \simeq 0$ follows from Theorem 1.3 applied to $\mathcal{M}_1$ and P_1. Fix $C \in P_1$ with $\mu(C) \neq 0$ and $x \in C$. By the definition of conditional expectation we have

$$\int_C {}^*E(Y, \mathcal{M}_1)\mathrm{d}^*\mu = \int_C {}^*Y\mathrm{d}^*\mu.$$

Clearly there is an $\eta \simeq 0$ so that

$$\int_C {}^*E(Y, \mathcal{M}_1)\mathrm{d}^*\mu = ({}^*E(Y, \mathcal{M}_1)(x) + \eta){}^*\mu(C).$$

If $I_C = \{i \in I : A_i \subset C\}$, then $\forall\, i \in I_C$, $\exists\, \delta_i \simeq 0$ so that

$$\sum_{i \in I_C} ({}^*Y(c_P(i)) + \delta_i){}^*\mu(A_i) = \int_C {}^*Y\mathrm{d}^*\mu.$$

Therefore,

$${}^*E(Y, \mathcal{M}_1)(x) = [\sum_{i \in I_C} {}^*Y(c_P(i)){}^*\mu(A_i)]/{}^*\mu(C) + [\sum_{i \in I_C} \delta_i{}^*\mu(A_i)]/{}^*\mu(C) - \eta.$$

Since

$$\min_{i \in I_C} \delta_i \leq [\sum_{i \in I_C} \delta_i{}^*\mu(A_i)]/{}^*\mu(C) \leq \max_{i \in I_C} \delta_i,$$

the theorem follows.

References

Berkson, E. and Porta, H., 1969, Representations of $\mathfrak{B}(X)$, *J. Funct. Anal.* 3, No. 1.

Dunford, N. and Schwartz, J. T., 1958, *Linear Operators, Part I: General Theory* (Interscience, New York).

Luxemburg, W. A. J. (editor), 1969, *Applications of Model Theory to Algebra, Analysis, and Probability* (Holt, Rinehart and Winston).

Machover, M. and Hirschfeld, J., 1969, *Lectures on Non-Standard Analysis*, Springer-Verlag Lecture Notes in Mathematics no. 94.

Robinson, A., 1964, On Generalized Limits and Linear Functionals, *Pacific J. Math.* 14, 269–283.

Robinson, A., 1966, *Non-Standard Analysis* (North-Holland, Amsterdam).

Royden, H. L., 1968, *Real Analysis* (The Macmillan Co.).

Yosida, K. and Hewitt, E., 1952, Finitely Additive Measures, *Trans. Amer. Math. Soc.* 72, pp. 46–66.

Received 11 January 1971

EIN NICHT-STANDARD-BEWEIS FÜR DIE EXISTENZ EINES STARKEN LIFTINGS IN $\mathscr{L}_\infty\langle 0, 1]$

Bernd EIFRIG

Universität Heidelberg

Ein starkes Lifting in $\mathscr{L}_\infty\langle 0, 1]$, ist ein Lifting, welches die stetigen Funktionen fest läßt (Ionescu and Tulcea [1969]).

Mit λ bezeichnen wir das Lebesguesche Maß auf $\langle 0, 1]$. Ferner sei $\mathscr{L}_\infty\langle 0,1]$ die Algebra der beschränkten λ-meßbaren Funktionen, $L_\infty\langle 0, 1]$ deren Klassen modulo Nullfunktionen. Man weiß, daß die Algebra $L_\infty\langle 0, 1]$ isomorph einer Algebra stetiger Funktionen über dem in geeigneter Topologie (Hewitt and Yosida[1952]) kompakten Raum X der maximalen Ideale von $L_\infty\langle 0, 1]$ ist. Den Isomorphismus $L_\infty\langle 0, 1] \to \mathscr{C}(X)$ deuten wir mit $\hat{}$ an. Die clopenen (offenen–abgeschlossenen) Mengen in X bilden eine Basis der Topologie und entsprechen den idempotenten Elementen in $L_\infty\langle 0, 1]$. Außerdem benötigen wir ein κ-saturiertes Modell (Luxemburg [1969]) von $\mathscr{L}_\infty\langle 0, 1]$ mit $\kappa > \aleph_1$. Schließlich benützen wir einen Choquetschen Ultrafilter $\mathfrak{U}$ auf N, der schnell im Sinne von Mokobodzki [1967/68] konvergiert. Ein solcher Filter hat die Eigenschaft, daß jede stochastisch konvergente Folge bereits auf einem gewissen Element $S \in \mathfrak{U}$ fast überall konvergiert (siehe Mokobodzki [1967/68]).

Zu einer dyadischen Zerlegung von $\langle 0, 1]$ sei U_n eine Abbildung von $\mathscr{L}_2\langle 0, 1] \to \mathscr{L}_2\langle 0, 1]$ wie folgt definiert:

1. DEFINITION.

$$(U_n f)(x) = \sum_{k=0}^{2^n-1} 2^n \left[\int_{I_{k,n}} f \,\mathrm{d}\lambda \right] c_{I_{k,n}}(x),$$

$$\textit{für } n = 1, 2, \dots \quad \textit{mit} \quad I_{k,n} = \left\langle \frac{k}{2^n}, \frac{k+1}{2^n} \right] \quad \textit{und}$$

$$k = 0, 1, \dots 2^n - 1, f \in \mathscr{L}_2\,\langle 0,1], x \in \langle 0,1].$$

Die U_n sind kontrahierende Abbildungen. Man sieht leicht, daß die Folge $(U_n f)_{n=1,2\ldots}$ stochastisch gegen f konvergiert. Nach Puritz [1972] ist $\mu(\mathfrak{U}) \neq \emptyset$. Sei $\nu \in \mu(\mathfrak{U})$ fest gewählt.

Für einen Standardpunkt $x \in \langle 0, 1]$ gilt nach der obigen Bemerkung

1.1. $f(x) = \mathrm{st}(U_\nu f)(x)$ für fast alle
$x \in \langle 0, 1]$, $f \in \mathscr{L}_\infty\langle 0, 1]$.

Den Intervallen $I_{k,\nu}$ entsprechen *-clopene Mengen in $^*X$. In Analogie zu Donoghue [1965] definieren wir für eine meßbare Menge A

2. Definition. Träger $A = \mathrm{Tr}A = \{x : \mathrm{st}(U_\nu c_A)(x) = 1\}$.

Nach 1.1 gilt: $\lambda\,(\mathrm{Tr}A \mathbin{\hat{-}} A) = 0$ ($\hat{-}$ = symmetrische Differenz). Außerdem ergibt sich schnell die Behauptung:

1.2. $x \in \mathrm{Tr}A_1 \cap \mathrm{Tr}A_2 \Rightarrow x \in \mathrm{Tr}A_1 \cap A_2$.

Sei $\mathscr{F}_x = \{A : x \in \mathrm{Tr}A,\ A \text{ meßbar}\}$, $x \in \langle 0, 1]$.
Wegen 1.2 existiert eine *-meßbare Menge B_∞^x mit:

$B_\infty^x \subset {}^*A$ für alle $A \in \mathscr{F}_x$ und

1.3. $$\mathrm{st}\, 2^\nu \int\limits_{I_{k_x,\nu}} c_{B_\infty^x}\, \mathrm{d}\lambda = 1,\ x \in \left\langle \frac{k_x}{2^\nu}, \frac{k_x+1}{2^\nu} \right].$$

Daher ist $\hat{I}_{k_x,\nu} \cap \hat{B}_\infty^x \neq \emptyset$ und *-clopen in $^*X$. Speziell existiert ein $\xi_x \in {}^*X$ und eine *-clopene Umgebung $\hat{F}_x \neq \emptyset$, die ganz in $\hat{I}_{k_x,\nu} \cap \hat{B}_\infty^x$ liegt und auf der die Funktionen aus $\mathscr{C}(X)$ eine Oszillation kleiner als eine gewisse infinitesimale Größe aufweisen. Zu $\hat{F}_x$ existiert eine *-meßbare Menge $F_x \subset I_{k_x,\nu} \cap B_\infty^x$. Man hat

1.4. $$\frac{\int\limits_{F_x} c_{B_\infty^x}\, \mathrm{d}\lambda}{\lambda(F_x)} = 1, \text{ somit auch}$$

1.5. $$\frac{\int\limits_{F_x} c_{^*A}\, \mathrm{d}\lambda}{\lambda(F_x)} = 1, \text{ falls } A \in \mathscr{F}_x.$$

3. Definition

1.6. $\rho(A)(x) = \text{st}\left[\dfrac{\lambda(F_x \cap {}^*A)}{\lambda(F_x)}\right]$

für meßbares A.

Es gelten die Beziehungen:

$$\{x:\rho(A)(x) = 1\} \supset \text{Tr}\,A$$
$$\{x:\rho(\text{C}A)(x) = 1\} \supset \text{TrC}A.$$

Wegen der Wahl von F_x gilt entweder

$$\rho(A)(x) = 1 \quad \text{oder} \quad = 0, \quad x \in \langle 0, 1].$$

Daher: $\text{Tr}A \subset \{x:\rho(A)(x) = 1\} \subset \text{CTrC}A$.

Nun ist $\lambda(\text{Tr}\,A) = \lambda(\text{CTrC}A)$, die Menge $\{x:\rho(A)(x) = 1\}$ ist also meßbar und stimmt fast überall mit A überein. Für $\xi_x \in {}^*X$ gilt überdies: $\rho(A)(x) = \hat{c}_A(\xi_x)$. ρ ist also bereits ein Lifting auf der σ-Algebra der λ-meßbaren Mengen. Insbesondere folgt durch gleichmäßige Approximation mittels Treppenfunktionen, daß

1.7. $\tilde{\varrho}(f)(x) = \text{st}\left[\dfrac{\int_{F_x} f\,\text{d}\lambda}{\lambda(F_x)}\right], f \in \mathscr{L}_\infty$

ein multiplikatives Lifting, wegen $F_x \subset \mu(x)$ sogar ein starkes Lifting definiert.

Literatur

Donoghue, W. F., 1965, On the Lifting Property, *Proc. Am. Math. Soc.* 16, pp. 913–914.
Hewitt, E. and Yosida, K., 1952, Representations of $\mathscr{L}_\infty$, *Trans. Am. Math. Soc.* 72.
Luxemburg, W. A. J., 1969, *Applications of Model Theory to Algebra, Analysis and Probability* (Holt, Rinehart and Winston).
Mokobodzki, G., 1967/68, *Seminaire Brelot-Choquet-Deny.*
Puritz, C., 1972, Skies, Constellations and Monads, *dieser Ausgabe.*
Ionescu C. and Tulcea, A., 1969, *Topics in the Theory of Lifting* (Springer, New York).

Received 18 January 1971

ON SOME CONCURRENT BINARY RELATIONS OCCURRING IN ANALYSIS

W. A. J. LUXEMBURG[1])
California Institute of Technology

1. Introduction. To present an adequate discussion of all the important concurrent binary relations occurring in analysis would be impossible within the confines of a short essay, to say nothing about the limitations of the writer. In view of this we shall only present a few examples of concurrent binary relations which occur in various parts of analysis and show how they can be applied successfully with the use of enlargements.

We recall that a binary relation $\Phi(\cdot, \cdot)$ in set theory is called *concurrent* whenever for each choice of elements $x_1, \ldots, x_n$ in the domain of Φ (dom Φ) there exists an element y in the range of Φ (ran Φ) such that $\Phi(x_i, y)$ holds for each i, $i = 1, 2, \ldots, n$.

Many results in mathematics can be reformulated to read that a certain binary relation is concurrent. That may not at all be so important if it were not for the fact that in certain nonstandard models, called enlargements, of the theory under consideration it can be shown that for each concurrent binary relation Φ there exists an ideal element z in the enlargement such that $\Phi(x, z)$ holds for each $x \in$ dom Φ under certain appropriate interpretations of the symbols involved. The existence of enlargements and their significance was first discovered by A. Robinson (see Robinson [1966] p. 30), who used them successfully in Nonstandard Analysis. Only somewhat later Robinson and the present author discovered independently that enlargements can be constructed in the form of ultrapowers. It is not the place to go into this here now. But the reader who is not too familiar with the theory of enlargements is referred to Luxemburg [1969b].

Some of the earlier applications of concurrent binary relations, made by the author, were in proving extension principles such as the Hahn-Banach Extension Theorem and Sikorski's Extension Theorem for Boolean homo-

[1]) Work on this paper was supported in part by NSF Grant GP 23392.

morphisms. For these results, in fact, one has to show that a certain concurrent binary relation can already be satisfied simultaneously for all its elements in its domain by an element in its range, which is then the required extension. Using enlargements in such a situation we obtain immediately that there is already an ideal element in the range with the required property, and the proof then proceeds in showing that the ideal element has a standard part which is the required extension. We shall not discuss in this paper any of the extension principles but refer the interested reader to Luxemburg [1962a, 1964a, 1969c].

In set theory one of the basic concurrent binary relations is the binary relation of membership between the elements of an infinite set and its family of finite subsets. This means that in any enlargement of a mathematical theory every infinite set is contained externally in the enlargement in a star-finite set of the enlargement. This fact was applied successfully by various authors to reduce various problems of combinatorial set theory to finite sets (see Luxemburg [1962b]). It may be pointed out that, in fact, this set-theoretic principle is sufficiently general as to handle any situation in which concurrent binary relations play a fundamental role (see Luxemburg [1969b] for a discussion). But we shall not follow this route in the present paper.

It is our purpose to discuss only four examples. In section 2 we shall treat the famous simultaneous approximation theorems of Dirichlet and Kronecker and apply them to obtain an interesting boundedness condition for finite sets of complex numbers. In section 3, we give a non-standard proof of the famous Radon–Nikodym Theorem based on the fact that a certain binary relation is concurrent. In the last section we shall discuss Helly-type theorems for linear functionals in the theory of normed linear spaces. It is applied to obtain an interesting representation theorem for linear functionals. In particular, we include a short discussion of the dual space of general l^{∞}-spaces.

Finally, we would like to remark that there exist even more comprehensive models than enlargements, the so-called saturated models, which role these models can play in analysis was first shown in Luxemburg [1969b]. We shall not be concerned with them here but refer the interested reader to Luxemburg [1969b].

2. An inequality for finite sets of complex numbers. Let R denote the field of real numbers and let $Z \subset R$ be the ring of integers. The subset of Z of the natural numbers $\{1, 2, \ldots, n, \ldots\}$ will be denoted by N. One of the basic approximation theorems in number theory is the so-called Dirichlet Approximation Theorem who's validity is a consequence of the pidgeon-hole principle. It can be stated as follows.

2.1. THEOREM *(Dirichlet's Principle). For each choice of real numbers* $x_1, \ldots, x_n \in R$ *and for each positive number* ε $(0 < \varepsilon \in R)$ *there exists an integer* $n \in Z$ *such that* nx_i *differs from an integer in absolute value by at most* ε *for all* $i = 1, 2, \ldots, n$.

For a proof and a discussion of Dirichlet's principle we refer to Hardy and Wright [1954]. For our purpose it is important to observe that Dirichlet's principle expresses that the binary relation Φ with dom $\Phi = R \times R^+$, where $R^+ = \{x : x > 0\}$, ran $\Phi = Z$ and defined by $\Phi((x, \varepsilon), m)$ holds whenever mx differs from an integer in absolute value by at most ε is concurrent. This fact was successfully applied by Kugler [1969] in the theory of Bohr-compactifications of the additive group of the real line and by Taylor [1969] for a result concerning bounded internal functions.

We shall use it to obtain an inequality for complex numbers. But first we shall draw a conclusion from Dirichlet's principle.

Consider an enlargement of the theory of a superstructure based in R (see Luxemburg [1972]). The set of nonstandard reals of the enlargement will be denoted by $^*R$ and its set of integers by $^*Z$. For any $a \in {}^*R$ we set $(a) = a - [a]$, where $[a]$ denotes the largest integer contained in a. By $a =_1 b$ we mean $a - b$ is infinitesimal.

As we indicated above, Dirichlet's principle states that the binary relation $\Phi((x, \varepsilon), m) \Leftrightarrow |(mx)| < \varepsilon$ or $|1 - (mx)| < \varepsilon$ is concurrent, and so using the enlargement we can even state the following theorem.

2.2. THEOREM. *There exists an infinitely large integer* $\omega \in {}^*Z$ *such that* $(\omega x) =_1 0$ *or* 1 *for all* $x \in R$.

We are now in a position to prove the following inequality.

2.3. THEOREM. *Let* $z_1, \ldots, z_n$, *be n-complex numbers such that for all* $p \in N$

2.4. $$\left|\sum_{k=1}^{n} a_k z_k^p\right| \leq M^p,$$

where $a_1, \ldots, a_n$ *and* M *are positive constants.*

Then $|z_i| \leq M$ *for all* $i = 1, 2, \ldots, n$.

Proof. We set $z_k = r_k \exp(2\pi i \alpha_k)$ $(k = 1, 2, \ldots, n)$. From 2.2 it follows that there exists an infinitely large integer $\omega \in {}^*Z$ such that $(\omega\alpha_k) =_1 0$ or 1 for $k = 1, 2, \ldots, n$. Hence, by 2.4, $|\sum_{k=1}^n a_k r_k^\omega b_k| \leq M^\omega$, where $b_k =_1 1$ for all $k = 1, 2, \ldots, n$. From this we conclude that $(1/2) \sum_{k=1}^n a_k r_k^\omega \leq M^\omega$, and so, in particular, $|z_k| = r_k \leq M(2/a_k)^{1/\omega}$. Since $(2/a_k)^{1/\omega} =_1 1$, we obtain finally that $|z_k| \leq M$ for all $k = 1, 2, \ldots, n$, and the proof is finished.

Remark. It is easy to see that in 2.3 the positive constants a_k may depend on p even to the extent that $\lim_{p\to\infty} a_k(p) = 0$ $(k = 1, 2, \ldots, n)$ without affecting the conclusion of the theorem, provided $\lim_{p\to\infty} (a_k(p))^{1/p} = 1$ for all $k = 1, 2, \ldots, n$.

It is natural to ask whether in condition 2.4 the constants $a_1, \ldots, a_n$ may be taken to be complex numbers. The answer to this question turns out to be affirmative provided the arguments $2\pi\alpha_1, \ldots, 2\pi\alpha_n$, where $\alpha_1, \ldots, \alpha_n$ are reduced mod. 1, of the complex numbers $z_1, \ldots, z_n$ satisfy an additional condition. The reason for this is that in case the constants $a_1, \ldots, a_n$ are complex we can no longer use Dirichlet's principle but we have to resort to Kronecker's Approximation Theorem.

For this purpose, we recall that a set $x_1, \ldots, x_n$ of real numbers are called to be *linearly independent* over the field of rationals Q whenever $\sum_{k=1}^n q_k x_k = 0$, $q_1, \ldots, q_n \in Q$ implies $q_1 = q_2 = \ldots = q_n = 0$, or in other words, if the numbers $x_1, \ldots, x_n$ are elements of a Hamel basis for R.

Kronecker's Theorem states.

2.5. Theorem *(Kronecker's Approximation Theorem). If the real numbers $1, \alpha_1, \ldots, \alpha_n$ are linearly independent and $\beta_1, \ldots, \beta_n$ are n-arbitrary real numbers, then for each natural number $m \in N$ and for each positive number $\varepsilon (0 < \varepsilon \in R)$ there exists a natural number $n > m$ such that $|(n\alpha_k + \beta_k)| < \varepsilon$ for each $k = 1, 2, \ldots, n$.*

Kronecker's Theorem is a deep result and for its proof we have to refer the reader to Hardy and Wright [1954] Chapter 23.

As in the case of Dirichlet's principle also Kronecker's Theorem implies that certain binary relations are concurrent. Let H be an arbitrary Hamel basis for R such that $1 \in H$, and let Φ_H be a binary relation with domain $H \times R \times N \times R^+$ and range N defined as follows:

$$\Phi_H((x, y, m, \varepsilon), n) \text{ holds whenever } n > m \text{ and } |(nx + y)| < \varepsilon \quad \text{or} \quad |1 - (nx + y)| < \varepsilon.$$

In an enlargement there are now infinitely large natural numbers with the following properties.

2.6. THEOREM. *For each Hamel basis H of R such that $1 \in H$ there exists an infinitely large natural number $\omega \in {}^*N$ such that $(\omega x + y) =_1 0$ or 1 for each $x \in H$ and for each $y \in R$.*

We shall leave it to the reader now to show that the following variant of 2.3 holds.

2.7. THEOREM. *Let $z_k = r_k \exp(2\pi i \alpha_k)$, $k = 1, 2, \ldots, n$, be n-complex numbers, where $\alpha_1, \ldots, \alpha_n$ are reduced* mod. 1 *and $\{1, \alpha_1, \ldots, \alpha_n\}$ form a linearly independent set. Then*

$$\left|\sum_{k=1}^{n} a_k z_k^p\right| \leq M^p$$

for all $p \in N$, where $\{a_1, \ldots, a_n\}$ is an arbitrary set of complex numbers $\neq 0$ and M is a positive constant, implies $|z_k| \leq M$ for all $k = 1, 2, \ldots, n$.

Without affecting the conclusion of the theorem, in this case, the constants $a_1, \ldots, a_n$ may also depend on p, provided $\lim_{p\to\infty} |a_k|^{1/p} = 1$ for each $k = 1, 2, \ldots, n$.

3. The Radon–Nikodym Theorem. It is a real pleasure for the author to acknowledge that the non-standard proof of the Radon–Nikodym Theorem, which will be presented in this section, was obtained jointly with Dr. I. Juhász (Budapest) in Oberwolfach during the meeting on nonstandard analysis. The ideas contained in this section have definite points of contact with the ideas contained in Loeb [1972] but were obtained independently.

In proving the Radon–Nikodym Theorem (see Zaanen [1967] Chapter 7 for a thorough discussion of this important result) one needs to establish the following special case.

4.1. THEOREM *(Radon–Nikodym). Let (X, Λ, μ) be a finite measure space and let ν be a non-negative countably additive measure defined on the σ-algebra Λ of the μ-measurable sets of X such that $\nu(E) \leq \mu(E)$ for all $E \in \Lambda$. Then there exists a non-negative μ-measurable function f on X which is unique* a.e. *such that $0 \leq f(x) \leq 1$, μ* - a.e., *and $\nu(E) = \int_E f(x)\, d\mu$ for all $E \in \Lambda$.*

A most elegant proof of this result via the F. Riesz Representation Theorem for linear functionals on Hilbert spaces is due to J. von Neumann and can be found in Zaanen [1967]. We shall essentially follow the same route, however, we shall replace part of the classical proof by observing that a certain binary relation is concurrent. The details are as follows.

4.2. LEMMA. *The binary relation* Φ *with domain* Λ *and range the convex set* P *of all* μ*-measurable* f *satisfying* $0 \leq f \leq 1$ a.e. *and defined by* $\Phi(E, f)$ *whenever* $\nu(E) = \int_E f \,d\mu$ *is concurrent in* E.

Proof. We shall first establish that the range of Φ is not empty. To this end, for each $E \in \Lambda$ we set $f = (\gamma(E)/\mu(E))E$, where E denotes the characteristic function of E, if $\mu(E) > 0$ and we set $f = 0$ if $\mu(E) = 0$. Since $\nu(E) = 0$ when $\mu(E) = 0$ it follows immediately that $f \in \operatorname{ran} \Phi$. We shall now show that Φ is concurrent. For this purpose, assume that $E_1, \ldots, E_n \in \Lambda$. Then the well-known basis theorem for semirings (see Zaanen [1967] p. 25) applied to the σ-algebra Λ implies that there exists a finite disjoint system $F_1, \ldots, F_p \in \Lambda$ such that for each $k = 1, 2, \ldots, n$, $E_k = \bigcup(F_i : F_i \subset E_k)$. Then we define $f = \sum_{j=1}^{p} (\nu(F_j)/\mu(F_j))F_j$, where we delete terms with $\mu(F_j) = 0$. Then obviously $\Phi(E_i, f)$ holds for all $i = 1, 2, \ldots, n$, and the proof is finished.

Remark. The reader does well to observe that the basis theorem for semirings of sets states that a certain binary relation is concurrent. Indeed, if Γ is a semi-ring and Φ the binary relation with domain Γ and range the family Ω of all finite disjoint families of elements of Γ such that $\Phi(E, \{F_1, \ldots, F_p\})$, $E \in \Gamma$ and $\{F_1, \ldots, F_p\} \in \Omega$ holds whenever $E = \bigcup(F_i : F_i \subset E)$, then the basis theorem for Γ is equivalent to the statement that Φ is concurrent in E.

We shall now turn to the proof of the Radon–Nikodym Theorem as formulated in 4.1.

Consider an enlargement of the theory of a superstructure based in X. Then it follows from 4.2 that there exists an internal ${}^*\mu$-measurable function f on ${}^*X$ such that $0 \leq f \leq 1$, ${}^*\mu$-a.e., and $\int_{{}^*E} f d^*\nu = {}^*\nu({}^*E)$ for all $E \in \Lambda$. For all $g \in L^2(X, \Lambda, \mu)$ we have, using Schwarz' inequality,

$$\left| \int_{{}^*X} f^*g \, d^*\mu \right| \leq \|g\|_2 \, \mu(X),$$

and so, $T_f(g) = \operatorname{st}(\int_{{}^*X} f^*g \, d^*\mu)$ defines a bounded linear functional on L^2. Then the F. Riesz' Representation Theorem implies that there exists an element $\varphi \in L^2(X)$ such that $\int_{{}^*X} f^*g \, d^*\mu =_1 \int_X \varphi g d\mu$ for all $g \in L^2$. In particular, since $\nu(E)$ is standard, we have for all $g = E \in \Lambda$

$$\nu(E) = \int_{*E} f \mathrm{d}^*\mu = \int_E \varphi \mathrm{d}\mu.$$

From $\int_E \varphi \mathrm{d}\mu \geq 0$ and $\int_E (1 - \varphi)\mathrm{d}\mu = \mu(E) - \nu(E) \geq 0$ for all $E \in \Lambda$ it follows finally that $0 \leq \varphi \leq 1$, μ-a.e., and the uniqueness of φ follows along similar lines, and the proof is finished.

Remark. Although the function $\mathrm{st}(f(x))$ may exist for almost all x it is not in any way related to φ pointwise. In fact, $\mathrm{st}(f)$ may not even be μ-measurable. The function φ is obtained in the proof as the standard part of f in the weak topology of L^2. From this it then follows that φ is even the $\sigma(L^\infty, L^1)$-standard part of $f \in {}^*(L^\infty)$.

4. An imbedding theorem for the second dual space of a normed linear space. It has been known for some time that the theory of topological linear spaces can be illuminated by looking at it from a nonstandard analysis' point of view. In this connection we like to refer the reader to the paper of Young [1972] on the subject and a recent Ph.D. thesis of Tacon [1971]. For a discussion of uniform structures and normed linear spaces we refer the reader to Luxemburg [1969b].

Some years ago, Robinson [1964] on the basis of his results on generalized limits, asked the author the following question. Is it possible to imbed the second dual space E'' of a normed linear space in an enlargement of E? The affirmative answer to this question was announced in Luxemburg [1964b] but until now it had not appeared in print.

In this final section of the paper we shall present a slightly more general result and we shall show how it can be applied to obtain various representation theorems for linear functionals. The number of applications we shall present is far from exhaustive and the ones which are given are only to illustrate the way the imbedding theorem can be used.

We shall begin with some notation and terminology from the theory of normed linear spaces.

Let $(E, \|\cdot\|)$ be a normed linear space over the real or complex numbers. Its Banach dual spaces will be denoted by $E', E'', \ldots$. The bilinear functionals which establish the duality between the pairs of dual spaces will be denoted by $\langle \cdot , \cdot \rangle$, that is, if $x' \in E'$, then $\langle x, x' \rangle$ denotes the value of $x' \in E'$ at x, and $\langle x', x'' \rangle$ denotes the value of $x'' \in E''$ at $x' \in E'$, and so on. We shall need the following concept.

4.1. DEFINITION. *Let W be a linear subspace of the dual space E' of a normed linear space E. Then a linear subspace $V \subset E$ is called a W-norm fundamental* (*abbr.* W-n.f.) *subspace of E whenever for each $x' \in W$*

$$\|x'\| = \sup(|\langle x, x'\rangle| : \|x\| \leq 1 \quad \text{and} \quad x \in V).$$

If $W = E'$, then V is called simply a norm-fundamental subspace of E.

A W-n.f. subspace V of E is always $\sigma(E, W)$-dense in E. A n.f. subspace of E is always norm-dense. Observe that the Hahn–Banach Extension Theorem implies that E' is E-n.f. The isometric imbedding of E in E'' defined by the mapping $x \to \langle x, \cdot\rangle$ is based on this fact.

There are various characterizations for linear subspaces of a normed linear space to be norm-fundamental in some sense. They will, however, not concern us here since in the applications it will always be perfectly clear whether the linear subspace in question is norm-fundamental in some sense or not. Our method is based on the following approximation property of W-n.f. subspaces of E, which is, in fact, the famous theorem of Helly in the theory of normed linear spaces.

4.2. THEOREM. *Let $V \subset E$ be a linear subspace of E which is W-n.f. $(W \subset E')$, and let $x'' \in E''$. Then for each choice of elements $x_1', \ldots, x_n' \in W'$ and for each $\varepsilon > 0$ there exists an element $x \in V$ such that $\langle x, x_i'\rangle = \langle x_i', x''\rangle$ for each $i = 1, 2, \ldots, n$ and $\|x\| \leq (1 + \varepsilon)\,\|x''\|$.*

Proof. There is no loss in generality to assume that $\|x''\| = 1$. Consider the mapping $x \to (\langle x, x_1'\rangle, \ldots, \langle x, x_n'\rangle)$ of E into C^n, where C^n denotes the n-dimensional complex Hilbert space. Let K_ε $(\varepsilon > 0)$ be the image under this mapping of the ball $\{x : x \in V \text{ and } \|x\| \leq 1 + \varepsilon\}$ of V. Then K_ε is a convex subset of C^n. Now, if the point $(\langle x_1', x''\rangle, \ldots, \langle x_n', x''\rangle) \notin K_\varepsilon$, then by the separation theorem for convex sets there exist complex numbers $a_1, \ldots, a_n$ such that $|\langle \sum_{i=1}^n a_i x_i', x''\rangle| \geq 1$ and $|\langle x, \sum_{i=1}^n a_i x_i'\rangle| \leq 1$ for all $x \in V$ satisfying $\|x\| \leq 1 + \varepsilon$. Since V is W-n.f. and $x_1', \ldots, x_n' \in W'$, the latter inequality implies that $\|\sum_{i=1}^n a_i x_i'\| \leq 1/(1 + \varepsilon)$. Hence, $1 \leq |\langle \sum_{i=1}^n a_i x_i', x''\rangle| \leq \|x''\|\,\|\sum_{i=1}^n a_i x_i'\| \leq 1/(1 + \varepsilon)$ is a contradiction, and the proof is finished.

Let us now examine this Helly-type theorem from the point of view of this paper. To this end, consider the binary relation Φ with domain $W \times R^+$ and range V defined as follows: $\Phi((x', \varepsilon), x)$ holds whenever $\langle x, x'\rangle = \langle x', x''\rangle$ and $\|x\| \leq (1 + \varepsilon)\,\|x''\|$. Then Theorem 4.2 is equivalent to the statement that Φ is concurrent.

Consider now an enlargement of the theory of a superstructure based in E. Then as a consequence of Helly's theorem we get the following imbedding theorem or rather a representation theorem for the elements of E'' in terms of certain finite elements of an enlargement $^*V$ of some linear subspaces V of E.

4.3. THEOREM. *If $V \subset E$ is a W-n.f. linear subspace of E, where $W \subset E'$ is a linear subspace of E', then for each $x'' \in E''$ there exists an element $v \in {}^*V$ such that $\langle x', x'' \rangle = \langle v, x' \rangle$ for all $x' \in W$ and* $\text{st}(\|v\|) \leq \|x''\|$. *In particular, if $W = E'$ or W is E''-norm fundamental, then $\|v\| =_1 \|x''\|$ and $\|x''\| \leq \|v\|$.*

Proof. We only need to prove the last part of the theorem. If W is E''-n.f., then $\langle x', x'' \rangle = \langle v, x' \rangle$ for all $x' \in W$ implies that $|\langle x', x'' \rangle| = |\langle v, x' \rangle| \leq \|v\| \; \|x'\|$, and so, by hypothesis, $\|x''\| = \sup(|\langle x', x'' \rangle| : x' \in W \text{ and } \|x'\| \leq 1) \leq \|v\|$, and the proof is finished.

Remarks. (i) The reader should observe that the element $v \in {}^*V$ is not uniquely determined by x''.

(ii) The imbedding of E'' into an enlargement of norm-fundamental subspaces of E has a natural counterpart. Given any finite element $u \in {}^*E$, where $^*E$ is an enlargement of the normed linear space E, then for each $x' \in E'$, $U(x') = \langle u, x' \rangle$ satisfies $|\langle u, x' \rangle| \leq \|u\| \; \|x'\|$, which is finite. Hence, the linear functional $\text{st}(U)$ defines a bounded linear functional on E'. From this we conclude that for each finite element $u \in {}^*E$ there exists an element $x'' \in E''$ such that $\langle x', x'' \rangle = \text{st}(\langle u, x' \rangle)$ for all $x' \in E'$ and $\|x''\| \leq \text{st}(\|u\|)$. Thus, we have shown, conversely, that the finite elements of $^*E$ can be represented in some sense by the elements of E''.

The reader who is familiar with the nonstandard hull of a normed linear space (see Luxemburg [1969b] section 16) will have no difficulties to reformulate Theorem 4.3 and the above Remark (ii) as to become results for the nonstandard hull of a normed linear space.

The main reason why the above result 4.3 is useful is contained in the fact that v can serve to represent x'' on $W \subset E'$, and, in case W is also E''-n.f., then $\|x''\| = \text{st}(\|v\|)$. We shall illustrate this by two examples. The first example we shall discuss is the dual space of $l^\infty(N)$. Our discussion of this space will be similar in many respect with Robinson [1964] Theorem 4.13.

The reader who is not too familiar with l^∞, its dual space, and the theory of finitely additive measures is advised to consult Dunford and Schwartz [1958] Chapters III and IV.

Let $l^\infty(N)$ denote as usual the Banach space of all bounded complex functions $x = x(n)$, $n \in N$ with norm $\|x\| = \sup(|x(n)| : n \in N)$. Since $l^\infty(N)$ is the dual space of the Banach space of all absolutely convergent series it follows from (4.3) that $(l^\infty)'$ can be imbedded or rather can be represented by elements of an enlargement of l^1. But we can now make this representation a little bit more special. Let V denote the linear subspace of l^1 of all the functions on N with only finitely many non-zero elements. Then V is obviously a norm-fundamental subspace of l^1. The space ${}^*V$ consists of all the internal functions on ${}^*N$ which vanish outside a star-finite subset of ${}^*N$. Hence, by 4.3, we have now the following representation theorem for the bounded linear functionals on l^∞.

4.4. THEOREM. *For each element $F \in (l^\infty(N))'$ there exists an internal function f on ${}^*N$ which vanishes outside a star-finite subset of ${}^*N$ such that*

$$\text{(i)}\ \sum_{n\in {}^*N} f(n)\,{}^*x(n) = F(x) \quad \textit{for all } x \in l^\infty, \quad \textit{and}$$

$$\text{(ii)}\ \|F\| = \mathrm{st}\Big(\sum_{n\in {}^*N} |f(n)|\Big) \quad \textit{and} \quad \|F\| \leq \sum_{n\in {}^*N} |f(n)|.$$

Observe that the summations in 4.4 are over star-finite subsets of N.

We would like to show now briefly how the Representation Theorem 4.4 can be used to derive the usual properties of $(l^\infty)'$.

To this end, it is first of all important to observe that the equality in 4.4 (i) implies, in particular, that $f(n)$ is standard for all standard $n \in N$. If we denote as usual by f^+ and f^- the positive and negative parts of a function and observing that for real F, f is real, we can formulate the following condition for a functional F on l^∞ to be non-negative, that is, $F(x) \geq 0$ for all $x \geq 0$.

4.5. *A linear functional $F \in (l^\infty)'$ is non-negative if and only if $f(n) \geq 0$ for all standard $n \in N$ and $\sum_{n\in {}^*N} f^-(n) =_1 0$.*

The easy proof is left to the reader.

Let us show now, restricting the discussion to the real $l^\infty(N)$, that every $F \in (l^\infty)'$ can be written as the difference of two positive linear functionals. To see this observe that from 4.4 (i) it follows that for each $x \in l^\infty$,

$$F(x) = \sum_{n\in{}^*N} f(n)^*x(n) = \sum_{n\in{}^*N} f^+(n)^*x(n) - \sum_{n\in{}^*N} f^-(n)^*x(n),$$

and so, setting $F^+(x) = \operatorname{st}(\sum_{n\in{}^*N} f^+(n)^*x(n))$ and $F^-(x) = \operatorname{st}(\sum_{n\in{}^*N} f^-(n)^*x(n))$ the required result is obtained.

It is well-known that every element $F \in (l^\infty)'$ can be split in an *absolutely continuous part* and a *purely finitely additive part*. We recall that an element $F \in (l^1)'$ is called *absolutely continuous* or *an integral* whenever there exists an element $\varphi \in l^1$ such that for each $x \in l^\infty$

$$F(x) = \sum_{n=1}^{\infty} \varphi(n)x(n).$$

An element $F \in (l^\infty)'$ is called *purely finitely additive* or *singular* whenever $|G(x)| \leq |F(x)|$ for all $x \in l^\infty$ and G is an integral implies $G \equiv 0$.

The integrals and the singular elements of $(l^\infty)'$ can be characterized in terms of f of 4.4 as follows. The easy proof is left to the reader.

4.6. (i) *A linear functional $F \in (l^\infty)'$ is an integral if and only if $\sum_{n\geqslant\nu}|f(n)| =_1 0$ for all infinitely large natural numbers ν.*

(ii) *A linear functional $F \in (l^\infty)'$ is singular if and only if $f(n) = 0$ for all standard n.*

We can now use 4.6 to obtain the absolutely continuous part and the singular part of a linear functional $F \in (l^\infty)'$.

If F is represented by $f \in {}^*V$ in the sense of 4.4, then we define first a standard function φ by means of the following definition $\varphi(n) = f(n)$ for all $n \in N$. Then for each $x \in l^\infty$ we write

4.7. $$F(x) = \sum_{n\in{}^*N} {}^*\varphi(n)^*x(n) + \sum_{n\in{}^*N} (f(n) - {}^*\varphi(n))^*x(n),$$

and since, $F(x)$ and $\sum_{n\in{}^*N} {}^*\varphi(n)^*x(n)$ are standard numbers it follows that $\sum_{n\in{}^*N} (f(n) - {}^*\varphi(n))^*x(n)$ is standard as well. We then set for each $x \in l^\infty$, $F_s(x) = \sum_{n\in{}^*N} (f(n) - {}^*\varphi(n))\, x(n)$, and, by 4.4, there is an element f_φ such that $\sum_{n=1}^{\infty} \varphi(n)x(n) = \sum_{n\in{}^*N} f_\varphi(n)^*x(n)$ with $f_\varphi(n) = \varphi(n)$ for all standard n. Hence, $\sum_{n\in{}^*N} (f(n) - f_\varphi(n))^*x(n)$ for all $x \in l^\infty$, is a representation of F_s in terms of 4.4. Since $f(n) - f_\varphi(n) = 0$ for all standard n it follows from 4.6 (ii) that F_s is singular. We conclude that 4.7 defines the decomposition of F into its absolutely continuous and its purely finitely additive part.

It is well-known that for each $F \in (l^\infty)'$ there exists a unique finitely additive measure μ_F on the Boolean algebra of all subsets of N such that

$$F(x) = \int_N x(n)\mathrm{d}\mu_F$$

for all $x \in l^\infty$.

The measure μ can be defined in terms of f of 4.4 by means of the following definition. For each $A \subset N$, $\mu_F(A) = \sum_{n \in {}^*A} f(n)$. Observe finally that 4.6 (ii) implies the well-known result: *F is singular if and only if $\mu_F(A) = 0$ for all finite subsets A of N.*

Our second and last example deals with the problem of representing the bounded linear functionals on the normed linear space of the bounded vector fields. As far as the author has been able to determine this problem was waiting a solution.

The normed space we have in mind, whose dual space we like to describe, is an l^∞-space of vector-valued functions and can be defined as follows.

Let T be an infinite set and let $\mathscr{E}$ be an infinite set of normed linear spaces. We assume that E is a mapping of T into $\mathscr{E}$, that is, for each $t \in T$, $E(t) \in \mathscr{E}$. By $l^\infty(E, T)$ we shall denote the normed linear space of all mappings x in $\prod_{t \in T} E(t)$ such that $\|x\| = \sup_{t \in T} \|x(t)\|_t < \infty$, where $\|\cdot\|_t$ is the norm of the space $E(t)$, $t \in T$. If $T = N$ and $E(t) = R$, the field of real numbers, then $l^\infty(E, T)$ is the real $l^\infty(N)$-space. The problem is now to describe the dual space of $l^\infty(E, T)$. The example $l^\infty(N)$ suggests that $(l^\infty(E, T))'$ should be, in some sense, a generalized sum of the family of dual spaces $E'(t)$, $t \in T$ of E. We shall show that this is indeed the case.

First we introduce the space $l^1(E', T)$ which consists of all mappings x' in $\prod_{t \in T} E'_t$ such that $\|x'\| = \sum_{t \in T} \|x'(t)\|'_t < \infty$, where $\|\cdot\|'_t$ is the norm of the dual space of $E(t)$, $t \in T$. The dual space of $l^1(E', T)$ contains $l^\infty(E, T)$ as a linear subspace. In addition, we consider the linear subspace V of all $x' \in l^1(E', T)$ which vanish outside a finite subset of T. It is easy to see that V in $l^1(E', T)$ is a $l^\infty(E, T)$-norm-fundamental subspace and that $l^\infty(E, T)$ is also $(l^1(E', T))''$-norm-fundamental.

Consider now an enlargement of the theory of a superstructure based in $l^\infty(E, T)$. Then $^*E$ is now a mapping of $^*T$ into $^*\mathscr{E}$ and the elements $f' \in {}^*V$ are mappings in $^*\prod_{t \in {}^*T} {}^*E'(t)$ which vanish off star-finite subsets of T and satisfy $\sum_{t \in {}^*T} \|f'(t)\|'_t$ is finite. Then, using Theorem 4.3, we obtain the following result.

4.8. THEOREM. *To each $F \in (l^\infty(E, T))'$ there corresponds an internal element $f' \in {}^*V$ such that for each $x \in l^\infty(E, T)$ we have*

(i) $F(x) = \sum_{t \in {}^*T} \langle x(t), f'(t) \rangle$, *and*

(ii) $\|F\| =_1 \sum_{t \in {}^*T} \|f'(t)\|'_t$ *and* $\|F\| \leq \sum_{t \in {}^*T} \|f'(t)\|'_t$.

It is not difficult to see that if T is finite the above result reduces immediately to the well-known description of the dual space of $\prod_{t \in T} E(t)$ with the maximum norm.

As in the previous example the representing element f' in 4.8 can be used to define a vector-valued measure for an integral representation of F. The details are left to the reader.

As we indicated earlier a norm-fundamental subspace V of a normed linear space E is a norm-dense linear subspace of E. From this it may seem reasonable to expect that if in Helly's Theorem 4.2 the element x'' is an element $x \in E$ that its conclusion may be strengthened. That this is indeed the case was shown by H. Yamabe (see Dunford and Schwartz [1958] p. 87). We will need only the following form of Yamabe's Theorem. For the sake of completeness we include a proof of the theorem. The proof differs in many respects from Yamabe's proof.

4.9. THEOREM *(H. Yamabe). Let V be a norm-fundamental subspace of a normed linear space E and let $x \in E$. Then for each positive real number $\varepsilon > 0$ and for each choice of elements $x'_1, \ldots, x'_n \in E'$ there exists an element $v \in V$ such that $\langle x, x'_i \rangle = \langle v, x'_i \rangle$ for each $i = 1, 2, \ldots, n$ and $\|x - v\| < \varepsilon$.*

Proof. For each $l = 1, 2, \ldots, n$, let $H_i = \{x : \langle x, x'_i \rangle = 0\}$ be the hyperplane on which x'_i vanishes, and let $K = \bigcap_{i=1}^n H_i$. We shall first observe that Yamabe's result is equivalent to the statement that $V \cap K$ is dense in K. It is obvious that Yamabe's Theorem implies that $V \cap K$ is dense in K. In order to prove the converse we have only to show that for each $x \in E$ there is an element $v \in V$ such that $x - v \in K$. To this end, consider the mappings $\varphi : x \to (\langle x, x'_1 \rangle, \ldots, \langle x, x'_n \rangle)$ of E into the n-dimensional complex Hilbert space C^n. It is obvious that $\varphi(E)$ and $\varphi(V)$ are linear subspace of C^n such that $\varphi(V) \subset \varphi(E)$. We shall prove that $\varphi(E) = \varphi(V)$. If there exists an element $x \in E$ such that $\varphi(x) \notin \varphi(V)$, then by observing that $\varphi(V)$ is a closed linear subspace of C^n, and by applying the separation theorem for closed convex sets, we conclude that there exist constants $c_1, \ldots, c_n$ such that $\langle x, \sum_{i=1}^n c_i x'_i \rangle = 1$ and $\langle v, \sum_{i=1}^n c_i x'_i \rangle = 0$ for all $v \in V$. Hence, $1 = \langle x - v, \sum_{i=1}^n c_i x'_i \rangle \leq \|x - v\| \, \|\sum_{i=1}^n c_i x'_i\|$ for all $v \in V$, contradicts the hypothesis that V is norm dense in E.

It is clear that in order to show that $V \cap K$ is dense in K it is sufficient to show that for each hyperplane H in E the linear subspace $H \cap V$ is dense in H. This can be further simplified, by observing that if we consider E (if necessary) as a normed linear space over R and if $x' \in E'$, then $H = \{x : \langle x, x' \rangle = 0\} = H' \cap H''$, where $H' = \{x : \mathrm{Re}\langle x, x' \rangle = 0\}$ and $H'' = \{x : \mathrm{Im}\langle x, x' \rangle = 0\}$, here Re and Im are the operations of taking the real part and the imaginary part respectively. Hence, we only need to show that $V \cap H'$ is dense in H', or in other words, we may assume that E is a real normed linear space. In view of this, let $H = \{x : \langle x, x' \rangle = 0\}$, $H^+ = \{x : \langle x, x' \rangle > 0\}$ and $H^- = \{x : \langle x, x' \} < 0\}$, where $x' \in E'$. Since H^+ and H^- are open it follows that $H^+ \cap V$ is dense in H^+ and $H^- \cap V$ is dense in H^-. Hence, if $x \in H$, and $\varepsilon > 0$, then there exist elements v_1, v_2 such that $v_1 \in H^+ \cap V$, $v_2 \in H^- \cap V$, $\|x - v_1\| < \varepsilon$ and $\|x - v_2\| < \varepsilon$. Since H separates H^+ from H^- and V is convex it follows that there exists a positive number $0 < \lambda < 1$ such that $v = \lambda v_1 + (1 - \lambda)v_2$ satisfies $v \in H \cap V$ and $\|x - v\| \leq \lambda\|x - v_1\| + (1 - \lambda)\|x - v_2\| < \varepsilon$, which completes the proof.

Remark. Observe that the proof shows that for the validity of Yamabe's Theorem it is sufficient to assume that V is a dense and convex subset of E, which is, in fact, Yamabe's original formulation of the theorem.

From Yamabe's Theorem we conclude that for a given $x \in E$ the binary relation Φ_x with domain $E' \times R^+$ and range V defined by $\Phi((x', \varepsilon), v)$ holds whenever $\langle x, x' \rangle = \langle v, x' \rangle$ and $\|x - v\| < \varepsilon$ is concurrent. Hence, this leads to the following result supplementing Theorem 4.3.

4.10. THEOREM. *Let V be a norm-fundamental subspace of a normed linear space E and let $^*V$ be an enlargement of V. Then for each $x \in E$ there exists an element $v \in {}^*V$ such that*

(i) $\langle x, x' \rangle = \langle v, x' \rangle$ *for all* $x' \in E'$, *and*

(ii) $\|x - v\| =_1 0$.

One of the interesting consequences of 4.10 is the fact that in the monad of every pre-near-standard point (see Luxemburg [1969b]) of V there is a pre-near-standard point v such that for each standard linear functional $x' \in E'$, $\langle v, x' \rangle$ is standard. Furthermore, observe that v is a near-standard point of $^*E$.

Theorem 4.10 can very well be used to represent the elements of a Banach space E in terms of the elements of a dense subspace. For instance, if applied to the subspace of polynomials of the Banach space $C[0, 1]$ we obtain that for each continuous function f there exists an internal polynomial p such that

(i) $\|f - p\| =_1 0$, and

(ii) $\int_0^1 f(x)\, \mathrm{d}g(x) = \int_0^1 p(x)\, \mathrm{d}^*g(x)$,

for all functions g on $[0, 1]$ of bounded variation. Of course, (i) implies that p is a near-standard element of $^*C[0,1]$.

References

Dunford, N. and Schwartz, J. T., 1958, *Linear Operators, Part I: General Theory* (Interscience, New York, London).

Hardy, G. H. and Wright, E. M., 1954, *An Introduction to the Theory of Numbers* (Oxford Press, third ed.).

Kugler, L. D., 1969, Nonstandard Analysis of almost Periodic Functions, in: Luxemburg [1969a].

Loeb, P., 1972, A non-standard Representation of Measurable Spaces L_∞ and $L_\infty{}^*$, *this volume*.

Luxemburg, W. A. J., 1969a, *Applications of Model Theory to Algebra, Analysis and Probability Theory*, Proc. of a Meeting on Nonstandard Analysis (Holt, Rinehart and Winston, New York).

Luxemburg, W. A. J., 1962a, Two Applications of the Method of Construction by Ultrapowers to Analysis, *Bull. Am. Math. Soc*, 68, pp. 233–237.

Luxemburg, W. A. J., 1962b, A Remark on a Paper by N. G. de Bruijn and P. Erdös, *Proc. Acad. Sci. Amsterdam* A65 (= *Indag. Math.* 24), pp. 343–345.

Luxemburg, W. A. J., 1964a, A Remark on Sikorski's Extension Theorem for Homomorphisms in the Theory of Boolean Algebras, *Fund. Math.* 55, pp. 239–247.

Luxemburg, W. A. J., 1964b, Ultrapowers of Normed Linear Space, *Notices Am. Math. Soc.* 11 (2) No. 73, pp. 64T–137.

Luxemburg, W. A. J., 1969b, A General Theory of Monads, in: Luxemburg [1969a].

Luxemburg, W. A. J., 1969c, Reduced Powers of the Real Number System and Equivalents of the Hahn-Banach Extension Theorem, in: Luxemburg [1969a].

Luxemburg, W. A. J., 1972, What is Nonstandard Analysis?, *Am. Math. Monthly*, to be published.

Robinson, A., 1964, On Generalized Limits and Linear Functionals, *Pacific J. Math.* 14, pp. 269–283.

Robinson, A., 1966, *Non-standard Analysis* (North-Holland, Amsterdam).

Tacon, G., 1971, *Compactness-type Problems in Topological Vector Spaces*, Ph.D. Thesis Australian National University, Canberra.

Taylor, R. F., 1969, On Some Properties of Bounded Internal Functions, in: Luxemburg [1969a].

Young, L., 1972, Functional Analysis — A Non-standard Treatment with Semifields, *this volume*.

Zaanen, A. C., 1967, *Integration* (North-Holland Amsterdam, second ed.).

Received 15 July 1971

RESTRICTED ULTRAPRODUCTS OF FINITE VON NEUMANN ALGEBRAS

Gerhard JANSSEN
Lehre, Germany

1. Introduction. Considerable progress has been made in the theory of II_1-algebras in the last few years. In particular McDuff [1971] and Sakai [1970] have shown the existence of an uncountable number of II_1-factors acting on a separable Hilbert space. The main result of the present note consists in showing that the restricted ultraproduct of finite von Neumann algebras, which is defined to be a certain algebra of residue classes of their ultraproduct, also is a finite von Neumann algebra. The class of finite von Neumann algebras contains e.g. all finite dimensional semisimple algebras over the field of complex numbers and all II_1-factors. Starting especially with an increasing sequence of simple finite dimensional algebras the restricted ultraproduct becomes an (infinite dimensional) II_1-factor.

2. Restricted ultraproducts of metric spaces and normed vectors spaces. Let (M_i, d_i), $i \in J$ be an indexed set of metric spaces with metric functions d_i: $M_i \times M_i \to \boldsymbol{R}$ and let $\boldsymbol{U}$ be a nontrivial = free = nonprincipal ultrafilter over J. Then $\boldsymbol{U}$-prod $M_i = {}^*M$ is a "metric" space, whose "metric" function $\boldsymbol{U}$-prod $d_i = {}^*d$: ${}^*M \times {}^*M \to {}^*\boldsymbol{R}$ has the usual formal properties of a metric except that its values lie in the corresponding ultrapower ${}^*\boldsymbol{R}$ of $\boldsymbol{R}$. We regard $\boldsymbol{R}$ as a subfield of ${}^*\boldsymbol{R}$ and denote by $\boldsymbol{B}$ ($\boldsymbol{S}$) the subrings of finite (infinitely small) elements of ${}^*\boldsymbol{R}$. Then $\boldsymbol{S}$ is a maximal ideal in $\boldsymbol{B}$ and the decomposition $\boldsymbol{B} = \boldsymbol{R} + \boldsymbol{S}$ is direct. The natural homomorphism st: $\boldsymbol{B} \to \boldsymbol{R}$, which maps every finite nonstandard real number onto its standard part is order preserving. Let Mon ${}^*a = \{{}^*m \in {}^*M | {}^*d({}^*a, {}^*m) \in \boldsymbol{S}\}$ denote the **monad** of ${}^*a \in {}^*M$ and Gal ${}^*p = \{{}^*m \in {}^*M | {}^*d({}^*p, {}^*m) \in \boldsymbol{B}\}$ the **galaxy** of ${}^*p \in {}^*M$. The triangular inequality ${}^*d({}^*a, {}^*b) \leq {}^*d({}^*a, {}^*p) + {}^*d({}^*p, {}^*b)$ applied to ${}^*a, {}^*b \in$ Gal ${}^*p$ shows that all distances in Gal ${}^*p$ are finite. If on the other hand ${}^*a \in$ Gal ${}^*p$, ${}^*d({}^*a, {}^*b) \in \boldsymbol{B}$, then ${}^*d({}^*b, {}^*p) \leq {}^*d({}^*a, {}^*b) + {}^*d({}^*a, {}^*p) \in \boldsymbol{B}$ implies ${}^*b \in$ Gal ${}^*p$. Hence Gal ${}^*p$ contains along with ${}^*a$ the whole monad of $^*a$. The monad of $^*a$ may be equally well defined to be the equivalence class of $^*a$ relative to the equivalence relation

$$^*x \sim {}^*y \Leftrightarrow {}^*d(^*x, {}^*y) \in \boldsymbol{S}$$

defined on $^*M$ or Gal $^*p$. It is obvious that if $^*a \sim {}^*a_1$ and $^*b \sim {}^*b_1$, then $\mathrm{st}^*d(^*a, {}^*b) = \mathrm{st}^*d(^*a_1, {}^*b_1)$ and so $d := \mathrm{st}^*d$ is welldefined on Gal $^*p/_\sim \times$ Gal $^*p/_\sim$. Since st preserves the order, it is clear that (Gal $^*p/_\sim, d$) is a metric space in the ordinary sense. This we call the **restricted ultraproduct** of the metric spaces (M_i, d_i), $i \in J$ with respect to the element $^*p \in {}^*M$.

2.1. Proposition. *If* (M_i, d_i), $i \in J$ *are complete metric spaces, then their restricted ultraproduct* $(M, d) :=$ (Gal $^*p/_\sim, d$) *is a complete metric space.*

Proof. Let $m(n)$, $n \in \boldsymbol{N}$ be a Cauchy sequence in (M, d). By extracting a subsequence we may assume

2.2. $d(m(n), m(k)) < 2^{-N}$ for all $n, k \geq N$ and for all $N \in \boldsymbol{N}$.

For every $n \in \boldsymbol{N}$ let $^*m(n) \in$ Gal $^*p$ be an element in the residue class $m(n)$. Then

2.2′. $^*d(^*m(n), {}^*m(k)) < 2^{-N}$ for all $n, k \geq N$ and for all $N \in \boldsymbol{N}$.

Let $m_i(n) \in \prod_{i\in J} M_i$ be elements such that $^*(m_i(n)) = {}^*m(n)$ for all $n \in \boldsymbol{N}$. Now we define by induction on n

2.3.

$$w_i(1) := m_i(1) \text{ and } w_i(n+1) := \begin{cases} m_i(n+1), \text{if } d_i(m_i(n+1), w_i(n)) < 2^{-n} \\ w_i(n) \text{ otherwise.} \end{cases}$$

Then we claim $^*(w_i(n)) = {}^*m(n)$ for all $n \in \boldsymbol{N}$, where * denotes transition to the ultraproduct. The equation holds true for $n = 1$ and if it is satisfied for n, then $^*d(^*w_i(n), {}^*m(n+1)) = {}^*d(^*m(n), {}^*m(n+1)) < 2^{-n}$ by 2.2′, which implies that the first alternative of 2.3 is fulfilled for all i in a set belonging to $\boldsymbol{U}$. Hence $^*w_i(n+1) = {}^*m(n+1)$. Furthermore the following inequality does not depend on $i \in J$:

$$\text{2.4.} \quad d_i(w_i(n+1), w_i(n)) \leq \sum_{k=0}^{l-1} d_i(w_i(n+k), w_i(n+k+1))$$
$$< \sum_{k=0}^{l-1} 2^{-(n+k)} < 2^{-n+1}.$$

Therefore, $w_i(n)$ is a Cauchy sequence for every $i \in J$ and has a limit w_i in M_i. Since $^*m(1) \in$ Gal $^*p$ and the distance $^*d(^*w_i(1), {}^*w_i) = {}^*d(^*m(1), {}^*w_i) < \sum_{k=1}^{\infty} 2^{-k} = 1$ is finite, it follows $^*w_i \in$ Gal $^*p$ by a previous remark. Let $w \in M$ be the image of $^*w_i$, then w is the limit of the sequence $m(n)$, since $d(w, m(n)) = \mathrm{st}^*d(^*w_i, {}^*m(n)) \leq 2^{-n+1}$. Q.e.d.

It should be remarked, that the assertion of the proposition remains true in many cases without assuming the (M_i, d_i) to be complete. For instance let $J = N$ be a denumerable index set, define $w_i(n)$ as before and put $u_i = w_i(i) \in \prod_{i \in J} M_i$. The image u of $*u_i$ is the limit of the given Cauchy sequence $m(n)$. For a complete treatment of this question in the special case of ultrapowers see Luxemburg [1969].

Let $\boldsymbol{K}$ denote the field of real or complex numbers. $\boldsymbol{K}$ is embedded in its ultrapower $*\boldsymbol{K}$ via the diagonal map. $\boldsymbol{K}_{\boldsymbol{B}}$ ($\boldsymbol{K}_{\boldsymbol{S}}$) denote the subrings of elements of $*\boldsymbol{K}$ having finite (infinitely small) absolute values. Again we have the direct decomposition $\boldsymbol{K}_{\boldsymbol{B}} = \boldsymbol{K} + \boldsymbol{K}_{\boldsymbol{S}}$ and the natural homomorphism st: $\boldsymbol{K}_{\boldsymbol{B}} \rightarrow \boldsymbol{K}$. The restricted ultraproduct $(V, \| \ \|)$ of normed $\boldsymbol{K}$-vector spaces $(V_i, \| \ \|_i)$, $i \in J$ is unambiguously defined to be taken with respect to the zero element $*0$ of the ultraproduct $*V$. Apparently Gal $*0$ and Mon $*0$ are closed with respect to vector addition and multiplication by finite scalars. Thus they are both $\boldsymbol{K}_{\boldsymbol{B}}$-modules and a fortiori $\boldsymbol{K}$-spaces. Moreover the previously introduced equivalence relation $\sim$ coincides with equivalence modulo Mon $*0$ and it follows that $V: = \text{Gal } {*0}/_{\sim} = \text{Gal } {*0}/\text{Mon } {*0}$ is a $\boldsymbol{K}$-vector space with norm $\| \ \|: = \text{st}{*\| \ \|}$. If furthermore all V_i are normed algebras, then the inequalities

$$\|v_i w_i\|_i \leq \|v_i\|_i \, \|w_i\|_i \quad \text{for all} \quad v_i, w_i \in V_i$$

imply

2.5. $$*\|{*v}\, {*w}\| \leq *\|{*v}\| \, *\|{*w}\| \quad \text{for all} \quad *v, *w \in *V.$$

From this inequality we conclude that Mon $*0$ and Gal$*0$ are multiplicatively closed and that Mon $*0$ is a twosided ideal in Gal $*0$. Thus in this case $V = \text{Gal } {*0}/\text{Mon } {*0}$ becomes a normed algebra over $\boldsymbol{K}$. The following corollary is an immediate consequence of Proposition 2.1.

2.6. Corollary. *The restricted ultraproduct of* **Banach** *spaces = complete normed vector spaces* (**Banach** *algebras = complete normed algebras*) *is a Banach space (Banach algebra).*

Suppose now that all V_i are prehilbert spaces over $\boldsymbol{K}$ with hermitian bilinear forms $(-,-)_i$ and the corresponding norms given by $\|x_i\|_i: = \sqrt{(x_i, x_i)_i}$. The fact that the norms arise from hermitian bilinear forms is equivalently expressed solely in terms of the norms by the equations

$$\|x_i + y_i\|_i^2 + \|x_i - y_i\|_i^2 = 2(\|x_i\|_i^2 + \|y_i\|_i^2).$$

Evidently this gives

$$\|x + y\|^2 + \|x - y\|^2 = 2(\|x\|^2 + \|y\|^2)$$

for all x, y in the restricted ultraproduct V. Then the bilinear form on V is defined by

$$(x, y) := \tfrac{1}{4}(\|x + y\|^2 - \|x - y\|^2) \quad \text{in the real case}$$

and by

$$(x, y) := \tfrac{1}{4}(\|x + y\|^2 - \|x - y\|^2 + \mathrm{i}\|x + \mathrm{i}y\|^2 + \mathrm{i}\|x - \mathrm{i}y\|^2) \quad \text{in case } \boldsymbol{K} = \boldsymbol{C}.$$

Thus the restricted ultraproduct also turns out to be a prehilbert space and from 2.1 we obtain

2.7. COROLLARY. *The restricted ultraproduct of Hilbert spaces is a Hilbert space.*

3. Von Neumann algebras. In this section we recall some facts concerning von Neumann algebras = W^*-algebras. The standard reference for the whole material is the book of Dixmier [1969]. A more detailed treatment of some aspects of the II_1-case can be found in the original papers by Murray and von Neumann [1936, 1937] or for the separable case in the book of Schwartz [1967].

Let H be a Hilbert space over the field $\boldsymbol{C}$ of complex numbers with hermitian bilinear form (–,–) and norm $\|x\| := \sqrt{(x, x)}$. A linear transformation or operator A of H into itself is **bounded** if and only if there exists a real number r such that $\|Ax\| \leq r\|x\|$ for all $x \in H$. The infimum of all these $r \in \boldsymbol{R}$ is $\|A\|$ the **norm** of A. The set $\mathfrak{B}(H)$ of all bounded linear transformations is a Banach algebra over $\boldsymbol{C}$ with respect to this norm. Every $A \in \mathfrak{B}(H)$ has an **adjoint** A^{T}, which is uniquely determined by the equation

$$(Ax, y) = (x, A^{\mathrm{T}}y) \quad \text{for all} \quad x, y \in H.$$

The map $A \mapsto A^{\mathrm{T}}$ of $\mathfrak{B}(H)$ onto itself is a **hermitian involution**, i.e.

3.1. $(A + B)^{\mathrm{T}} = A^{\mathrm{T}} + B^{\mathrm{T}}, (AB)^{\mathrm{T}} = B^{\mathrm{T}}A^{\mathrm{T}}, A^{\mathrm{TT}} = A, (rA)^{\mathrm{T}} = r^{\mathrm{T}}A^{\mathrm{T}},$

where r^{T} denotes the conjugate complex number of $r \in \boldsymbol{C}$.

The **weak topology** of H is given by the set $\{x \mapsto |(x, y)| \mid y \in H\}$ of seminorms of H. The **weak (operator) topology** of $\mathfrak{B}(H)$ is defined by the seminorms $\{A \ |(\mapsto Ax, y)| \mid x, y \in H\}$ and the **strong (operator) topology** of $\mathfrak{B}(H)$

by the seminorms $\{A \mapsto \|Ax\| \mid x \in H\}$ of $\mathfrak{B}(H)$. For **selfadjoined** operators $A = A^{\mathrm{T}}$, $B = B^{\mathrm{T}}$ in $\mathfrak{B}(H)$ there is an **order** defined by

$$A \leq B \Leftrightarrow (Ax, x) \leq (Bx, x) \quad \text{for all } x \in H.$$

Let $\mathfrak{E} . = \{E \in \mathfrak{B}(H) \mid E = E^2 \text{ and } E = E^{\mathrm{T}}\}$ denote the set of **projections**. For every selfadjoined $A \in \mathfrak{B}(H)$ there exists a unique **spectral function** $E(t)$ defined on $\boldsymbol{R}$ with values in $\mathfrak{E}$, which satisfies the following conditions.

3.2. a. $t_1 \leq t_2 \Rightarrow E(t_1) \leq E(t_2)$ for all $t_1, t_2 \in \boldsymbol{R}$.

b. $E(t)$ is strongly continuous from the left.

c. There exists $0 \leq M \in \boldsymbol{R}$ such that $E(-M) = 0$ and $E(M) = 1$. (1 is the identity operator.)

d. A has the spectral representation $A = \int t \, \mathrm{d}E(t)$ the integral being strongly convergent.

For later use we note that the infimum of the numbers appearing in c. is $\|A\|$.

3.3. Definition. *A subalgebra* $\mathfrak{A}$ of $\mathfrak{B}(H)$ *is a* **von Neumann algebra** *if and only if*

a. $\mathfrak{A}$ *contains the identity operator* 1 *of* $\mathfrak{B}(H)$.

b. $A \in \mathfrak{A} \Rightarrow A^{\mathrm{T}} \in \mathfrak{A}$.

c. $\mathfrak{A}$ *is weakly closed in* $\mathfrak{B}(H)$.

Usually condition a. is dropped, since it can always be satisfied replacing H by a suitable closed subspace H'.

Condition c. may be replaced by the following equivalent ones:

c'. The unit ball $\mathfrak{A}_1 : = \{A \in \mathfrak{A} \mid \|A\| \leq 1\}$ is weakly closed in $\mathfrak{B}(H)$.

c''. $\mathfrak{A}_1$ is weakly compact.

c'''. $\mathfrak{A}_1$ is strongly complete.

This is a consequence of Dixmier [1969] Chap. I, §3.1 and Chap. I, §3.4, Theorem 2.

The following theorem is well known.

3.4. *If A is a selfadjoined operator in a von Neumann algebra $\mathfrak{A}$, then the range of its spectral function is contained in $\mathfrak{A}$. Hence the spectral representation takes place in $\mathfrak{A}$.*

A von Neumann algebra is called a **factor**, if its center is $\boldsymbol{C}1$.

After these preparations we are going to define the class $\mathfrak{F}$ of algebras, which will be studied in the sequel. Let $\mathfrak{A}$ be an arbitrary algebra over $\boldsymbol{C}$

with unit element 1 and hermitian involution $a \mapsto a^{\mathrm{T}}$. We say that $\mathfrak{A}$ has a **trace**, if there is a linear form tr: $\mathfrak{A} \to \boldsymbol{C}$ such that the following conditions hold for all $a, b \in \mathfrak{A}$.

3.5. a. $\mathrm{tr}(1) = 1$. (This normalization is essential in the next section.)
b. $\mathrm{tr}(ab) = \mathrm{tr}(ba)$.
c. $\mathrm{tr}(a^{\mathrm{T}}) = (\mathrm{tr}(a))^{\mathrm{T}}$.
d. $\mathrm{tr}(aa^{\mathrm{T}}) > 0$, if $a \neq 0$.
e. For every $a \in \mathfrak{A}$ there exists $0 \leq M \in \boldsymbol{R}$ such that $\mathrm{tr}(axx^{\mathrm{T}}a^{\mathrm{T}}) \leq M^2 \mathrm{tr}(xx^{\mathrm{T}})$ for all $x \in \mathfrak{A}$.

Properties b., c., d. imply that $(a, b) := \mathrm{tr}(ab^{\mathrm{T}})$ is a positive definite hermitian bilinear form on $\mathfrak{A}$. Let $\|a\| := \sqrt{(a, a)} = \sqrt{\mathrm{tr}(aa^{\mathrm{T}})}$ denote the corresponding norm and let $\hat{\mathfrak{A}}$ be the Hilbert space obtained by completion. Rewriting e. gives

$$\|ax\| \leq M\|x\| \quad \text{for all} \quad x \in \mathfrak{A}.$$

The infimum of these $M \in \boldsymbol{R}$ gives a second norm $N(a)$ on $\mathfrak{A}$. Thus the operator $L(a)$ defined by $L(a)x := ax$ is bounded on $(A, \| \ \|)$. We denote the extension of $L(a)$ by continuity to an operator of $\hat{\mathfrak{A}}$ by the same letter. Now it is easily seen that

$$L: \mathfrak{A} \to \mathfrak{B}(\hat{\mathfrak{A}})$$

is an algebra isomorphism mapping $\mathfrak{A}$ onto a subalgebra of $\mathfrak{B}(\hat{\mathfrak{A}})$, which satisfies

$$L(1) = 1, \quad L(a^{\mathrm{T}}) = (L(a))^{\mathrm{T}}, \quad N(a) = N(L(a)),$$

where the last N denotes the operator norm in $\mathfrak{B}(\hat{\mathfrak{A}})$. Thus the algebra $L(\mathfrak{A})$ has properties 3.3 a. and b. of a von Neumann algebra. Now we derive a criterion, which enables us to decide in terms of $\mathfrak{A}$ whether $L(\mathfrak{A})$ is a von Neumann algebra.

3.6. THEOREM. *L is a homeomorphic map of the unit ball $\mathfrak{A}_1 := \{a \in \mathfrak{A} \mid N(a) \leq 1\}$ onto $L(\mathfrak{A}_1)$, if we endow $\mathfrak{A}_1$ with the weak Hilbert space topology and $L(\mathfrak{A}_1)$ with the weak operator topology induced from $\mathfrak{B}(\hat{\mathfrak{A}})$. The same holds, if we give $\mathfrak{A}_1$ the $\| \ \|$-topology and $L(\mathfrak{A}_1)$ the strong operator topology.*

Proof. The inverse mapping of L is given by $A \mapsto A1$, $A \in L(\mathfrak{A})$, $1 \in \mathfrak{A}$ and it follows readily from the definitions that this map is continuous in both cases. To show continuity in the other direction let $a_\alpha \to a$ be a weakly convergent generalized sequence in $\mathfrak{A}_1$. The sequence $L(a_\alpha)$ is contained in the weakly compact unit ball of $\mathfrak{B}(\hat{\mathfrak{A}})$ and has, therefore, a cluster point A. We must show $A = L(a)$. For arbitrary $x, y \in \mathfrak{A}$ we have $((A - L(a))x, y) = (Ax, y) - (ax, y) = (Ax, y) - \mathrm{tr}(axy^{\mathrm{T}}) = (Ax, y) - (a, (xy^{\mathrm{T}})^{\mathrm{T}}) = (Ax, y) - \lim\,(a_\alpha, (xy^{\mathrm{T}})^{\mathrm{T}}) = (Ax, y) - \lim \mathrm{tr}(a_\alpha xy^{\mathrm{T}}) = (Ax, y) - \lim\,(a_\alpha x, y) = (Ax, y) - \lim\,(L(a_\alpha)x, y) = \lim\,((A - L(a_\alpha))x, y) = 0$. Hence the bounded linear transformations A and $L(a)$ coincide on the dense subset $\mathfrak{A}$ of $\mathfrak{A}$ and consequently on all of $\hat{\mathfrak{A}}$.

To prove the remaining assertion let $a_n \to a$ be a Cauchy sequence in $\mathfrak{A}_1$. We must show that $L(a)$ is the strong limit of $L(a_n)$. To do this let x be an arbitrary element in $\mathfrak{A}$. We have $\|(L(a) - L(a_n))x\|^2 = \|(a - a_n)x\|^2 = \mathrm{tr}((a - a_n)xx^{\mathrm{T}}(a - a_n)^{\mathrm{T}}) = \mathrm{tr}(x^{\mathrm{T}}(a - a_n)^{\mathrm{T}}(a - a_n)x) = \|x^{\mathrm{T}}(a - a_n)^{\mathrm{T}}\|^2 \leq N^2(x^{\mathrm{T}})\,\|(a - a_n)^{\mathrm{T}}\|^2 = N^2(x)\,\|a - a_n\|^2$ and the last expression tends to zero as $n \to \infty$. Since $\mathfrak{A}$ is dense in $\hat{\mathfrak{A}}$ it follows that $L(a)$ is in fact the strong limit of $L(a_n)$. Q.e.d.

It should be remarked, however, that L is **not** in general a homeomorphism between $\mathfrak{A}$ and $L(\mathfrak{A})$ with respect to the above topologies.

From 3.3.c″ and c‴ we conclude the following.

3.7. COROLLARY. *If $\mathfrak{A}$ is an algebra with trace, then the three conditions are equivalent*

a. *$L(\mathfrak{A})$ is a von Neumann algebra in $\mathfrak{B}(\hat{\mathfrak{A}})$.*

b. *The unit ball $\mathfrak{A}_1 = \{a \in \mathfrak{A} | N(a) \leq 1\}$ is compact in the weak Hilbert space topology.*

c. *$\mathfrak{A}_1$ is complete in the Hilbert space norm $\| \ \|$.*

3.8. DEFINITION. *We call an algebra* **finite**, *if it has a trace and satisfies one of the equivalent conditions of the preceding corollary. Let $\mathfrak{F}$ denote the class of finite algebras.*

This definition is more restrictive than the common one. Usually one calls an algebra finite, if it is a direct product of finite algebras in the above sense. There is no principal difficulty in dealing with the more general case in our context, but it induces some arbitrariness in the later definition of the restricted ultraproduct.

The class $\mathfrak{F}$ contains all algebras of $n \times n$-matrices the usual trace being divided by n to meet the normalization 3.5a. The factors of infinite dimension in $\mathfrak{F}$ are in one-to-one correspondence with the von Neumann factors of type II_1.

4. Restricted ultraproducts of finite algebras. Let $(\mathfrak{A}_i, \mathrm{tr}_i)$, $i \in J$ be a set of finite algebras and $^*\mathfrak{A}$ their ultraproduct with respect to a nontrivial ultrafilter $\boldsymbol{U}$ over J. We conserve the notations introduced in sections 2 and 3. Specifically if $a_i \in \prod_{i\in J} \mathfrak{A}_i$, then $^*a$ denotes the corresponding element in $^*\mathfrak{A}$ and if $^*a \in {}^*\mathfrak{A}$ is given, then $a_i \in \prod_{i\in J} \mathfrak{A}_i$ denotes an element, which is mapped onto $^*a$. Now $^*\mathfrak{A}$ is an algebra over $^*\boldsymbol{C}$ with unit element ^{*1}, "hermitian" involution $^*a \mapsto {}^*a^{*\mathrm{T}}$, trace $^*\mathrm{tr}\colon {}^*\mathfrak{A} \to {}^*\boldsymbol{C}$, "hermitian" bilinear form $^*(^*a, {}^*b) = {}^*\mathrm{tr}(^*a^*b^{*\mathrm{T}})$, corresponding norm $^*\|^*a\| = \sqrt{^*(^*a, {}^*a)}$ and the second norm $^*N(^*a) = \inf\{0 \le {}^*M \in {}^*\boldsymbol{R} \mid {}^*\|^*a^*x\| \le {}^*M^*\|^*x\| \text{ for all } {}^*x \in {}^*\mathfrak{A}\}$. All formal properties of finite algebras carry over to $^*\mathfrak{A}$ in the usual way. Now we set $\mathfrak{A}_{\boldsymbol{B}} := \{^*a \in {}^*\mathfrak{A} \mid {}^*N(^*a) \in \boldsymbol{B}\}$ and $\mathfrak{A}_{\boldsymbol{S}} := \{^*a \in \mathfrak{A}_{\boldsymbol{B}} \mid {}^*\|^*a\| \in \boldsymbol{S}\}$. $\boldsymbol{B}$, $\boldsymbol{S}$, $\boldsymbol{C}_{\boldsymbol{B}}$, $\boldsymbol{C}_{\boldsymbol{S}}$ have the same meaning as in section 2. Note the difference in the definition of $\mathfrak{A}_{\boldsymbol{B}}$ and $\mathfrak{A}_{\boldsymbol{S}}$. Apparently they both are $\boldsymbol{C}_{\boldsymbol{B}}$-modules and a fortiori $\boldsymbol{C}$-vector spaces. Moreover the inequalities

4.1. $^*N(^*a^*b) \le {}^*N(^*a)^*N(^*b)$ and

4.2. $^*\|^*a^*b\| \le {}^*N(^*a)^*\|^*b\|, \quad {}^*\|^*a^*b\| \le {}^*N(^*b)^*\|^*a\|$

show that $\mathfrak{A}_{\boldsymbol{B}}$ is multiplicatively closed and that $\mathfrak{A}_{\boldsymbol{S}}$ is a twosided ideal in $\mathfrak{A}_{\boldsymbol{B}}$. Hence $\mathfrak{A} := \mathfrak{A}_{\boldsymbol{B}}/\mathfrak{A}_{\boldsymbol{S}}$ is an algebra over $\boldsymbol{C}$, which we call the **restricted ultraproduct** of the finite algebras $\mathfrak{A}_i$. From $^*\|^*a^{*\mathrm{T}}\| = {}^*\|^*a\|$ it follows that $(^*a + \mathfrak{A}_{\boldsymbol{S}})^{*\mathrm{T}} = {}^*a^{*\mathrm{T}} + \mathfrak{A}_{\boldsymbol{S}}$ is well defined on the residue classes and, therefore, gives a hermitian involution $a \mapsto a^{\mathrm{T}}$ on $\mathfrak{A}$. Furthermore $N_i(1_i) = 1$ and $\|1_i\|_i = 1$ imply $^*1 \in \mathfrak{A}_{\boldsymbol{B}}$ and $^*\mathrm{tr}(^*1) = 1$. In 4.2 we set $^*b = {}^*1 \in \mathfrak{A}_{\boldsymbol{B}}$ and obtain

$$^*\|^*a\| \le {}^*N(^*a)^*\|^*1\| = {}^*N(^*a).$$

Thus $^*\mathrm{tr}$ is finite on $\mathfrak{A}_{\boldsymbol{B}}$ and $\mathrm{tr} := \mathrm{st}^*\mathrm{tr}$ is well defined on $^*\mathfrak{A}$. This function evidently has properties 3.5a–d of a trace. To see that e. is satisfied we define two new functions on $\mathfrak{A}$ by

$$N_1(a) := \inf\{0 \le M \in \boldsymbol{R} \mid \|ax\| = \sqrt{\mathrm{tr}(axx^{\mathrm{T}}a^{\mathrm{T}})} \le M\|x\|\}$$
$$= \sup\{\|ax\|/\|x\| \mid x \ne 0\} \quad \text{and}$$
$$N_2(a) := \inf\{\mathrm{st}^*N(^*a) \mid {}^*a \in a\}.$$

The inequality $\|ax\| = \mathrm{st}^*\|^*a^*x\| \le \mathrm{st}(^*N(^*a)^*\|^*x\|) = \mathrm{st}^*N(^*a)\ \|x\|$ implies $N_1(a) \le N_2(a)$ for all a in $\mathfrak{A}$, thereby showing the existence of N_1 and 3.5e., too. Hence it has turned out that $\mathfrak{A}$ is an algebra with trace. To derive this result we made no use of the additional assumption that the $\mathfrak{A}_i$ are finite algebras. Now we come to the main theorem.

4.3. THEOREM. *The restricted ultraproduct of finite algebras is finite.*

Proof. We conserve the notations of the foregoing discussion. All that remains to be proved is one of the properties of Corollary 3.7. We are going to show the last one. The first step consists in proving $N_1 = N_2$. This means that we can lift $a \in \mathfrak{A}$ without changing the operator norm essentially. Let $^*a$ lie in a and let a_i be mapped on $^*a$. The element $a_i^{\mathrm{T}}a_i$ is selfadjoined and has componentwise spectral representation

$$a_i^{\mathrm{T}}a_i = \int_0^{M_i} t\,\mathrm{d}e_i(t).$$

Since $a_i^{\mathrm{T}}a_i \geq 0$ we may assume as we have done that 0 is the lower bound of all integrals and from $^*a^{*\mathrm{T}*}a \in \mathfrak{A}_{\boldsymbol{B}}$ we derive that we may assume that there exists $M \in \boldsymbol{R}$ such that $M_i \leq M$ for all $i \in J$. Evidently the element

$$s_i = \int_{t_i}^{M_i} t\,\mathrm{d}e_i(t),\ t_i \in I := \left\{r_i \in \prod_{i\in J} \boldsymbol{R} \,\middle|\, {}^*\|1_i - e_i(r_i)\| \in \boldsymbol{S}\right\}$$

is mapped into $\mathfrak{A}_{\boldsymbol{S}}$.

Thus $a_i^{\mathrm{T}}a_i$ and $a_i^{\mathrm{T}}a_i - s_i$ have the same image $a^{\mathrm{T}}a$ in $\mathfrak{A}$ and we obtain

$$\begin{aligned} N_2^2(a) &= \inf\{\mathrm{st}^*N_i^2(b_i) | {}^*b_i \in a\} = \inf\{\mathrm{st}^*N_i(b_i^{\mathrm{T}}b_i) | {}^*(b_i^{\mathrm{T}}b_i) \in a^{\mathrm{T}}a\} \\ &\leq \mathrm{st}^*N_i(a_i^{\mathrm{T}}a_i - s_i) = \mathrm{st}^*t_i. \end{aligned}$$

This implies $N_2^2(a) \leq \inf\{\mathrm{st}^*r_i | r_i \in I\}$. On the other hand we get

$$\begin{aligned} N_1^2(a) &= \sup_{x\neq 0}\left(\frac{\|ax\|}{\|x\|}\right)^2 = \sup\left\{\left(\frac{\mathrm{st}^*\|a_ix_i\|_i}{\mathrm{st}^*\|x_i\|_i}\right)^2 \,\middle|\, {}^*x_i \in \mathfrak{A}_{\boldsymbol{B}},\ {}^*x_i \notin \mathfrak{A}_{\boldsymbol{S}}\right\} \\ &= \sup\left\{\frac{\mathrm{st}^*(a_i^{\mathrm{T}}a_ix_i, x_i)_i}{\mathrm{st}^*(x_i, x_i)_i} \,\middle|\, {}^*x_i \in \mathfrak{A}_{\boldsymbol{B}},\ {}^*x_i \notin \mathfrak{A}_{\boldsymbol{S}}\right\} \\ &\geq \sup\left\{\frac{\mathrm{st}^*(a_i^{\mathrm{T}}a_i(1_i - e_i(t_i)), 1_i - e_i(t_i))_i}{\mathrm{st}^*(1_i - e_i(t_i), 1_i - e_i(t_i))_i} \,\middle|\, t_i \notin I\right\} \\ &\geq \sup\left\{\frac{\mathrm{st}^*(t_i(1_i - e_i(t_i)), 1_i - e_i(t_i))_i}{\mathrm{st}^*(1_i - e_i(t_i), 1_i - e_i(t_i))_i} \,\middle|\, t_i \notin I\right\} \\ &= \sup\{\mathrm{st}^*t_i | t_i \notin I\} = \inf\{\mathrm{st}^*t_i | t_i \in I\} \geq N_2^2(a), \end{aligned}$$

which gives us the desired result. From now on we shall drop the index and write $N = N_1 = N_2$.

Since all $\mathfrak{A}_i$ are finite algebras their unit balls $\mathfrak{A}_i(1)\colon = \{a_i \in \mathfrak{A}_i \mid N_i(a_i) \leq 1\}$ are complete metric spaces with respect to the norms $\| \;\|_i$. Their restricted ultraproduct $\mathfrak{D}$ with respect to the zero element of $^*\mathfrak{A}$ is contained in the unit ball $\mathfrak{A}(1)\colon = \{a \in \mathfrak{A} \mid N(a) \leq 1\}$ and is $\| \;\|$-complete according to 2.1. Hence $\mathfrak{D}$ is $\| \;\|$-closed and a fortiori N-closed. Now $N_2(a) = \inf\{\mathrm{st}\, {}^*N({}^*a) \mid {}^*a \in a\}$ implies that $\mathring{\mathfrak{A}}(1)\colon = \{a \in \mathfrak{A} \mid N(a) < 1\}$ is contained in $\mathfrak{D}$. Thus we have $\mathring{\mathfrak{A}}(1) \subset \mathfrak{D} \subset \mathfrak{A}(1)$. Transition to the N-closure gives $\mathfrak{D} = \mathfrak{A}(1)$. Q.e.d.

Next we prove a result on lifting of projections, which will be needed later on.

4.4. PROPOSITION. *Let e be a projection in $\mathfrak{A}$, then there exist projections $e_i \in \mathfrak{A}_i$ for all $i \in J$ such that $^*e_i \in e$.*

Proof. Let $a_i \in \prod_{i \in J} \mathfrak{A}_i$ be mapped onto e, then $f_i\colon = \frac{1}{2}(a_i + a_i^{\mathrm{T}})$ is also mapped onto e and is selfadjoint. Hence we have the spectral representation $f_i = \int t \,\mathrm{d}f_i(t)$, where $f_i(t)$ denotes the spectral function of f_i. Without loss of generality we may assume

$$f_i(t) = \begin{cases} 0, & \text{if } t \leq 0 \\ 1_i, & \text{if } t > 1. \end{cases}$$

From $e - e^2 = 0$ we derive $^*f_i - {}^*f_i^2 = {}^*(\int (t - t^2)\,\mathrm{d}f_i(t)) \in \mathfrak{A}_{\boldsymbol{S}}$. Since $^*(t_i - t_i^2)$ is infinitesimal if and only if $^*t_i$ or $^*t_i - {}^*1$ is infinitesimal we conclude that

$$^*f_i(t_i) - {}^*f_i(t_i') \in \mathfrak{A}_{\boldsymbol{S}}, \quad \text{if} \quad 0 < \varepsilon_1 \leq t_i,\ t_i' \leq \varepsilon_2 < 1,$$

where $\varepsilon_1, \varepsilon_2 \in \boldsymbol{R}$.

In other words $^*f_i(t_i)$ is constant up to infinitesimal elements. Hence we may replace $f_i(t)$ by the spectral functions

$$d_i(t)\colon = \begin{cases} 0, & \text{if } t \leq 0 \\ f_i(\frac{1}{2}), & \text{if } 0 < t \leq 1 \\ 1_i, & \text{if } 1 > t, \end{cases}$$

then $e_i\colon = \int t \,\mathrm{d}d_i(t)$ is a set of projections, which is still mapped onto $e \in \mathfrak{A}$. Q.e.d.

Finally we may mention that the Jacobson radical of $\mathfrak{A}_{\boldsymbol{B}}$ consists of the elements $^*a$ such that $^*N({}^*a) \in \boldsymbol{S}$.

5. The center of a restricted ultraproduct. This section is devoted to the study of the behaviour of the center. We start with some additional definitions and properties of von Neumann algebras.

5.1. DEFINITION. *Two projections e, f of a von Neumann algebra $\mathfrak{A}$ acting on the complex Hilbert space H are said to be* **equivalent** $(\sim)$, *if there exists an element $u \in \mathfrak{A}$ such that $u^{\mathrm{T}}u = e$ and $uu^{\mathrm{T}} = f$.*

Let us compute $0 \leq (u - fue)^{\mathrm{T}}(u - fue) = u^{\mathrm{T}}u - u^{\mathrm{T}}fue - eu^{\mathrm{T}}fu + eu^{\mathrm{T}}ffue = e - u^{\mathrm{T}}uu^{\mathrm{T}}ue - eu^{\mathrm{T}}uu^{\mathrm{T}}u + eu^{\mathrm{T}}uu^{\mathrm{T}}ue = 0$. This shows $u = fue = fu = ue$. If $\mathfrak{A}$ has a trace tr, then $\mathrm{tr}(e) = \mathrm{tr}(u^{\mathrm{T}}u) = \mathrm{tr}(uu^{\mathrm{T}}) = \mathrm{tr}(f)$ shows that equivalent projections have the same trace. Moreover it is easily seen that $N(u) = N(e) = 1$, if $e \neq 0$. If $e(\beta), \beta \in B$ $(f(\beta), \beta \in B)$ are sets of pairwise orthogonal projections in $\mathfrak{A}$ and $e(\beta) \sim f(\beta)$ for every $\beta \in B$, then it follows $\sum_{\beta \in B} e(\beta) \sim \sum_{\beta \in B} f(\beta)$.

The **commutant** $\mathfrak{A}'$ of the von Neumann algebra $\mathfrak{A}$ acting on H is the set $\mathfrak{A}' := \{b \in \mathfrak{B}(H) \mid ab = ba \text{ for all } a \in \mathfrak{A}\}$. $\mathfrak{A}'$ is itself a von Neumann algebra. $\mathfrak{A}$ is called **discrete** if its commutant $\mathfrak{A}'$ is commutative or if $\mathfrak{A}$ is isomorphic to a discrete von Neumann algebra as an abstract algebra with involution. If there is no projection $e \neq 0$ in the center of $\mathfrak{A}$ such that the von Neumann algebra $e\mathfrak{A}e$ acting on eH is discrete, then $\mathfrak{A}$ is **continuous**. Selecting the maximal projection e in the center of $\mathfrak{A}$ such that $e\mathfrak{A}e$ is discrete, one concludes that every von Neumann algebra $\mathfrak{A}$ is naturally isomorphic to the direct product $e\mathfrak{A}e \times (1 - e)\mathfrak{A}(1 - e)$ where $e\mathfrak{A}e$ is discrete and $(1 - e)\mathfrak{A}(1 - e)$ is continuous (Dixmier [1969] Chap. I, §8.1, Cor. 2 of Prop. 1). The structure of discrete von Neumann algebras is given by the following proposition (Dixmier [1969] Chap. III, §3.1, Prop. 2).

5.2. PROPOSITION. *Every discrete von Neumann algebra $\mathfrak{A}$ can be written as a direct product $\prod_{\beta \in B} (\mathfrak{Z}(\beta) \otimes \mathfrak{B}(H(\beta)))$, where the $\mathfrak{Z}(\beta)$ are commutative von Neumann algebras and $H(\beta)$ suitable Hilbert spaces. Moreover, if $\mathfrak{A}$ is finite, then all $H(\beta)$ are necessarily finite dimensional.*

Now we turn to the case of continuous algebras. We begin with a general definition.

5.3. DEFINITION. *A projection e of a von Neumann algebra $\mathfrak{A}$ is called* **fundamental** *of order $n = 0, 1, 2, \ldots$, if there exist 2^n mutually orthogonal* *equivalent projections* $e = e(1), e(2), \ldots, e(2^n)$ *such that* $\sum_{l=1}^{2^n} e(l)$ *is contained in the center of* $\mathfrak{A}$.

If $\mathfrak{A}$ is finite and e fundamental, then the order n of e and $\sum_{l=1}^{2^n} e(l)$ are uniquely determined by e (Dixmier [1969] Chap. III, §8.3, Lemma 3). We state the following.

5.4. PROPOSTION. *Every projection e in a finite continuous von Neumann algebra is the sum of a family of mutually orthogonal fundamental projections* (Dixmier [1969] Chap. III, §8.2, Cor.).

5.5. LEMMA. *Let* $e = \sum_{\beta \in B} e(\beta)$ *be the sum of mutually orthogonal projections* $e(\beta)$ *in a finite algebra* $\mathfrak{A}$ *and let each* $e(\beta) = \sum_{l=1}^{r(\beta)} f(\beta, l)$ *be the sum of* $r(\beta)$ *mutually orthogonal equivalent fundamental projections of order* $n(\beta)$ *such that* $f(\beta, l) \sim f(\gamma, k)$, *if* $\beta \neq \gamma$, *then e is contained in the center* $\mathfrak{Z}$ *of* $\mathfrak{A}$ *if and only if* $r(\beta) = 2^{n(\beta)}$ *for all* $\beta \in B$.

Proof. If $r(\beta) = 2^{n(\beta)}$ for all $\beta \in B$, then $e(\beta) = \sum_{l=1}^{2^{n(\beta)}} f(\beta, l)$ is contained in $\mathfrak{Z}$ by Definition 5.3. Consequently $e = \sum_{\beta \in B} e(\beta) \in \mathfrak{Z}$. If in the contrary there exists $\gamma \in B$ such that $r(\gamma) < 2^{n(\gamma)}$, then there exists $0 \neq u \in \mathfrak{A}$ such that $u^{\mathrm{T}}u = f(\gamma, 1)$ and $uu^{\mathrm{T}} = f(\gamma, r(\gamma) + 1)$, which is a projection equivalent to $f(\gamma, 1)$ and orthogonal to all $f(\gamma, 1), f(\gamma, 2), \ldots, f(\gamma, r(\gamma))$. According to a remark at the beginning of this section we obtain $ue = uf(\gamma, 1)e = uf(\gamma, 1) = u \neq 0$ and $eu = ef(\gamma, r(\gamma) + 1)u = 0u = 0$.

If $\mathfrak{A}$ is a finite algebra with trace tr and center $\mathfrak{Z}$, then clearly $\mathfrak{Z}$ is a finite algebra the restriction of tr to $\mathfrak{Z}$ giving the trace in the correct normalization.

5.6. THEOREM. *If* $(\mathfrak{A}_i, \mathrm{tr}_i)$, $i \in J$ *are finite algebras with centers* $\mathfrak{Z}_i$, *then the center* $\mathfrak{Z}$ *of the restricted ultraproduct* $\mathfrak{A}$ *is the restricted ultraproduct of the* $\mathfrak{Z}_i$.

Proof. Evidently the restricted ultraproduct of the $\mathfrak{Z}_i$ is contained in $\mathfrak{Z}$. Therefore, we need only to show that $z \in \mathfrak{Z}$ comes from an element $z_i \in \prod_{i \in J} \mathfrak{Z}_i$. Every $z \in \mathfrak{A}$ can be written as a linear combination of two selfadjoint elements in the form $z = \frac{1}{2}(z + z^{\mathrm{T}}) + \frac{1}{2}\mathrm{i}((z - z^{\mathrm{T}})/\mathrm{i})$. It is easily seen that $z \in \mathfrak{Z}$ if and only if its selfadjoint constituents belong to $\mathfrak{Z}$. So we may assume $z = z^{\mathrm{T}}$. Now z has the spectral function $e(t)$ and $z \in \mathfrak{Z}$ if and only if $e(t) \in \mathfrak{Z}$ for every $t \in \boldsymbol{R}$. Hence it suffices to treat the case of a projection $e \in \mathfrak{Z}$. By 4.4 we can lift this projection to a set of projections $e_i \in \prod_{i \in J} \mathfrak{A}_i$. Every $\mathfrak{A}_i$ is the direct product of a discrete and a continuous von Neumann algebra, thus $e_i = c_i \times d_i$, where c_i (d_i) is a projection in the continuous (discrete) part of $\mathfrak{A}_i$. Now by 5.4 each

$$c_i = \sum_{\substack{\beta \in B_i \\ 1 \leq l \leq r_i(\beta)}} f_i(\beta, l)$$

is the sum of orthogonal fundamental projections $f_i(\beta, l)$ of order $n_i(\beta)$ such that $f_i(\beta, l) \sim f_i(\gamma, k)$ if and only if $\beta = \gamma$. Let $r_i(\beta) + t_i(\beta) = 2^{n_i(\beta)}$ and $m_i(\beta) = \mathrm{Min}(r_i(\beta), t_i(\beta))$. Then a slight modification of the proof of 5.5 gives the following result: the image c of c_i is in $\mathfrak{Z}$ if and only if

$$^*\mathrm{tr}_i \left(\sum_{\beta \in B_i} \sum_{l=1}^{m_i(\beta)} f_i(\beta, l) \right) \in \boldsymbol{S}.$$

If we replace c_i by

$$c_i' = \sum_{\substack{\beta \\ m_i(\beta) = t_i(\beta)}} \sum_{l=1}^{2^{n_i(\beta)}} f_i(\beta, l),$$

then $c_i' \in \mathfrak{Z}$ and

$$c_i' - c_i = \sum_{\substack{\beta \\ m_i(\beta) = t_i(\beta)}} \sum_{k = r_i(\beta)+1}^{2^{n_i(\beta)}} f_i(\beta, k) - \sum_{\substack{\beta \\ m_i(\beta) \neq t_i(\beta)}} \sum_{l=1}^{m_i(\beta)} f_i(\beta, l).$$

But

$$^*\mathrm{tr}_i(c_i' - c_i, c_i' - c_i) = {}^*\mathrm{tr}_i(c_i + c_i') = {}^*\mathrm{tr}_i \left(\sum_{\beta \in B_i} \sum_{l=1}^{m_i(\beta)} f_i(\beta, l) \right) \in \boldsymbol{S},$$

where we used that equivalent projections have the same trace. Hence c_i' is mapped onto $c \in \mathfrak{Z}$. In essentially the same way it can be shown with the help of 5.2 that the discrete parts d_i may be chosen in the center $\mathfrak{Z}_i$, if their image lies in $\mathfrak{Z}$. Taking both results together into account we conclude that the restricted ultraproduct of the $\mathfrak{Z}_i$ coincides with $\mathfrak{Z}$. Q.e.d.

5.7. Corollary. *The restricted ultraproduct of finite factors is a finite factor.*

Now we can give an example of an infinite dimensional finite factor. Set $J = \boldsymbol{N}$ and $\mathfrak{A}_n = \mathfrak{M}_n$ = full algebra of $n \times n$-matrices with complex entries. The usual trace divided by n gives tr_n in the correct normalization. According to the corollary the restricted ultraproduct of $(\mathfrak{M}_n, \mathrm{tr}_n)$, $n \in \boldsymbol{N}$ is a finite factor ($\mathfrak{M}$, tr) and it is not difficult to see that $\mathfrak{M}$ cannot have finite dimension. We note without proof, that $\mathfrak{M}$ is nothing else but the well known socalled hyperfinite factor (Dixmier [1969] Chap. III, §7.2).

References

Dixmier, J., 1969, Les algèbre d'opérateurs dans l'espace Hilbertien (Gauthiers-Villars, Paris, 2ième éd.).

McDuff, D., 1969, A Countable Infinity of II_1-Factors, *Ann. Math.* 90, pp. 361–371.

McDuff, D., 1971, *Uncountable Many II_1-Factors*, to appear.

Luxemburg, W. A. J., 1969, A General Theory of Monads, in: *Applications of Model Theory to Algebra, Analysis and Probability*, ed. W. A. J. Luxemburg (Holt, Rinehart and Winston, New York).

Murray, F. J. and von Neumann, J., 1936, On Rings of Operators, *Ann. Math.* 37, pp. 116–229.

Murray, F. J. and von Neumann, J., 1937, On Rings of Operators II, *Trans. Am. Math. Soc.* 41, pp. 208–248.

Sakai, S., 1970, An Uncountable Number of II_1- and II_∞-Factors, *J. Functional Analysis* 5, pp. 236–246.

Schwartz, J. T., 1967, *W*-algebras* (Gordon and Breach, New York-London-Paris).

Received 16 March 1971

ALMOST PERPENDICULAR VECTORS

Christian W. PURITZ
University of Glasgow

The purpose of this note is to show how the methods of Nonstandard Analysis can illuminate the study of the weak topology of a Hilbert space. The main results are a transparent proof of the fact that the unit ball is weakly compact and a new characterisation of compact operators. We conclude by looking at vectors that are of infinite norm but are "infinitely close" to 0 in the weak topology.

1. Let H be a Hilbert space over the complex field $\boldsymbol{C}$, let M be the full higher order structure based on $H \cup \boldsymbol{C}$, and let $^*M$ be a nonstandard model of M (see Robinson [1966], Luxemburg [1969] or Staples [1969]). $^*M$ is an extension of M which in a certain sense has the same properties as M. The objects of $^*M$ that were already in M are called *standard* and will sometimes be denoted with a *; this applies particularly to sets. Thus $\boldsymbol{C}$ becomes $^*\boldsymbol{C}$, which is a non-archimedean extension of $\boldsymbol{C}$. A number $x \in {}^*\boldsymbol{C}$ is said to be *infinitesimal*, $x =_1 0$, if $|x| < \varepsilon$ for every standard positive ε, to be *finite* if there is a standard natural number n such that $|x| < n$, and to be *infinite* if it is not finite. A vector of $^*H$ will be called infinitesimal, finite or infinite according to the size of its norm.

The neighbourhood filter of 0 in the weak topology is generated by the subbasis $\{S_{h,\varepsilon} : h \in H,\ 0 < \varepsilon \in R\}$, where $S_{h,\varepsilon} = \{f \in H : |f, h| < \varepsilon\}$. This filter is characterised[1]) in $^*M$ by its *monad*

$$\mu_{\mathrm{w}}(0) = \cap({}^*S_{h,\varepsilon} : h \in H, 0 < \varepsilon \in R).$$

This is called the *weak monad* of 0 and contains the points of $^*H$ that are "infinitely close to 0" in the weak topology. It is immediate from the definition of the $S_{h,\varepsilon}$ that $\mu_{\mathrm{w}}(0)$ consists precisely of those vectors of $^*H$ that have

[1]) The characterisation is complete if $^*M$ is an *enlargement* of M, i.e. if all filters of M have non-empty monads in $^*M$.

an infinitesimal inner product with every standard vector. Such vectors f will be said to be *almost perpendicular to* H, $f \perp_1 H$. Thus

$$\mu_w(0) = \{f \in {}^*H : f \perp_1 H\}.$$

To obtain examples of vectors $\perp_1 H$ we use

1.1. LEMMA. *Let S be a dense subset of H, and let $f \in {}^*H$ be $\perp_1 S$, i.e. $(f, h) =_1 0$ for all $h \in S$. Then if f is finite, $f \perp_1 H$.*

Proof. Given $h \in H$, let (h_n) be a sequence of points of S that tends to h. (Here as throughout unqualified topological terms refer to the norm topology.) For every $n \in N$ we have

$$|f, h| \leq |f, h_n| + |f, h - h_n|.$$

Let ε be any standard positive number. As $h_n \to h$ and f is finite, there exists n_1 such that $|f, h - h_{n_1}| < \frac{1}{2}\varepsilon$. Also $|f, h_{n_1}| < \frac{1}{2}\varepsilon$, being infinitesimal. Thus $|f, h| < \varepsilon$, so as ε is arbitrary $(f, h) =_1 0$.

The lemma can fail dramatically when f is infinite: see §6.

1.2. COROLLARY. *If H is separable with orthonormal basis $(e_n : n \in N)$ then in ${}^*H$ a finite vector $f = {}^*\sum_{n=1}^{\infty} c_n e_n$* [1]*) is $\perp_1 H$ iff $c_n =_1 0$ for all finite n.*

Proof. The condition is obviously necessary, and sufficiency follows from the fact that if $c_n =_1 0$ for all $n \in N$, then f is $\perp_1$ to the linear span of the e_n.

An example of the above is $f = e_\nu$ where $\nu \in {}^*N - N$. It should be noted that e_ν is not exactly perpendicular ($\perp$) to H; for instance if $h = \sum_{n=1}^{\infty} e_n/n$, $(e_\nu, h) = 1/\nu$.

2. (The results sketched in this section will hardly be needed in the sequel.) If ${}^*M$ is an enlargement of M then there *are* vectors $\perp H$ in ${}^*H$, because the relation of orthogonality is concurrent in a Hilbert space. Furthermore one can show that if ${}^*M$ is κ-saturated (Luxemburg [1969] p. 28) for some cardinal $\kappa > \text{card}(H)$, then every vector $\perp_1 H$ can be expressed as a vector $\perp H$ plus an infinitesimal vector. However it seems impossible to give an "example" of a vector $\perp H$, for such a vector does not belong to ${}^*S$ for any countable subset S of H; and no basic ultrapower $H^N/\mathcal{U}$ has vectors $\perp H$. (The last two statements follow from the fact that if

[1]) ${}^*\Sigma_{n=1}^{\infty}$ means that the summation is over all $n \in {}^*N$.

$S \subseteq H$ is countable, there exists $h \in H$ such that $(h, f) \neq 0$ for all $f \in S$.)

3. Weak compactness of the unit ball. The weak monads of standard points other than 0 are obtained by simply translating $\mu_w(0)$, and a point $f \in {}^*H$ is called *weakly near-standard* if it lies in some weak monad, i.e. if $f = f_0 + f_1$ for some $f_0 \in H, f_1 \perp_1 H$. It is easily seen that weak monads of distinct points are disjoint: $f_0 + f_1 = f_0' + f_1'$ implies that $f_0 - f_0' = f_1' - f_1$ is both standard and $\perp_1 H$, and hence $= 0$. This shows that the weak topology is Hausdorff (Robinson [1966] p. 92).

3.1. THEOREM. *Every finite point of* $^*H$ *is weakly near-standard.*

Proof. Given f such that $\|f\|$ is finite, the product (f, h) is also finite whenever $h \in H$ (Schwarz' inequality). We can therefore define $\Phi_0(h) = {}^\circ(f, h)$; (${}^\circ a$ denotes the *standard part* of a, the unique standard number such that $a - {}^\circ a =_1 0$, see Robinson [1966] p. 57). Φ_0 is a functional on H (with values in $\boldsymbol{C}$) and is additive and homogeneous, because ${}^\circ(a + b) = {}^\circ a + {}^\circ b$ and ${}^\circ(ka) = k \cdot {}^\circ a$ hold whenever a, b are finite and k is standard. Also Φ_0 is bounded, in fact ${}^\circ\|f\| \geq \|\Phi_0\|$. Thus by the theorem of Riesz there is an $f_0 \in H$ such that $\Phi_0(h) = (f_0, h)$ for all $h \in H$. Then $(f_0, h) = {}^\circ(f, h)$ so that $(f - f_0, h) =_1 0$, i.e. $f - f_0 \perp_1 H$ as required.

3.2. COROLLARY *(Standard). The closed unit ball in H is weakly compact.*

Proof. Let B_1 be the unit ball. Using Robinson's characterisation of a compact sub-space (Robinson [1966] p. 94)[1]) we need to show that every point of $^*B_1$ lies in the weak monad of a point of B_1. Given $f \in {}^*B_1$, so that $\|f\| \leq 1$, we have $f = f_0 + f_1$ with $f_0 \in H, f_1 \perp_1 H$, and all we have to show is that $f_0 \in B_1$. Now

$$\|f\|^2 = (f, f) = \|f_0\|^2 + \|f_1\|^2 + 2\,\mathrm{Re}(f_0, f_1).$$

The last term on the right-hand side is infinitesimal as $f_1 \perp_1 H$, and the middle term is non-negative. If $\|f_0\| > 1$, then $\|f_0\|^2$ exceeds 1 by a *standard* positive amount, which is greater than every infinitesimal, so that we get $\|f\| > 1$, contradicting the fact that $f \in {}^*B_1$. Thus $\|f_0\| \leq 1$, which completes the proof.

The weak sequential compactness of B_1 can also be deduced from Theorem 3.1, though less easily.

[1]) We here take $^*M$ to be an enlargement.

4. Compact operators. Robinson [1966, p. 119] has given a nonstandard characterisation of compact operators in terms of the norm topology, in which the monad of a standard point f_0 is

$$\mu(f_0) = \{f \in {}^*H : \|f - f_0\| =_1 0\},$$

and points belonging to such a monad are called *near-standard.* A linear operator $A : H \to H$ is compact iff in ${}^*H$ ${}^*A$ maps all finite points into near-standard points. I shall give here a characterisation relating to the weak topology. We first need

4.1. LEMMA. *If A is a bounded linear operator: $H \to H$ then ${}^*A$ maps $\mu_w(0)$ into $\mu_w(0)$.*

Proof. Let $A^\dagger$ be the adjoint of A and let f_1 be $\perp_1 H$. Then for any $h \in H$ we have

$$(h, {}^*Af_1) = ({}^*A^\dagger h, f_1) =_1 0;$$

so ${}^*Af_1 \perp_1 H$ as claimed.

4.2. THEOREM. *The operator $A : H \to H$ is compact iff ${}^*A$ maps finite vectors $\perp_1 H$ into infinitesimal vectors.*

Proof. $\Rightarrow$. If A is compact and f_1 is finite and $\perp_1 H$, then ${}^*Af_1$ is near-standard and (Lemma 4.1) $\perp_1 H$; but this is only possible if ${}^*Af_1 =_1 0$.

$\Leftarrow$. Given any finite vector $f \in {}^*H$, let $f = f_0 + f_1$ with $f_0 \in H, f_1 \perp_1 H$; then ${}^*Af = {}^*Af_0 + {}^*Af_1$, and by assumption ${}^*Af_1 =_1 0$, so ${}^*Af \in \mu({}^*Af_0)$; thus A is compact.

We easily deduce from the above that a compact operator maps weakly converging sequences into strongly converging ones. Another easily obtained result is

4.3. THEOREM *(Standard). If $A : H \to H$ is bounded and $A^\dagger A$ is compact, then A is compact.*

Proof. For any finite $f_1 \perp_1 H$ we have $A^\dagger A f_1 =_1 0$ by hypothesis (writing A instead of ${}^*A$ for convenience). Hence, as f_1 is finite,

$$0 =_1 (f_1, A^\dagger A f_1) = (Af_1, Af_1); \quad \text{so} \quad Af_1 =_1 0.$$

5. Infinite vectors $\perp_1$ *H*. The uniform boundedness principle implies that a sequence of vectors that weakly converges to 0 is bounded in norm. This seems to suggest that all vectors $\perp_1 H$ are finite (for a sequence $f_n \to 0$ weakly iff $f_\nu \in \mu_w(0)$ for all infinite ν, and is bounded in norm iff f_ν is finite for all ν (Robinson [1966] pp. 96, 59). That is not the case however, for weak neighbourhoods of 0 are always unbounded, so in an enlargement $^*H$ has infinite vectors in $\mu_w(0)$. Indeed, if $f \perp H$ then $kf \perp H$ for every $k \in {}^*\mathbf{C}$, so that $\|kf\|$ can be arbitrarily large. This shows incidentally that a compact operator need not map infinite vectors $\perp_1 H$ into $\mu(0)$; for if A is chosen to have a trivial null-space then $^*A(kf) = k \cdot {}^*Af$ is non-zero and can be made arbitrarily large.

It is possible to give a more explicit example of an infinite vector $\perp_1 H$ as follows.

Let ν_1, ν_2 be infinite natural numbers. We define $\nu_1 \ll \nu_2$ to mean that, for every function $f:\mathbf{N} \to \mathbf{N}$, $^*f(\nu_1) < \nu_2$; i.e. ν_2 is in a higher sky than ν_1 (Puritz [1971]). Such a pair of numbers (called a *random pair* by Luxemburg [1969] p. 71 [1])) must exist in an enlargement; one can take $\nu_2 = p(\nu_1)$ where p is any function that dominates every standard function throughout $^*\mathbf{N}$.

5.1. LEMMA. *If* $\nu_1 \ll \nu_2$ *and if* $f_1 : N \to N$ *is such that* $f_1(n) \to \infty$ *as* $n \to \infty$ *then* $\nu_1/{}^*f_1(\nu_2) =_1 0$.

Proof. Suppose that for some $k \in \mathbf{N}$, $\nu_1/{}^*f_1(\nu_2) > 1/k$, i.e. $^*f_1(\nu_2)/k < \nu_1$. Let $f:\mathbf{N} \to \mathbf{N}$ be defined as follows:

$$f(n) = \text{the largest number } m \text{ such that } f_1(m)/k < n.$$

Such a largest number always exists (except perhaps for $n \leq f_1(1)/k$) because $f_1(m) \to \infty$ as $m \to \infty$. When we pass to $^*N$ and take $n = \nu_1$ the largest m must be $\geq \nu_2$, so $^*f(\nu_1) \geq \nu_2$, which contradicts $\nu_1 \ll \nu_2$.

5.2. EXAMPLE. *Let* $(e_n : n \in N)$ *be an orthonormal sequence in H and let* $\nu_1 \ll \nu_2 \in {}^*N - N$. *Then* $\nu_1 e_{\nu_2}$ *is infinite and* $\perp_1 H$.

Proof. Let $h = \sum_{n=1}^{\infty} c_n e_n + h'$ be any vector of H, with $h' \perp e_n$ for all n. In $^*H, h' \perp e_\nu$ for all $\nu \in {}^*N$, so $|h, \nu_1 e_{\nu_2}| = \nu_1 |c_{\nu_2}|$. Let $f_1 : N \to N$ be defined by

$$f_1(n) = \begin{cases} 1 + \left[\dfrac{1}{|c_n|}\right] & \text{if } c_n \neq 0 \\ n & \text{if } c_n = 0. \end{cases}$$

[1]) Luxemburg shows there that, if $\nu_1 \ll \nu_2$, the point $e_{\nu_2}/\nu_1 \in {}^*H$ is not compact, i.e. does not belong to any standard compact set.

Then $f_1(n) \to \infty$ as $n \to \infty$ because $c_n \to 0$, and $\nu_1|c_{\nu_2}| < \nu_1/{}^*f_1(\nu_2)$, and this is $=_1 0$ from the lemma. Thus $\nu_1 e_{\nu_2} \perp_1 H$.

The set of infinite vectors $\perp_1 H$ can be seen to be the monad $\mu(\mathscr{T})$ of the filter $\mathscr{T}$ generated by the sets $T_{h,n}$, $h \in H$, $n \in \mathbf{N}$, where

$$T_{h,n} = \{f \in H: \|f\| > n \quad \text{and} \quad |f, h| < 1/n\}.$$

What the uniform boundedness principle tells us is just that no elementary filter[1]) refines $\mathscr{T}$, or in other words that $\mu(\mathscr{T})$ does not contain $\{f_\nu : \nu \in {}^*N - N\}$ for any standard sequence (f_n). I have shown (Puritz [1970]) that, assuming the Continuum Hypothesis and that card$(H) = c$, it follows that there exists an ultrapower $H^N/\mathscr{U}_1$, in which $\mu(\mathscr{T})$ is empty (this means incidentally that $N^N/\mathscr{U}_1$ has no numbers $\nu_1 \ll \nu_2$, i.e. has only one sky, so that the ultrafilter $\mathscr{U}_1$ must be δ-stable, a P-point of $\beta N - N$ (Puritz [1971]). But this does not conflict with the fact that in other nonstandard models there are infinite almost perpendicular vectors.

6. The vector $\nu_2 e_{\nu_1}$ with $\nu_1 \ll \nu_2$ provides a striking counterexample to Lemma 1.1. Let S be the set of points $h \in H$ such that $(h, e_{\nu_1}) = 0$. Both S and $H - S$ are dense in H, for S contains the span of the e_n and $H - S$ contains all vectors that have a non-zero component along every e_n. Now let $h = \sum_{n=1}^{\infty} c_n e_n + h'$ be any vector of H and let $f_2(n) = [1/|c_n|]$ whenever $c_n \neq 0$. Then since $\nu_1 \ll \nu_2$, $\nu_2/{}^*f_2(\nu_1)$ is infinite when $c_n \neq 0$, and we have

$$\begin{aligned} |h, \nu_2 e_{\nu_1}| &= 0 && \text{if } h \in S, \\ &\geq \nu_2/{}^*f_2(\nu_1) && \text{if } h \in H - S. \end{aligned}$$

Thus $(h, \nu_2 e_{\nu_1})$ is either 0 or infinite.

References

Luxemburg, W. A. J., 1969, editor, *Applications of Model Theory to Algebra, Analysis and Probability* (Holt, Rinehart and Winston, New York).

Puritz, C. W., 1971, Ultrafilters and Standard Functions in Non-Standard Arithmetic, *Proc. London Math. Soc.* (3) 22, pp. 705–733.

[1]) Filter generated by the tails $\{f_n : n > m\}$, $m \in \mathbf{N}$, of a sequence.

Puritz, C. W., 1970, *Skies and Monads in Non-standard Analysis*, Ph.D. Thesis, Glasgow (partly published as Skies, Constellations and Monads, *this volume*).
Robinson, A., 1966, *Non-Standard Analysis*, Studies in Logic and the Foundations of Mathematics (North-Holland, Amsterdam).
Staples, J., 1969, A Non-Standard Representation of Boolean Algebras, and Applications, *Bull. London Math. Soc.* 1, pp. 315–320.

Received 22 April 1971

FUNCTIONAL ANALYSIS – A NON-STANDARD TREATMENT WITH SEMIFIELDS

Leslie YOUNG
Wolfson College, Oxford

1. Introduction. The chief results of this paper arise from the application of Non-Standard Analysis to the theory of topological vector spaces. This theory was a generalisation of the classical theory of normed vector spaces, examining the relations which arise in a space with both a topological and a vector space structure. We give a comprehensive non-standard treatment which will deal with most of the important standard constructions and theorems. Naturally, the most illuminating results are those relating the algebraic structure to the various classes of non-standard points which reflect the topological structure.

Underlying the deepest results of the standard theory is a powerful duality enabling us to discuss properties of a topological vector space in terms of its dual–the associated space of continuous linear functionals. We can go a considerable way toward establishing a non-standard duality theory relating the non-standard extension of a space to its dual.

As with all accounts of functional analysis we find that frequently we need to call upon results in the theory of function spaces–that is, the study of topological structures on classes of functions–and in our case we need some theorems concerning the non-standard structure. Rather than invoking these piecemeal we devote a separate chapter to a systematic account of the most important results of the theory using Non-Standard Analysis. This does not appear to have been attempted before and in any case it seems worthwhile to look at such concepts as equicontinuity and uniform convergence in the more general setting before adding the vector space structure.

To explain our use of the notion of a semifield we point out that extant work in Non-Standard Analysis on function spaces and topological vector spaces, for example in Robinson [1966] and Luxemburg [1969], is confined to the special cases of sequences of functions into metric spaces and to normed spaces. We venture an explanation: Non-Standard Analysis gives an attractive development of "pure" topology, of topological groups, Banach and Hilbert Spaces using the concept of a monad. In these theories the topological and uniform structure is either given or immediately derived so that the monads are readily specified. But the interesting topological structures for function spaces are defined in terms of the topologies of the domain and range spaces; for one member of a dual pair of vector spaces, in terms of subsets of the other member–they are complex derived entities and the monads are correspondingly awkward–except of course for metric and normed spaces, the special cases which have been treated.

Our approach to the general case has been to discard the traditional treatment of topology in terms of open sets, neighbourhoods and vicinities in favour of a treatment using an abstract concept of distance; that is, in terms of "metrics" and "norms" taking values in a structure more general than the real line–a topological semifield. We chanced upon this concept while idly leafing through the Russian Mathematical Surveys. The survey article there, however, treats only uniform spaces. We extend the theory to topological spaces and then apply it to function spaces and to locally convex topological vector spaces.

Linking with Non-Standard Analysis we find that Topology reduces largely to examining which points are on infinitesimal distance apart–a rather satisfactory situation given that this now has a rigorous as well as an intuitive meaning. Further, we are able to give a non-standard treatment of general function spaces and topological vector spaces in a style which recalls closely the treatment of the special cases which have already been put forward.

In large part the introduction of semifields is merely a stylistic change making the arguments clearer and more attractive. For our study of topological vector spaces, however, essential use is made of the notion of a seminorm over a field. This allows a definition of boundedness more tractable than the conventional one through which we are lead to introduce the class of "norm bounded" points in the enlargement of a space. This class is the natural analogue of the norm-finite points which appear in the non-standard theory of normed spaces and stands in the same relation to bounded filters and bounded sets as do the pre-near-standard points to Cauchy-filters and precompact sets and near-standard points to convergent filters and compact sets. Relations between this class–which is peculiar to the theory of topological vector spaces–and the other specifically "topological" classes of points underly important concepts in the standard theory.

This paper contains preliminary results toward a D.Phil. thesis to be submitted to the University of Oxford. The area covered is undoubtedly capable of considerable further development.

1.1. Non-standard analysis. Familiarity wlth the sections of Luxemburg [1969] dealing with the logical foundations and elementary results in non-standard topology is assumed. The monograph of Machover and Hirschfeld [1969] is recommended for that painless introduction. For later reference we collect here the principal definitions and results and establish our notation.

Given a higher-order structure $\mathfrak{M}$–that is, a domain of individuals together with higher order entities of all types–let K be the set of all sentences in a higher-order language L which hold in $\mathfrak{M}$. Let $\hat{\mathfrak{M}}$ be a higher order non-standard model of K i.e. an *extension* of $\mathfrak{M}$. Thus $\hat{\mathfrak{M}}$ has every property of $\mathfrak{M}$ which can be expressed by sentences of L. Note that $\hat{\mathfrak{M}}$ need not contain every higher order entity based on its domain. Those in $\hat{\mathfrak{M}}$ are said to be *internal.* To every entity a of $\mathfrak{M}$ there corresponds an entity in $\hat{\mathfrak{M}}$ namely that denoted by the constant in K denoting a in $\mathfrak{M}$. This we write as "$\hat{a}$". Entities of $\hat{\mathfrak{M}}$ which can be obtained in this way are called *standard.* If S is a set of entities in $\mathfrak{M}$ and $a \in S$ then in $\hat{\mathfrak{M}}$, $\hat{a} \in \hat{S}$. When S is infinite $\hat{S}$ may contain entities which are non-standard. Hence we speak of $\hat{S}$ as the *extension* of S. Similarly a function in $\mathfrak{M}$ has an extension in $\hat{\mathfrak{M}}$.

We find the following convention best suited to our needs: only where we are concerned with the membership of a standard entity–i.e. we are thinking of it as a set– shall we continue to use the notation "$\hat{S}$". If we are considering a standard individual we shall omit the "$\wedge$" and similarly when we consider the extension of a function. Furthermore we shall use "S" to denote the standard elements of the standard set $\hat{S}$. Thus when we write "$\exists x \in \hat{Q}$ such that $y \in E \Rightarrow f(y) \simeq \langle x, y\rangle$" we are asserting that there is a (possibly non-standard) element in the extension of Q such that if y is a standard element in the extension of E then $f(y) \simeq \langle x, y\rangle$ where $\langle x, y\rangle$ is the image of the pair (x, y) under the extension of the function $\langle .,.\rangle$. The trendy logical symbols $\exists$ (exists), $\forall$ (all) and $\Rightarrow$ (implies) will be used frequently in informal discussion.

A binary relation $R(x, y)$ in $\mathfrak{M}$ is *concurrent in x* if for every finite subset $\{x_1, \ldots, x_n\}$ of the domain of its first argument there is a y such that for $i = 1, \ldots, n$ $R(x_i, y)$ holds in $\mathfrak{M}$. A higher order extension $\hat{\mathfrak{M}}$ of $\mathfrak{M}$ is an *enlargement* if for every concurrent binary relation R in $\mathfrak{M}$ there is a y such that $R(\hat{x}, y)$ holds in $\hat{\mathfrak{M}}$ for all standard $\hat{x}$ in the domain of the first argument of $\hat{R}$.

When discussing a number of mathematical structures e.g. a pair of vector spaces $\langle E, F\rangle$ together with the reals R we take it for granted that we have a *full* higher order structure–one containing all entities of all types–based on some domain containing all the individuals arising in the various structures. An enlargement of this structure then contains the extensions $\hat{E}, \hat{F}, \hat{R}$.

A structure $\mathfrak{M}$ is *κ-saturated* if for every internal binary relation R which is concurrent on a subset A of the domain of its first argument [i.e. for all finite subsets $\{x_1, \ldots, x_n\}$ of A there is a y such that for $i = 1, \ldots, n$ $R(x_i, y)$ in $\mathfrak{M}$] with $\bar{\bar{A}} < \kappa$ there is a z such that for each $x \in A$ $R(x, z)$ in $\mathfrak{M}$.

The construction of enlargements and of κ-saturated enlargements of higher-order structures is carried out in Luxemburg [1969] by means of ultrapowers and ultralimits. In that paper the proof of the following result is entangled with a number of other considerations so we give a streamlined version here. In the following the monad of a filter $\mathfrak{F}$ is defined by

$$\mu(\mathfrak{F}) = \cap\{\hat{S} | S \in \mathfrak{F}\}.$$

1.1.1. THEOREM. *Let $\mathfrak{F}$ be a filter on a set of entities of $\mathfrak{M}$. There is an enlargement of $\mathfrak{M}$ such that if Φ is an internal subset of $\hat{\mathfrak{F}}$ with the property that*

$$U \in \hat{\mathfrak{F}} \text{ and } U \subset \mu(\mathfrak{F}) \Rightarrow U \in \Phi$$

then $\exists S \in \mathfrak{F}$ such that $\hat{S} \in \Phi$.

Proof. Suppose the internal subset Φ of $\hat{\mathfrak{F}}$ is such that $\forall S \in \mathfrak{F}, \hat{S} \notin \Phi$. If Λ is the internal set consisting of elements of $\hat{\mathfrak{F}}$ not in Φ then clearly the set of standard elements of Λ is precisely $\mathfrak{F}$. Consider the filter $\mathfrak{F}_\theta$ generated by the sets $\mathscr{E}_E = \{S | S \in \mathfrak{F} \text{ and } S \subset E\}$ for $E \in \mathfrak{F}$. We have that

$$\mu(\mathfrak{F}_\theta) = \{U | U \in \hat{\mathfrak{F}} \quad \text{and} \quad U \subset \mu(\mathfrak{F})\}.$$

Also, for $\mathscr{E} \in \mathfrak{F}_\theta$ we have that $\Lambda \cap \mathscr{E} \neq \emptyset$.

Let $\hat{\mathfrak{M}}$ be a κ-saturated enlargement of $\mathfrak{M}$ with $\kappa > \bar{\bar{\mathfrak{F}}}_\theta$. Consider the relation $R(x, y)$ of $\hat{\mathfrak{M}}$ which holds if x and y are of the type of subsets of $\hat{\mathfrak{F}}$ and $y \in \hat{\mathfrak{F}}_\theta$ and $y \subset x$ and $\Lambda \cap y \neq \emptyset$. This relation is internal and is concurrent in x on the set of standard elements of $\hat{\mathfrak{F}}_\theta$. As $\hat{\mathfrak{M}}$ is κ-saturated there is a $y \in \hat{\mathfrak{F}}_\theta$ such that $y \in \hat{\mathscr{E}}$ for $\mathscr{E} \in \mathfrak{F}_\theta$ and $\Lambda \cap y \neq \emptyset$, i.e. there is a $U \in \hat{\mathfrak{F}}$ such that $U \subset \mu(\mathfrak{F})$ and $U \in \Lambda$.

Therefore if $\forall S \in \mathfrak{F} : \hat{S} \notin \Phi$ then $\exists U \in \hat{\mathfrak{F}} : U \subset \mu(\mathfrak{F})$ and $U \notin \Phi$

Therefore if $\forall U \in \hat{\mathfrak{F}} : U \subset \mu(\mathfrak{F}) \Rightarrow U \in \Phi$ then $\exists S \in \mathfrak{F}$ such that $\hat{S} \in \Phi$.

q.e.d.

The remainder of this section merely lists a number of results in the non-standard theory of topological and uniform spaces. Proofs can be found in Luxemburg [1969] and Machover and Hirschfeld [1969].

1.1.2. If $\mathfrak{F}$ is a filter then there is an $S \in \hat{\mathfrak{F}}$ such that $S \subset \mu(\mathfrak{F})$.

1.1.3. If $\mathfrak{F}$ is a filter on X then a subset S of X is in $\mathfrak{F}$ iff $\mu(\mathfrak{F}) \subset \hat{S}$.

1.1.4. If $\mathfrak{F}$ is a filter and $\mathscr{D}$ an ultrafilter on X such that $\mu(\mathscr{D}) \cap \mu(\mathfrak{F}) \neq \emptyset$ then $\mu(\mathscr{D}) \subset \mu(\mathfrak{F})$.

If $\mathfrak{F}$ is the neighbourhood filter of a point p in a topological space X we write its monad as $\mu(p)$. Points in $\hat{X}$ in the monad of some standard point are said to be *near-standard*. They are used to characterise topological properties as follows:

1.1.5. A filter $\mathfrak{F}$ on X converges to $p \in X$ iff $\mu(\mathfrak{F}) \subset \mu(p)$.

1.1.6. $\mu(p) = \cup\{\mu(\mathfrak{F}) | \mathfrak{F}$ an ultrafilter converging to $p\}$.

1.1.7. $p \in X$ is in the closure of a set $S \subset X$ iff $\mu(p) \cap \hat{S} \neq \emptyset$.

1.1.8. $S \subset X$ is closed iff $\mu(p) \cap \hat{S} \neq \emptyset \Rightarrow p \in S$.

1.1.9. X is Hausdorff iff for $p, q \in X$, $\mu(p) \cap \mu(q) = \emptyset$.

1.1.10. $S \subset X$ is compact iff $\forall x \in \hat{S}\ \exists p \in S : x \in \mu(p)$.

1.1.11. If $S \subset X$ is relatively compact then for all $x \in \hat{S}$ there is a $p \in X$ such that $x \in \mu(p)$.

If X is regular and for all $x \in \hat{S}$ there is a $p \in X$ such that $x \in \mu(p)$ then S is relatively compact. Since all uniformizable spaces and therefore all topological vector spaces are regular we can apply this result in these spaces.

1.1.12. X is locally compact iff for each near-standard point x in $\hat{X}$ there is a compact subset S of X such that $x \in \hat{S}$.

A point r in the extended reals $\hat{R}$ is *finite* if there is a standard $q \in R$ such that $|r| < q$.

1.1.13. Every finite point in $\hat{R}$ is near-standard.

As the usual topology on R is Hausdorff every finite r in $\hat{R}$ is in the monad of a unique standard point–the *standard part* of r written "st(r)". Points in the monad of 0 are called *infinitesimal*. If for $p, q \in \hat{R}$ $p - q$ is infinitesimal we write $p \simeq q$.

1.1.14. A function $f: X \to Y$ between topological spaces is continuous iff $\forall p \in X\ f(\mu(p)) \subset \mu(f(p))$.

1.1.15. If for each $i \in I$ X_i is a topological space then in the extension of the topological product $\prod X_i$ $q \in \mu(p)$ iff $\forall i \in I\ q_i \in \mu(p_i)$.

Let $\mathscr{U}$ be a uniformity on X. In the uniform space $(X, \mathscr{U})$ a point $x \in \hat{X}$ is *pre-near-standard* if it is in the monad of a Cauchy filter.

1.1.16. $x \in \hat{X}$ is pre-near-standard iff for every $V \in \mathscr{U}$ there is a standard $p \in X$ such that $x \in \hat{V}(p)$.

1.1.17. $(X, \mathscr{U})$ is complete iff every pre-near-standard point in $\hat{X}$ is near-standard with respect to the induced topology.

1.1.18. A subset A of X is precompact iff $x \in \hat{A} \Rightarrow x$ is pre-near-standard.

1.2. Topological semifields. Locally convex topological vector spaces can be "normed" and topological and uniform spaces "metrized" by functions taking values in a semifield–an entity with algebraic, topological and order properties generalising the real line. In fact the Tychonoff semifields–products of real lines suffice for this purpose. Since the reals have a particularly rich and lucid non-standard theory we might expect the combination of non-standard analysis and Tychonoff semifields to form an effective instrument in topology and functional analysis. We do not suggest that the links between the two groups of ideas are particularly intimate–the use of semifields could have been avoided entirely, but with considerable loss in clarity, efficiency and appeal. General semifields have been studied for their own sake but we do not touch on such results since we are using semifields only as a means of clarifying relations in other structures.

A survey of the general theory is in Antonovskii et al. [1966] where the applications to the study of uniform spaces are developed. The extension to the study of topological and vector spaces given here is our own as are the connexions with non-standard analysis. But (therefore?) the results are quite simple and we shall omit proofs where they seem obvious once the proposition has been put. There are some inessential differences from the definitions in Antonovskii et al. [1966] which speed the theory.

Let Δ be a set. R^Δ is the set of functions $h:\Delta \to R$. The function always taking value r is also denoted by "r". The operations of addition, multiplication and scalar multiplication by elements of R are defined co-ordinate-wise.

The term semifield is used because in the ring R^Δ with unit 1 if $h \in R^\Delta$ never takes value 0 then we can define a multiplicative inverse h^{-1} by $h^{-1}(d) = (h(d))^{-1}$ for $d \in \Delta$.

R^Δ viewed as the cartesian product of copies of R is given the product topology which makes it a topological vector space over R. It is, in fact, locally convex since the convex sets $\{h \in R^\Delta \mid |h(d)| < \varepsilon\}$ for $\forall d \in \Delta, \varepsilon > 0$ form a sub-base for the neighbourhoods of 0.

Henceforth we use "$\mathfrak{N}^\Delta$" to denote the filter of neighbourhoods of 0 in the semifield R^Δ. We define an order relation $\leq$ on R^Δ by

$$g \leq h \quad \text{if} \quad g(d) \leq h(d), \forall d \in \Delta.$$

R_0^Δ is the subset of elements ≥ 0.

Any set $S \subset R^{\Delta}$ bounded above in this ordering has a least upper bound $\vee S$, namely the element of R^{Δ} defined by

$$(\vee S)(d) = \sup\{f(d) : f \in S\}.$$

Similarly a subset S of R^{Δ} bounded below has a greatest lower bound $\wedge S$.

For $f \in R^{\Delta}$ we define $|f| \in R^{\Delta}$ by

$$|f|(d) = |f(d)| \quad \text{for} \quad d \in \Delta.$$

Let X be a set. A map $\phi : X \times X \to R_0^{\Delta}$ is a *quasimetric* over R^{Δ} if

$$\left.\begin{array}{l}\phi(x, x) = 0 \\ \phi(x, y) \leq \phi(x, z) + \phi(z, y)\end{array}\right\} \text{for} \quad x, y, z \in X.$$

ϕ is a *pseudometric* if also

$$\phi(x, y) = \phi(y, x) \quad \text{for} \quad x, y \in X.$$

ϕ is a *metric* if also

$$\phi(x, y) = 0 \Rightarrow x = y.$$

The topology induced by a quasimetric ϕ on X is that obtained by taking as neighbourhood filter at x that filter with sub-base consisting of sets of the form $\{y \in X | \phi(x, y) \in u\}$ where u ranges over $\mathfrak{N}^{\Delta}$ the neighbourhood filter of 0 in R^{Δ}. Clearly the same neighbourhood filters would be generated if u ranged over a sub-base of $\mathfrak{N}^{\Delta}$.

It is a standard result that if to each $x \in X$ we can assign a filter $\mathfrak{F}_x$ on X such that

1. $\forall S \in \mathfrak{F}_x, x \in S$,
2. $\forall V \in \mathfrak{F}_x \, \exists W \in \mathfrak{F}_x : y \in W \Rightarrow V \in \mathfrak{F}_y$,

then there is a unique topology $\mathscr{I}$ on X such that $\mathfrak{F}_x$ is the neighbourhood filter at x in $\mathscr{I}$ namely:

$$\mathscr{I} = \{S | S \subset X \quad \text{and} \quad \forall x \in S : S \in \mathfrak{F}_x\}.$$

Our assignment of neighbourhood filters using the quasimetric satisfies the conditions for:

1. each member of the sub-base at x contains x since $\phi(x, x) = 0$;
2. if $V \in \mathfrak{F}_x$ then $\exists$ positive reals $\varepsilon_1, \ldots, \varepsilon_n, \exists d_1, \ldots, d_n \in \Delta$:
$$\phi(x, y)(d_i) < \varepsilon_i, \; i = 1, \ldots, n \Rightarrow y \in V.$$

Define $W \in \mathfrak{F}_x$ as the set of y such that $\phi(x, y)(d_i) < \frac{1}{2}\varepsilon_i$. If $y \in W$ and

$\phi(y, z)(d_i) < \frac{1}{2}\varepsilon_i$ then by the triangle inequality $\phi(x, z)(d_i) < \varepsilon_i$ so $z \in V$. Thus

$$\begin{aligned} y \in W \Rightarrow V &\supset \{z \mid \phi(y, z)(d_i) < \tfrac{1}{2}\varepsilon_i,\ i = 1, \ldots, n\} \\ &\Rightarrow V \in \mathfrak{F}_y. \end{aligned}$$

The uniformity induced by a pseudometric ϕ on X is the filter on $X \times X$ with sub-base consisting of sets of the form $\{(x, y) \mid \phi(x, y) \in u\}$ where u ranges over $\mathfrak{N}^\Delta$. Using the properties of the pseudometric it is easy to show that this is indeed a uniformity. Also, if the pseudometric is in fact a metric then the induced uniformity is Hausdorff.

Semifields would be useful only if they could be used to describe every topological and uniform space. We have shown that this is indeed the case below. In the following "CS" denotes the complement of the set S.

1.2.1. THEOREM. *For every topological space $(X, \mathcal{I})$ there is a semifield R^Δ and a quasimetric ϕ over R^Δ which induces the topology $\mathcal{I}$ on X.*

Proof. $\mathcal{I}$ is the class of open sets in X. Consider the function $\phi: X \times X \to R^{\mathcal{I}}$ defined by

$$\phi(x, y)(S) = \begin{cases} 0 & \text{if} \quad (x, y) \in (S \times S) \cup (\mathrm{C}S \times X) \\ 1 & \text{if} \quad (x, y) \in S \times \mathrm{C}S. \end{cases}$$

This is a quasimetric. Firstly, $\phi(x, x)(S) = 0\ \forall x \in X\ \forall S \in \mathcal{I}$ so $\phi(x, x) = 0$. If $(x, y) \in (S \times S) \cup (\mathrm{C}S \cup X)$ then $\phi(x, y)(S) = 0 \leq \phi(x, z)(S) + \phi(z, y)(S)$ for any z. If $(x, y) \in S \times \mathrm{C}S$ then since for any $z \in X$ either $z \in S$ or $z \in \mathrm{C}S$ we have that either $(x, z) \in S \times \mathrm{C}S$ or $(z, y) \in S \times \mathrm{C}S$ so either $\phi(x, z)(S) = 1$ or $\phi(z, y)(S) = 1$ and in either case $\phi(x, y)(S) \leq \phi(x, z)(S) + \phi(z, y)(S)$. Thus the triangle inequality holds.

We show that the induced neighbourhood filter coincides with the original. Take a sub-base member of the induced filter $\{y \mid \phi(x, y)(S) < \varepsilon\}$. This clearly includes the set $\{y \mid \phi(x, y)(S) = 0\}$. This set is either S or X and both sets are neighbourhoods of x in the original topology. Now take a neighbourhood N of x in the original topology. Then N contains some open neighbourhood S of x. Since $x \in S$ $\{y \mid \phi(x, y)(S) < 1\} = S$ so S is a sub-base member of the induced filter at x. We have thus shown that at every $x \in X$ the original and the induced neighbourhood filters coincide.

q.e.d.

1.2.2. THEOREM. *For every uniform space $(X, \mathcal{U})$ there is a semifield R^Δ and a pseudometric ϕ over R^Δ which induces the uniformity $\mathcal{U}$ on X.*

Proof. By a well-known argument (e.g. Kelley [1955] p. 185) for each $U \in \mathscr{U}$ we can find a function $d_u : X \times X \to R$ such that:

1. $0 \leq d_u(x, y) \leq 1$.
2. If $(x, y) \notin U$ then $d_u(x, y) = 1$.
3. $d_u(x, y) = d_u(y, x)$.
4. $d_u(x, y) \leq d_u(x, z) + d_u(z, y)$.
5. For every $\varepsilon > 0$ there is a $V \in \mathscr{U}$ such that $(x, y) \in V \Rightarrow d_u(x, y) < \varepsilon$.

Let Δ be the set of d_u so obtained as U ranges over $\mathscr{U}$. Define $\phi : X \times X \to R^{\Delta}$ by

$$\phi(x, y)(d_u) = d_u(x, y).$$

This is clearly a pseudometric. We show that the induced uniformity coincides with $\mathscr{U}$.

A sub-base of the induced uniformity consists of the sets $\{(x, y) | d_u(x, y) < \varepsilon\}$ and such sets belong to $\mathscr{U}$ by 5. Conversely if $U \in \mathscr{U}$ then $\{(x, y) | d_u(x, y) < 1\} = U$ so U is a member of the induced uniformity. q.e.d.

The above simplifies greatly a proof of the same result in Antonovskiĭ et al. [1966].

It is now clear that the semifield approach to uniform spaces is a variant of the treatment using the set of pseudometrics over R which are uniformly continuous on $X \times X$ as is found for example in Gillman and Jerison [1960]. Our subsequent "norming" of locally convex topological vector spaces is a variant of the treatment using continuous seminorms over R. The benefit of our method lies in the use we can make of the topological vector space structure and order structure of R^{Δ}.

We now introduce the directed quasimetrics which give a convenient characterisation of closure.

Given a quasimetric $\phi : X \times X \to R^{\Delta}$ we define an order relation $\prec$ on Δ by

$$d \prec d' \quad \text{iff} \quad \forall x, y \in X \quad \phi(x, y)(d) \leq \phi(x, y)(d').$$

ϕ is a *directed* quasimetric if the resulting partial ordering makes Δ a directed set. The following theorem shows that every topology can be described by a directed quasimetric.

1.2.3. THEOREM. *For any quasimetric $\phi : X \times X \to R^{\Delta}$ we can define a directed quasimetric $\phi' : X \times X \to R^{\Delta}$ which induces the same topology on X.*

Proof. For each finite subset $\{d_1, \ldots, d_n\}$ of Δ define a quasimetric $\delta : X \times X \to R$ by

$$\delta(x, y) = \max_{i=1,\ldots,n} \phi(x, y)(d_i).$$

Let Δ' be the set of such δ as $\{d_1, \ldots, d_n\}$ ranges over the finite subsets of Δ. Define $\phi' : X \times X \to R^{\Delta'}$ by

$$\phi'(x, y)(\delta) = \delta(x, y).$$

Clearly Δ' is directed by the relation $\prec$ above.

A sub-base for the neighbourhoods at $x \in X$ in the topology induced by ϕ' consists of sets

$$\{y | \delta(x, y) < \varepsilon\} = \{y | \max_{i=1,\ldots,n} \phi(x, y)(d_i) < \varepsilon\} \text{ for some } \{d_1, \ldots, d_n\} \subset \Delta$$

$$= \bigcap_{i=1}^{n} \{y | \phi(x, y)(d_i) < \varepsilon\},$$

i.e. of finite intersections of sub-basic members of the neighbourhood filter at x induced by ϕ. Thus the topologies are identical. q.e.d.

1.2.4. THEOREM. *Let $\phi : X \times X \to R^\Delta$ be a directed quasimetric. In the induced topology on X*

$$x \in \overline{M} \quad \text{iff} \quad \wedge \{\phi(x, m) : m \in M\} = 0.$$

Proof. Necessity: If $x \in \overline{M}$ then each neighbourhood of x meets M so $\forall \varepsilon > 0 \; \forall d \in \Delta \; \exists y \in M : \phi(x, y)(d) < \varepsilon$ i.e. $\wedge \{\phi(x, m) : m \in M\} = 0$.

Sufficiency: By hypothesis $\forall \varepsilon > 0 \; \forall d \in \Delta \; \exists y \in M : \phi(x, y)(d) < \varepsilon$. For any neighbourhood U of x there exist $d_1, \ldots, d_n \in \Delta$, $\varepsilon_i, \ldots, \varepsilon_n > 0$ such that

$$\phi(x, y)(d_i) < \varepsilon_i, \text{ i} = 1, \ldots, n \Rightarrow y \in U.$$

Choose $d \in \Delta$ such that $d \prec d_i$, i $= 1, \ldots, n$ and let

$$\varepsilon = \min_{i=1,\ldots,n} \varepsilon_i.$$

Then $\exists y \in M \; \phi(x, y)(d) < \varepsilon$, i.e. $\exists y \in M \; \phi(x, y)(d_i) < \varepsilon_i$, i $= 1, \ldots, n$, i.e. $\exists y \in M \; y \in U$. Thus $x \in \overline{M}$. q.e.d.

We can deduce that a uniform space X is regular in its induced topology for with a directed pseudometrisation $\phi : X \times X \to R^\Delta$ suppose that M is a closed set and $x \notin M$, i.e. $x \notin \overline{M}$, i.e. $\wedge \{\phi(x, m) | m \in M\} \neq 0$. Then

$\exists d \in \Delta\ \exists \varepsilon > 0\ \forall y \in M,\ \phi(x, y)(d) > \varepsilon$. The sets $\{v \mid \phi(x, z)(d) < \frac{1}{2}\varepsilon\}$ and $\bigcup_{y \in M} \{z \mid \phi(y, z)(d) < \frac{1}{2}\varepsilon\}$ are disjoint open sets containing respectively x and M.

A quasimetric ϕ is *bounded* if $\vee \{\phi(x, y) \mid x, y \in X\}$ exists. For any quasimetric $\phi : X \times X \to R^{\Delta}$ we can define a bounded quasimetric $\phi' : X \times X \to R^{\Delta}$ which induces the same topology by

$$\phi'(x, y) = \phi(x, y)/(1 + \phi(x, y)).$$

This is well defined since the denominator is never 0.

Thus without loss of generality we can assume that our quasimetrics and pseudometrics are directed and bounded.

We now link these ideas with Non-Standard-Analysis.

An element $h_0 \in \hat{R}_0$ is *finite* if for each $d \in \Delta$, $h_0(d)$ is a finite element of $\hat{R}$. An element $h_0 \in \hat{R}^{\Delta}$ is *bounded* if there is a standard h in $\hat{R}^{\Delta}$ such that $h_0 \leq h$.

There also exist "infinite" members h_0 of $\hat{R}^{\Delta}$ such that for all standard h in $\hat{R}^{\Delta}$ $h \leq h_0$. The relation $R(x, y)$ which holds if $x, y \in R^{\Delta}$ and $x \leq y$ is clearly concurrent in x so in the enlargement there are infinite members of $\hat{R}^{\Delta}$.

If $h \in \hat{R}^{\Delta}$ is in the monad of 0 we write $h \simeq 0$. The topology on R^{Δ} is the product topology when R is considered as the topological product of copies of R. By Theorem 1.1.15 $h \simeq 0$ iff $h(d) \simeq 0$ for each $d \in \Delta$.

1.2.5. THEOREM. *If X is quasimetrised by ϕ over R^{Δ} then in the induced topology $x \in \mu(p)$ iff $\phi(p, x) \simeq 0$.*

Proof.

$x \in \mu(p)$ iff $x \in \hat{N}$ for each N in a sub-base of neighbourhoods of p,
iff $x \in \cap\{\{y \in \hat{X} \mid \phi(p, y) \in \hat{u}\} \mid u \in \mathfrak{N}^{\Delta}\}$,
iff $\forall d \in \Delta\ \forall \varepsilon > 0\ \phi(p, x)(d) < \varepsilon$,
iff $\phi(p, x) \simeq 0$. q.e.d.

Similarly if X is pseudometrised by ϕ over R^{Δ} and $\mathscr{U}$ is the induced uniformity then

$$(x, y) \in \mu(\mathscr{U}) \quad \text{iff} \quad \phi(x, y) \simeq 0.$$

Note that by the symmetry of ϕ

$$\phi(x, y) \simeq 0 \quad \text{iff} \quad \phi(y, x) \simeq 0 \quad \text{for} \quad x, y \in \hat{X}$$

and that by the triangle inequality

$$\phi(x, z) \simeq 0 \quad \text{and} \quad \phi(z, y) \simeq 0 \Rightarrow \phi(x, y) \simeq 0.$$

2. Function Spaces. We are considering Y^x thecl ass of functions from the set X to the topological space Y. If Y is quasimetrized by $\theta: Y \times Y \to R^{\Gamma}$ and C is a family of subsets of X then the topology of uniform convergence on members of C on Y^X [henceforth the "C-topology"] is that quasimetrized by $\phi_C: Y^X \times Y^X \to R^{\Gamma \times C}$ where

$$\phi_C(f_1 g)(d, A) = \sup_{x \in A} \theta(f(x)_1 g(x))(d) \quad \text{for} \quad f, g \in Y^X, d \in \Gamma, A \in C.$$

We have seen that there is no loss in supposing θ to be bounded so that the supremum is always defined.

ϕ_C is indeed a quasimetric for

$$\phi_C(f, f)(d, A) = \sup_{x \in A} \theta(f(x), f(x))(d) = 0$$

as θ is a quasimetric and for any $h \in Y^X$

$$\begin{aligned}
\phi_C(f, g)(d, A) &= \sup_{x \in A} \theta(f(x), g(x))(d) \\
&\leq \sup_{x \in A} \{\theta(f(x), h(x))(d) + \theta(h(x), g(x))(d)\} \\
&\leq \sup_{x \in A} \{\theta(f(x), h(x))(d)\} + \sup_{x \in A} \{\theta(h(x), g(x))(d)\} \\
&= \phi_C(f, g)(d, A) + \phi_C(h, g)(d, A).
\end{aligned}$$

The resulting topology on Y^X is the C topology as conventionally defined for a sub-base of the neighbourhood filter at f consists of the sets

$$\begin{aligned}
\{g \mid \phi_C(f, g)(d, A) < \varepsilon\} &= \{g \mid \forall x \in A \ \theta(f(x), g(x))(d) < \varepsilon\} \\
&= \{g \mid \forall x \in A \ g(x) \in N(f(x))\}
\end{aligned}$$

where for each x in A $N(f(x))$ is the neighbourhood of $f(x)$ determined by d, ε. As d, ε varies $N(f(x))$ will range over a sub-base of the neighbourhood filter at $f(x)$ as required.

If Y is a uniform space and θ its pseudometric then the same definition of ϕ_C gives the pseudometric inducing the uniformity of uniform convergence on members of C [the "C-uniformity"]. If θ is a metric then clearly so is ϕ_C.

If C is the set of singletons of X the C topology is known as the *topology of pointwise convergence* [the "weak topology"]. We write the quasimetric as ϕ_X.

If $C = \{X\}$ then the C topology is the *topology of uniform convergence on X*.

If X is a topological space and C is the class of compact subsets of X then the C topology is known as the *compact-open topology*. We write the quasimetric as ϕ_{co}.

Let $(X, \mathscr{I})$ be a topological space with quasimetric $\phi : X \times X \to R^{\Delta}$ and let $(Y, \mathscr{U})$ be a uniform space with pseudometric $\theta: Y \times Y \to R^{\Gamma}$. A subset F of Y^X is *equicontinuous* if

$$\forall x \in X \ \forall V \in \mathscr{U} \ \exists \text{ nhd } G \text{ of } x \ \forall f \in F \ \forall y \in G \ (f(x), f(y)) \in V.$$

This is clearly equivalent to

$$\forall x \in X \ \forall u \in \mathfrak{N}^{\Gamma} \ \exists v \in \mathfrak{N}^{\Delta} \ \forall f \in F \ \forall y \in X \ \phi(x, y) \in v \Rightarrow \theta(f(x), f(y)) \in u.$$

The above use of ϕ and θ is maintained throughout this section.

Most of our results are obtained by non-standard methods. However for the following two essential results concerning the closures of sets of functions in the weak topology the non-standard proofs are no more transparent than the classical ones because there is no simple way of treating the non-standard extension of the closure of a set. We are able to use the characterisation of closure in terms of semifields (Theorem 1.2.4) in some rather nonchalant proofs.

For topological spaces X, Y we use "$C(X, Y)$" to denote the class of functions from X to Y which are continuous on members of C and "$c(X, Y)$" to denote the class of continuous functions from X to Y.

2.1. THEOREM. *$C(X, Y)$ is closed in Y^X with the C topology.*

Proof. We need only show that $c(X, Y)$ is closed in Y^X with the topology of uniform convergence on X. The result then follows by relativisation to the members of C.

Let $g \in \overline{c(X, Y)}$ so by Theorem 1.2.4. $\wedge \{\phi_C(f, g) \mid f \in c(X, Y)\} = 0$

$$\text{i.e. } \wedge \{ \bigvee_{x \in X} \theta(f(x), g(x)) \mid f \in c(X, Y)\} = 0.$$

As

$$f \in c(X, Y), \forall x \in X \ \forall u \in \mathfrak{N}^{\Gamma} \ \exists v \in \mathfrak{N}^{\Delta} \ \forall y \in X : \phi(x, y) \in v \Rightarrow \theta(f(x), f(y)) \in u$$
$$\Rightarrow \wedge \{|\theta(f(x), f(y)) - m| : m \in u\} = 0.$$

But by the triangle inequality, for $m \in u$

$$|\theta(g(x), g(y)) - m| \leq \theta(g(x), f(x)) + |\theta(f(x), g(x)) - m| + \theta(f(y), g(y))$$
$$\leq |\theta(f(x), g(x)) - m| + 2 \bigvee_{x \in X} \theta(f(x), g(x)).$$

Therefore for given x, u, v, y

$$\phi(x, y) \in v \Rightarrow \wedge\{|\theta(g(x), g(y)) - m| : m \in u\} = 0$$

$$\Rightarrow \theta(g(x), g(y)) \in \bar{u} \quad \text{by Theorem 1.2.4.}$$

Thus $\forall x \in X\ \forall u \in \mathfrak{N}^\Gamma\ \exists v \in \mathfrak{N}^\Delta\ \forall y \in X\ \phi(x, y) \in v \Rightarrow \theta(g(x), g(y)) \in \bar{u}$. But the closed neighbourhoods of 0 in R^Γ are clearly a base for the neighbourhood filter at 0 so g is continuous i.e.

$$g \in \overline{c(X, Y)} \Rightarrow g \in c(X, Y).$$

Thus $c(X, Y)$ is closed. q.e.d.

2.2. THEOREM. *If $F \subset c(X, Y)$ is equicontinuous then the closure of F in Y^X with the weak topology is contained in $c(X, Y)$ and is equicontinuous.*

Proof. By Theorem 1.2.4:

$$g \in \bar{F} \Rightarrow \wedge\{\phi_X(f, g) | f \in F\} = 0$$

$$\Rightarrow \forall x \in X\ \wedge\{\theta(f(x), g(x)) | f \in F\} = 0 \quad \text{by definition of } \phi_X$$

If F is equicontinuous then

$$\forall x \in X\ \forall u \in \mathfrak{N}^\Gamma\ \exists v \in \mathfrak{N}^\Delta\ \forall y \in X : \phi(x, y) \in v \Rightarrow \forall f \in F\ \theta(f(x), f(y)) \in u$$

$$\Rightarrow \wedge\{|\theta(f(x), f(y)) - m| : f \in F, m \in u\} = 0.$$

But

$$|\theta(g(x), g(y)) - m| \leq \theta(g(x), f(x)) + |\theta(f(x), f(y)) - m| + \theta(f(y), g(y)).$$

Therefore

$$\wedge\{|\theta(g(x), g(y)) - m| : m \in u\} = 0,$$

i.e.

$$\theta(g(x), g(y)) \in \bar{u}.$$

Thus

$$\forall x \in X\ \forall u \in \mathfrak{N}^\Gamma\ \exists v \in \mathfrak{N}^\Delta\ \forall y \in X : \phi(x, y) \in v \Rightarrow \forall g \in \bar{F}\ \theta(f(x), f(y)) \in \bar{u}.$$

But the closed neighbourhoods of 0 in R^Γ form a base so the result follows. q.e.d.

The better-known versions of these two results are that the uniform limit of a sequence of continuous functions is continuous and that the pointwise limit of an equicontinuous sequence is continuous. Our interest in these results arises because they give us properties of certain linear functionals on the dual of a vector space which we construct from points in the extension of the space.

We now turn to results using Non-Standard Analysis.

Using the established notation we note that for $f, g \in Y^X$

$$\phi_C(f, g)(d, A) \leq \varepsilon \quad \text{iff} \quad \forall x \in A \ \theta(f(x), g(x))(d) \leq \varepsilon.$$

Transferring this to the enlargement it is clear that for $f, g \in Y^X$

$$\phi_C(f, g)(d, A) \simeq 0 \quad \text{iff} \quad \forall x \in \hat{A} \ \theta(f(x), g(x))(d) \simeq 0.$$

Writing $v(C) = \cup\{\hat{A} | A \in C\}$ this becomes

$$\phi_C(f, g) \simeq 0 \quad \text{iff} \quad \forall x \in v(C) \ \theta(f(x), g(x)) \simeq 0.$$

For the weak topology this condition becomes $\forall x \in X \ \theta(f(x), g(x)) \simeq 0$. For the topology of uniform convergence on X it becomes $\forall x \in \hat{X}$

$$\theta(f(x), g(x)) \simeq 0.$$

The proof of the following characterisation of equicontinuity is routine and is omitted.

2.3. Theorem. *A subset F of Y^X is equicontinuous if and only if*

$$\forall x \in X \ \forall y \in \hat{X} \ \phi(x, y) \simeq 0 \Rightarrow \forall f \in \hat{F} \ \theta(f(x), f(y)) \simeq 0.$$

We use this characterisation to prove the following theorems which lead up to the central result in the theory of function spaces–the Theorem of Ascoli. With the machinery we have built up very lucid proofs, amounting to little more than applications of the triangle inequality, are possible.

2.4. Theorem. *Let X be a locally compact topological space, Y a uniform space and give $c(X, Y)$ the compact open topology. If $F \subset c(X, Y)$ is relatively compact then F is equicontinuous.*

Proof. By Theorem 1.1.11 if F is relatively compact then for every $g \in \hat{F}$ there is an $f \in c(X, Y)$ such that $\phi_{co}(f, g) \simeq 0$. If C is the class of compact subsets of X then we have that $\forall x \in v(C) \ \theta(f(x), g(x)) \simeq 0$. (*)

To demonstrate equicontinuity take any $x \in X, y \in \hat{X}$ such that $\phi(x, y) \simeq 0$. As $f \in c(X, Y)$ $\theta(f(x), f(y)) \simeq 0$ by Theorem 1.1.14.

As X is locally compact the near standard y is in $v(C)$ by Theorem 1.1.12 so by (*) $\theta(f(y), g(y)) \simeq 0$.

As the compact open topology is stronger than the weak topology $\theta(f(x), g(x)) \simeq 0$ since $\phi_{co}(f, g) \simeq 0$.

But

$$\theta(g(x), g(y)) \leq \theta(g(x), f(x)) + \theta(f(x), f(y)) + \theta(f(y), g(y)).$$

Thus

$$\theta(g(x), g(y)) \simeq 0.$$

Thus

$$\forall x \in X\ \forall y \in \hat{X}\ \forall g \in \hat{F} : \phi(x, y) \simeq 0 \Rightarrow \theta(f(x), g(x)) \simeq 0.$$

Thus F is equicontinuous. q.e.d.

2.5. THEOREM. *If F is an equicontinuous subset of $c(X, Y)$ then the weak topology and the compact open topology coincide on F.*

Proof. We need only show that if $\forall x \in X\ \theta(f(x), g(x)) \simeq 0$ then for every compact subset A of X $\forall y \in \hat{A}\ \theta(f(y), g(y)) \simeq 0$.

If $y \in \hat{A}$ and A is compact we have by Theorem 1.1.10 that there is an $x \in A$ such that $\phi(x, y) \simeq 0$.

As F is equicontinuous we have by Theorem 2.3 that for h in $\hat{F}$ $\theta(h(x), h(y)) \simeq 0$. In particular, $\theta(f(x), f(y)) \simeq 0$ and $\theta(g(x), g(y)) \simeq 0$. But

$$\theta(f(y), g(y)) \leq \theta(f(y), f(x)) + \theta(f(x), g(x)) + \theta(g(x), g(y))$$

so

$$\theta(f(y), g(y)) \simeq 0.$$

Thus for compact subsets A of X $\forall y \in \hat{A}\ \theta(f(y), g(y)) \simeq 0$ as required. q.e.d.

2.6. THEOREM *(Ascoli). Let X be a locally compact topological space, Y a uniform space. A subset F of $c(X, Y)$ is relatively compact in the compact open topology if and only if F is equicontinuous and for each x in X $F(x) = \{f(x) \mid f \in F\}$ is relatively compact.*

Proof. Necessity: Theorem 2.4 shows that relatively compact subsets of $c(X, Y)$ are equicontinuous. For each $x \in X$ consider $y \in \hat{F}(x)$. There is an $f \in \hat{F}$ such that $y = f(x)$. By the relative compactness of F there is a $g \in c(X, Y)$ such that $\phi_C(f, g) \simeq 0$. Then $\theta(f(x), g(x)) = \theta(y, g(x)) \simeq 0$ and y is near-standard. Thus each $F(x)$ is relatively compact by Theorem 1.1.11.

Sufficiency: We show that the hypothesis implies that for each f in $\hat{F}$ there is a $g \in c(X, Y)$ such the $\phi_{co}(f, g) \simeq 0$. Each $F(x)$ is relatively compact so for each $x \in X$ we can choose a p_x in Y such that $\theta(f(x), p_x) \simeq 0$. Define $g \in Y^X$ by $g(x) = p_x$ for $x \in X$. Then $\theta(f(x), g(x)) \simeq 0$ for $x \in X$ so

$\phi_X(f(x), g(x)) \simeq 0$. By Theorem 1.1.7 g belongs to the closure of F in the weak topology. But F is equicontinuous so by Theorem 2.2 $g \in c(X, Y)$. Further by Theorem 2.2 the closure of F is equicontinuous and by Theorem 2.5 the weak topology and the compact open topology coincide on equicontinuous sets so $\phi_{co}(f, g) \simeq 0$. Thus F is relatively compact in the compact open topology by Theorem 1.1.11. q.e.d.

The other natural question to ask about function spaces is: which topologies on $c(X, Y)$ make the evaluation map $e:(f, x) \mapsto f(x)$ a continuous map from $c(X, Y) \times X$ to Y when $c(X, Y) \times X$ has the product topology. Using the propositions characterising continuity and the product topology we see that if ψ is the quasimetric on $c(X, Y)$ associated with the topology on $c(X, Y)$ then the condition for the evaluation map to be continuous is:

$$\forall f \in c(X, Y)\ \forall x \in X\ \forall g \in \hat{c}(X, Y), \forall y \in \hat{X}\ \phi(x, y) \simeq 0 \quad \text{and} \quad \psi(f, g) \simeq 0$$
$$\Rightarrow \theta(f(x), g(y)) \simeq 0.$$

In fact a satisfactory answer for the most general situation can be obtained only with a more general concept of continuity using the "convergence structures" of Fischer [1959]. But we have the following results.

2.7. THEOREM. *If a topology on $c(X, Y)$ makes the evaluation map continuous then it is stronger than the compact-open topology.*

Proof. Allowing ψ to be the associated quasimetric on $c(X, Y)$ we show that if $\forall f \in c(X, Y), \forall g \in \hat{c}(X, Y), \psi(f, g) \simeq 0$ then for all compact subsets A of X we have that $\forall y \in \hat{A}\ \theta(f(y), g(y)) \simeq 0$.

For each y in the extension of the compact set A there is a standard x in $\hat{A}$ such that $\phi(x, y) \simeq 0$. As $f \in c(X, Y)$ we have that $\theta(f(x), f(y)) \simeq 0$. But $\psi(f, g) \simeq 0$ and $\theta(x, y) \simeq 0 \Rightarrow \theta(f(x), g(y)) \simeq 0$ by hypothesis. Also

$$\theta(f(y), g(y)) \leq \theta(f(y), f(x)) + \theta(f(x), g(y))$$

so $\theta(f(y), g(y)) \simeq 0$. This holds for any y in the extension of some compact set A so $\psi(f, g) \simeq 0 \Rightarrow \phi_{co}(f, g) \simeq 0$ as required. q.e.d.

2.8. THEOREM. *If X is locally compact then the compact-open topology makes the evaluation map continuous.*

Proof. Suppose $x \in X$, $y \in \hat{X}$, $\phi(x, y) \simeq 0$, $f \in c(X, Y)$, $g \in \hat{c}(X, Y)$, $\phi_{co}(f, g) \simeq 0$. We have to show that $\theta(f(x), g(y)) \simeq 0$.

As $f \in c(X, Y)$,

$$\theta(f(x), f(y)) \simeq 0.$$

As y is near-standard and X is locally compact there is by Theorem 1.1.12 some compact subset A of X such that $y \in \hat{A}$. But $\phi_{co}(f, g) \simeq 0$ so $\theta(f(y), g(y)) \simeq 0$. But

$$\theta(f(x), g(y)) \leq \theta(f(x), f(y)) + \theta(f(y), g(y))$$

so $\theta(f(y), g(y)) \simeq 0$ as required. q.e.d.

These two theorems show that for locally compact spaces the compact open topology is the weakest topology on $c(X, Y)$ which makes the evaluation map continuous.

Finally we establish a theorem on the non-standard structure of a function space which we require for deducing properties of certain linear functionals on the dual which we construct from the points in the extension of a vector space.

2.9. THEOREM. *If $f \in Y^X$ is ϕ_C pre-near-standard and $\phi_X(f, g) \simeq 0$ for some g in Y^X then $\phi_C(f, g) \simeq 0$.*

Proof. If f is ϕ_C pre-near-standard we have by Theorem 1.1.16 and the construction of the C uniformity:

$$\forall A \in C\ \forall d \in \Delta\ \forall \varepsilon > 0\ \exists h \in Y^X\ \forall x \in \hat{A}\ \theta(f(x), h(x))(d) < \varepsilon.$$

But for standard $x \in X$ $\phi(f(x), g(x)) \simeq 0$ as $\phi_X(f, g) \simeq 0$, so for any $\varepsilon > 0$ we have that $\theta(g(x), h(x))(d) < \varepsilon$. Transferring to the enlargement we see that

$$\forall x \in \hat{X}\ \theta(g(x), h(x))(d) < \varepsilon.$$

But

$$\theta(f(x), g(x))(d) \leq \theta(f(x), h(x))(d) + \theta(h(x), g(x))(d)$$

so we can assert that

$$\forall \varepsilon > 0\ \forall A \in C\ \forall d \in \Delta\ \forall x \in \hat{A}\ \theta(f(x), g(x))(d) < 2\varepsilon,$$

i.e. $\phi_C(f, g) \simeq 0$. q.e.d.

There are two immediate COROLLARIES:

If $\mathfrak{F}$ is a filter on Y^X which is ϕ_C Cauchy and converges to $g \in Y^X$ in the weak topology then $\mathfrak{F}$ converges to g in the C topology.

Proof. The hypothesis implies that each f in $\mu(\mathfrak{F})$ is ϕ_C pre-near-standard and is such that $\phi_X(f, g) \simeq 0$ by Theorem 1.1.5. By Theorem 2.9 $\phi_C(f, g) \simeq 0$ so $\mathfrak{F}$ converges to g in the C topology. q.ed.

If Y is complete then so is Y^X under the C uniformity for a cover C of X.

Proof. We show that every ϕ_C pre-near-standard f in $\hat{Y}^X$ is ϕ_C near-standard. As C covers X for each standard x $f(x)$ is clearly θ pre-near-standard. By the completeness of Y there is for each $x \in X$ a $p_x \in Y$ such that $\theta(f(x), p_x) \simeq 0$. Define $g \in Y^X$ by $g(x) = p_x$ for $x \in X$. Then $\phi_X(f, g) \simeq 0$. By Theorem 2.9. $\phi_C(f, g) \simeq 0$ so f is ϕ_C near-standard. q.e.d.

3. Topological Vector Spaces. Accounts of the standard theory can be found in Köthe [1969], Edwards [1965], Schaefer [1966] and Kelley and Namioka [1963]. The monograph of Robertson and Robertson [1966] gives a swift readable treatment which is recommended for a quick introduction.

After setting up the basic theory we group our results into those concerning the weak topology and the uniform structure and conclude with some applications to the theory of compact maps.

3.1. We shall be concerned with real vector spaces. We list some basic definitions and results. α, β, λ etc. denote reals. The usual notation for a scalar multiple of a set of vectors and the vector sum of two sets of vectors is used. In the vector space X:

A set A is *convex* if for $\alpha > 0, \beta > 0, \alpha + \beta = 1$ we have $\alpha A + \beta A \subset A$.

A set A is *circled* if for $\forall \lambda \in R : |\lambda| \leq 1 \; \lambda A \subset A$.

The smallest convex circled set containing A–the *convex circled hull* of A consists of finite linear combinations $\sum_{i=1}^{n} \lambda_i x_i$ where $x_i \in A$ and $\sum_{i=1}^{n} |\lambda_i| \leq 1$.

A set A is *radial* if $\forall x \in X \; \exists \alpha > 0 \; \forall \lambda : \alpha \leq |\lambda| \Rightarrow x \in \lambda A$.

A topological vector space has a topological structure compatible with its vector space structure: the map $x \mapsto -x$ is a continuous map from X to X; vector addition defines a continuous map from $X \times X$ to X; scalar multiplication defines a continuous map from $R \times X$ to R where $X \times X$, $R \times X$ have the product topologies. It is immediate that the neighbourhood filter at any point is merely the translation of the neighbourhood filter at 0 and in topological questions we only need consider the neighbourhoods of 0. Thus a linear map from X to R is continuous if and only if it is continuous at 0. Because X is a topological group we can define on it a uniform structure compatible with its topology. We have seen that it follows that X is regular. Note also that the axioms also imply that every neighbourhood of 0 is radial.

For an interesting theory we need the additional hypothesis that the neighbourhood filter at 0 has a base of convex sets that is, our vector space is *locally convex*. It is then a consequence of the axioms that there is a base of closed convex circled radial neighbourhoods of 0. We now show how semifields are used to describe locally convex spaces.

A *seminorm* on the vector space X over the semifield R^{Δ} is a function $\phi : X \to R^{\Delta}_{o}$ such that:

$$\phi(0) = 0,$$

$$\phi(\lambda x) = |\lambda| \phi(x) \quad \lambda \in R, x \in X,$$

$$\phi(x + y) \leq \phi(x) + \phi(y) \quad x, y \in X.$$

If in addition, $\phi(x) = 0 \Rightarrow x = 0$ then ϕ is a *norm*.

In the topology on X arising from the pseudometric $\theta(x, y) = \phi(x - y)$ a sub-base for the neighbourhoods of 0 consists of sets $\{x | \phi(x)(d) < \varepsilon\}$ for $d \in \Delta$, $\varepsilon > 0$. It is clear that in this topology $x \in \mu(0)$ iff $\phi(x) \simeq 0$. A routine check using the properties of the seminorm shows that with this topology X is a locally convex topological vector space.

To show that every locally convex space can be described in this way we shall need the following well-known result (see e.g. Schaefer [1966] p. 39) which is also needed for a later construction.

3.1.1. THEOREM. *Let A be a closed convex circled subset of the topological vector space E. $\mathbf{A} = \cup\{\lambda A | \lambda > 0\}$ is a linear subspace of E. The Minkowski functional of A defined by*

$$g_A(x) = \inf\{\lambda > 0 | x \in \lambda A\}$$

is a seminorm on $\mathbf{A}$ over R and $A = \{x \in \mathbf{A} | g_A(x) \leq 1\}$.

If A is radial then $\mathbf{A} = E$ and g_A is defined on all of E.

3.1.2. THEOREM. *For every locally convex topological vector space E there is a semifield R^{Δ} and a seminorm $\phi : X \to R^{\Delta}$ which induces the initial topology on E.*

Proof. Let Δ be a sub-base of closed convex circled neighbourhoods of 0. Define a seminorm $\phi : X \to R^{\Delta}$ by

$$\phi(x)(A) = g_A(x) \quad \text{for} \quad x \in E, A \in \Delta.$$

This is everywhere defined since neighbourhoods of 0 are radial.

Since each g_A is a seminorm over R it is clear that ϕ is a seminorm over R^{Δ}.

ϕ induces a topology on X such that a sub-base for the neighbourhood filter at 0 consists of sets of the form $\{x | \phi(x)(A) \leq \varepsilon\}$ for $A \in \Delta$, $\varepsilon > 0$. But $\{x | \phi(x)(A) \leq \varepsilon\} = \{\varepsilon x | g_A(x) \leq 1\} = \varepsilon A$ by Theorem 3.1.1. As Δ is a sub-base for the neighbourhoods at 0 in the initial topology it follows that this coincides with the initial topology. q.e.d.

A subset B of the topological vector space E is *bounded* if B is absorbed by every neighbourhood N of 0, i.e. $\forall N\ \exists \alpha > 0 : |\lambda| \leq \alpha \Rightarrow \lambda B \subset N$. It suffices to examine the members of a sub-base of neighbourhoods of 0.

The following natural characterisation of bounded sets accounts for much of the usefulness of seminorms over semifields.

3.1.3. THEOREM. *If the vector space X is seminormed by $\phi : X \to R^{\Delta}$ then a subset A is bounded if and only if there is an $f \in R^{\Delta}$ such that $x \in A \Rightarrow \phi(x) \leq f$.*

Proof. Necessity: By the definition of the induced topology on X, if A is bounded then

$$\forall d \in \Delta\ \exists \alpha_d > 0 : \alpha_d A \subset \{x \mid \phi(x)(d) \leq 1\}$$

i.e.

$$\forall d \in \Delta\ \exists \alpha_d > 0 : x \in A \Rightarrow \phi(\alpha_d x)(d) \leq 1,$$

so that $\phi(x)(d) \leq 1/\alpha_d$. The required $f \in R^{\Delta}$ is defined by $f(d) = 1/\alpha_d$.

Sufficiency: suppose there is an $f \in R^{\Delta}$ such that $x \in A \Rightarrow \phi(x)(d) \leq f(d)$. For each member of the sub-base of neighbourhoods of 0 of the form $\{x \mid \phi(x)(d) < \varepsilon\}$ choose $\alpha < \varepsilon/f(d)$. Now suppose $|\lambda| \leq \alpha$. If $y \in \lambda A$ then for some $x \in A$ $\phi(y)(d) = |\lambda|\phi(x)(d) \leq |\lambda| f(d) \leq \alpha f(d) < \varepsilon$ so $y \in \{x \mid \phi(x)\ (d) < \varepsilon\}$. Thus A is absorbed by every member of a sub-base of neighbourhoods of 0. q.e.d.

Since $\{z \mid \phi(z) \leq f\}$ is a bounded closed convex circled set containing A it follows that the closed convex circled hull of a bounded set is bounded. In fact if we choose f to be the "smallest" possible then $\{z \mid \phi(z) \leq f\}$ is precisely the closed convex circled hull of A.

If X is seminormed by $\phi : X \to R^{\Delta}$ then $x \in \hat{X}$ is ϕ *finite* if $\phi(x)$ is finite i.e. $\forall d \in \Delta\ \phi(x)(d)$ is finite and is ϕ *bounded* if $\phi(x)$ is bounded, i.e. $\exists f \in R^{\Delta}$: $\phi(x) \leq f$. A ϕ bounded x is obviously in some standard set–namely the extension of $S = \{z \mid \phi(z) \leq f\}$ which is bounded. With any other seminorm ϕ' which yields the same topology on X we have by Theorem 3.1.3 that x is ϕ' bounded, i.e. ϕ boundedness does not depend on the particular seminorm used. In fact any topology compatible with the dual pair $\langle X, X' \rangle$ yields the same ϕ bounded points, but we do not use this fact.

Analogous to Theorems 1.1.5, 1.1.10, 1.1.18 we have that a set is bounded iff all points in its extension are ϕ bounded and a filter $\mathfrak{F}$ on X is bounded iff all points in $\mu(\mathfrak{F})$ are ϕ bounded.

We shall require the following two forms of the Hahn–Banach Theorem.

3.1.4. THEOREM. *Let E be a real vector space; p a function from E to the positive reals such that $p(x + y) \leq p(x) + p(y)$, $x, y \in E$ and $p(\alpha x) = \alpha p(x)$; $\alpha \geq 0$, $x \in E$. If f is a real linear functional on a linear subspace G of E such that for $x \in G$ $|f(x)| \leq p(x)$ then there is an extension F of f to E such that $|F(x)| \leq p(x)$ for $x \in E$.*

3.1.5. THEOREM. *If A is a closed convex circled subset of the locally convex topological vector space E and $x_0 \notin A$ then there is a continuous linear functional f on E such that $x \in A \Rightarrow |f(x)| \leq 1$ and $f(x_0) > 1$.*

In fact non-standard proofs of these results can be derived.

Vector spaces E, F form a *dual pair* $\langle E, F\rangle$ if there is a bilinear functional from $E \times F$ to $R:(x, y) \mapsto \langle x, y\rangle$ which separates points of E (that is, if $\forall y \in F$ $\langle x, y\rangle = 0$ then $x = 0$) and also points of F. By the symmetry of the definition there is, for each statement about E, a dual statement about F obtained by transposing "E" and "F".

For each y in F the function: $(x, y) \mapsto \langle x, y\rangle$ for $x \in E$ is a linear functional on E so we can identify F with a linear subspace of $\mathbf{E}^*$ the class of linear functionals on E. This identification is henceforth implicit.

The most important example of a dual pair is $\langle E, E'\rangle$ where E is a locally convex Hausdorff topological vector space and E' is the space of linear functionals continuous on E. The bilinear functional is merely the evaluation map. It is obvious that members of E separate E' and it follows from the Hahn-Banach Theorem that the members of E' separate E.

The *weak topology* $\sigma(E, F)$ on E is that induced by the seminorm ϕ_F: $E \rightarrow R^F$ where

$$\phi_F(x)(y) = |\langle x, y\rangle| \quad \text{for} \quad y \in F,\, x \in E.$$

The bilinearity of $\langle\cdot,\cdot\rangle$ and the properties of the modulus function on R ensure that ϕ_F is a seminorm so that E becomes a locally convex topological vector space. Further, if $\phi_F(x)(y) = 0$ for all $y \in F$ then $x = 0$ so ϕ_F is in fact a norm and the weak topology is Hausdorff. We denote the monad of 0 in the weak topology on E by "$\mu_E(0)$".

3.1.6. THEOREM. *In the dual pair $\langle E, F\rangle$ a linear functional $f:E \rightarrow R$ is* *continuous with the respect to the* $\sigma(E, F)$ *topology iff there is a* $y \in F$ *such that* $\forall x \in E\, f(x) = \langle x, y\rangle$.

This is a simple consequence of the following elementary algebraic result which we shall call upon frequently.

3.1.7. THEOREM. *Let E be a vector space and* $f_1, \ldots, f_n$ *linear functionals on E. If f is a linear functional on E such that* $f_i(x) = 0, i = 1, \ldots, n \Rightarrow f(x) = 0$ *then there exist* $c_1, \ldots, c_n \in R$ *such that* $f = \sum_{i=1}^{n} c_i f_i$.

The concept of polarity is important in the duality theory of vector spaces. We shall see that it is also important for the non-standard theory. In the dual pair $\langle E, F\rangle$ the *polar* of a subset A of E is defined by

$$A^{\circ} = \{y \in F \mid \forall x \in A\ |\langle x, y\rangle| \leq 1\}.$$

It is immediate that $A \subset A^{\circ\circ}$; $A \subset B \Rightarrow B^{\circ} \subset A^{\circ}$; $\cap\{A_i^{\circ} \mid i \in I\} = [\cup\{A_i \mid i \in I\}]^{\circ}$.

The bilinear functional associated with the dual pair $\langle E, F\rangle$ extends to a "bilinear functional" from $\hat{E} \times \hat{F}$ to $\hat{R}$. We can define polars of subsets of $\hat{E}$–whether internal or external–with respect to this bilinear functional. With the usual arguments we see that the polar of the extension of a standard set in $\langle \hat{E}, \hat{F}\rangle$ is the extension of the polar of that set in $\langle E, F\rangle$. The spaces with respect to which polars are being taken will always be evident.

Let $\mu(0)$ be the monad of 0 for some topology on E making it a topological vector space. If $y \in \mu(0)^{\circ}$ then $\forall x \in \mu(0)\ |\langle x, y\rangle| \leq 1$. But $\mu(0)$ is closed under multiplication by standard scalars that is, $\forall x \in \mu(0)\ \forall \alpha \in R\ |\langle \alpha x, y\rangle| \leq 1$. By the bilinearity of $\langle \cdot, \cdot\rangle$ we have that $\forall x \in \mu(0)\ \forall \alpha \in R\ |\langle x, y\rangle| \leq 1/|\alpha|$. That is, $\forall x \in \mu(0)\ \langle x, y\rangle \simeq 0$. Thus $\mu(0)^{\circ} = \{y \in \hat{F} \mid \forall x \in \mu(0)\ \langle x, y\rangle \simeq 0\}$. In fact for a locally convex space we can show through the Hahn-Banach Theorem that $\mu(0)^{\circ\circ} = \mu(0)$. We have the following criterion for equicontinuity.

3.1.8. THEOREM. *A subset M of E′ is equicontinuous iff* $\hat{M} \subset \mu(0)^{\circ}$.
Proof. M is equicontinuous

iff $\forall$ nhds V of 0 in $R\ \exists$ nhd U of 0 in $E: \forall y \in M\ y(U) \subset V$

iff $\forall y \in \hat{M}\ \phi(x) \simeq 0 \Rightarrow \langle x, y\rangle \simeq 0$

iff $\hat{M} \subset \mu(0)^{\circ}$.

An equivalent condition is to require that $\hat{M}^{\circ} \supset \mu(0)$.

In the dual pair $\langle E, F\rangle$ let C be a cover of F by ϕ_E bounded sets. The topology of uniform convergence on members of C–[henceforth the "C topology"] is that induced by the norm $\phi_C : E \to R^C$ where

$$\phi_C(x)(A) = \sup_{y \in A} (|\langle x, y\rangle|) \quad \text{for} \quad x \in E, A \in C.$$

The supremum is always defined since the members of A are ϕ_E bounded. We shall frequently use the notation $C' = \{\varepsilon A \mid \varepsilon > 0, A \in C\}$; $v(C) = \cup\{\hat{A} \mid A \in C\}$.

3.1.9. THEOREM. *The monad of* 0 *in* E *with the* C *topology is* $[v(C')]^\circ$.
Proof.

$$\begin{aligned}[v(C')]^\circ &= [\cup\{\varepsilon\hat{A} \mid \varepsilon > 0, A \in C\}]^\circ \\ &= \cap\{(\varepsilon\hat{A})^\circ \mid \varepsilon > 0, A \in C\}.\end{aligned}$$

Therefore

$$\begin{aligned} x \in [v(C')]^\circ \quad &\text{iff} \quad \forall A \in C\, \forall \varepsilon > 0\, \forall y \in \hat{A}\, |\langle x, y\rangle| \leq \varepsilon \\ &\text{iff} \quad \phi_C(x) \simeq 0. \end{aligned}$$

q.e.d.

In particular, the monad of 0 in E with the $\sigma(E, F)$ topology $\mu_E(0) = F^\circ$. The neighbourhoods of 0 in E with the C topology have as sub-base $\{S^\circ \mid S \in C'\}$. Since the closed convex circled hull of S has the same polar as S the topology of uniform convergence on such hulls coincides with the C topology.

Also if C is directed by $\subset$ then if a linear functional f on E is continuous with respect to the C topology then $\exists B \in C' : x \in B^\circ \Rightarrow |f(x)| \leq 1$.

3.2. The weak topology. In this section we treat the main results of duality theory linked with the weak topology using in particular two tools from Non-Standard Analysis.

Given a dual pair $\langle E, F\rangle$ we shall associate with every ϕ_F finite point x of $\hat{E}$ a linear functional $\tilde{x}$ on F defined by:

$$\tilde{x}(y) = \text{st}(\langle x, y\rangle).$$

As x is ϕ_F finite this is defined for all $y \in F$. In the $\sigma(F^*, F)$ topology on F^* it is clear that $\phi_F(\tilde{x} - x) \simeq 0$.

In the other direction we have a theorem which asserts that under certain circumstances a linear functional on F can be "represented" by a point in $\hat{E}$. Thus we can discuss $\hat{E}$ in terms of linear functionals on F and conversely. That is, we have a non-standard duality theory.

3.2.1. THEOREM. *Let B be a subset of E; A its closed convex circled hull and f a linear functional on F such that $y \in B^{\circ} \Rightarrow |f(x)| \leq k$. Then there is an $x \in \hat{A}$ such that*

$$\frac{1}{k} f(y) \simeq \langle x, y \rangle \quad \text{for} \quad y \in F.$$

Proof. We show that the relation $R(\langle y, \varepsilon \rangle, x)$ which holds if ε is a positive real number, $y \in F$, $x \in A$ and $|f(y)/k - \langle x, y \rangle| \leq \varepsilon$, is concurrent in (y, ε). If not, then for some $y_1, \ldots, y_n \in F$ and positive reals $\varepsilon_1, \ldots, \varepsilon_n$ we have

$$\forall x \in A \left| \frac{1}{k} f(y_i) - \langle x, y \rangle \right| > \min \{\varepsilon_i : 1 \leq i \leq n\} \text{ for } i = 1, \ldots, n,$$

i.e. there is a $\sigma(F^*, F)$ neighbourhood of f/k disjoint from A (considered as a subset of F^*) i.e. f is not in the $\sigma(F^*, F)$ closure of A.

By the Hahn-Banach Theorem (3.1.5) there is a $\sigma(F^*, F)$ continuous Y in F^{**} such that $\langle Y, f/k \rangle > 1$ and $\forall x \in A \; |\langle Y, x \rangle| \leq 1$. But a $\sigma(F^*, F)$ continuous function on F^{**} is represented by some y in F by Theorem 3.1.6 so there is a $y \in A^{\circ}$ such that $\langle y, f/k \rangle > 1$. As $A^{\circ} = B^{\circ}$ this contradicts the fact that f is bounded by k on B°.

Thus R is concurrent so there is an $x \in \hat{A}$ such that

$$\frac{1}{k} f(y) \simeq \langle x, y \rangle \quad \text{for} \quad y \in F. \qquad \text{q.e.d.}$$

In fact a finer result holds if we accept more stringent conditions on f: for then f can be represented explicitly by an $x \in \hat{E}$. Since we do not need this result for further developments we merely state it:

"Let F be a family of linear functionals y on the vector space E; B a convex circled subset of E; $\theta : F \to R$ a map such that for any scalars $a_1, \ldots, a_n$

$$\left| \sum_{i=1}^{n} a_i \theta(y) \right| \leq \sup_{x \in B} \left\{ \left| \sum_{i=1}^{n} a_i \langle x, y_i \rangle \right| \right\}.$$

Then there is an $x \in \mu(1)\hat{B}$ such that for $y \in F$ $\langle x, y \rangle = \theta(y)$ where $\mu(1)$ is the monad of 1 in the usual topology on R."

As an application of our ideas suppose $y \in \hat{E}'$ is in the extension of some equicontinuous set M. As M is contained in the polar of some neighbourhood of 0 in E it is in the polar of some radial set and so is ϕ_E bounded. Thus $\tilde{y} : E \to R$ is defined. Now $\tilde{y}$ is in the weak closure of the equicontinuous set

M so it is continuous by Theorem 2.2, i.e. $\tilde{y} \in E'$. That is, y is ϕ_E near standard. We have thus proved the following theorem.

3.2.2. THEOREM *(Alaoglu-Bourbaki). Every equicontinuous subset of E' is $\sigma(E', E)$ relatively compact.*

Another approach to this theorem is to observe that $\tilde{y}$ is bounded on M° and $\widehat{M}^{\circ} \supset \mu(0)$ so $\tilde{y}$ is continuous and is in E'.

Theorem 3.2.1 may be used to approach the question of which topologies $\mathscr{I}$ on F are *consistent* with the dual pair $\langle E, F\rangle$ that is, are such that for every $\mathscr{I}$-continuous linear functional f on F there is an $x \in E$ such that for every $y \in F, f(y) = \langle x, y\rangle$. The theorem shows how f can be approximated by an $x \in \hat{A}$ for some subset A of E. If, in addition x is ϕ_F near some x_0 in E then this x_0 must represent f. Thus the obvious condition to impose on A is that it be $\sigma(E, F)$ relatively compact:

3.2.3. THEOREM *(Mackey Arens). Let C be a cover of E by a class of convex circled $\sigma(E, F)$ relatively compact sets which is directed by $\subset$. Then the C topology on F is consistent with $\langle E, F\rangle$.*

Proof. Let f be a linear functional on F which is continuous with respect to the C-topology. As C is directed by $\subset$ there is an $S \in C' = \{\varepsilon A \mid \varepsilon > 0, A \in C\}$ such that $x \in S^{\circ} \Rightarrow |f(x)| \leq 1$. By Theorem 3.2.1 there is an $x \in \hat{S}$ such that for $y \in F\, f(x) \simeq \langle x, y\rangle$. But S is $\sigma(E, F)$ relatively compact so there is an $x_0 \in E$ such that $\phi_F(x - x_0) \simeq 0$. But the $\sigma(F^*, F)$ topology is Hausdorff so $x_0 = f$. q.e.d.

In fact the condition is also necessary for we shall see that any topology $\mathscr{I}$ on F can be considered as the topology of uniform convergence on the convex circled equicontinuous subsets of the dual and by Theorem 3.2.2 these are $\sigma(E', E)$ relatively compact. If $\mathscr{I}$ is consistent with $\langle E, F\rangle$ the condition must therefore be satisfied.

The approach to the last two results suggests the following general criterion for weak compactness.

3.2.4. THEOREM. *Let B be a convex circled subset of E. B is $\sigma(E, F)$ relatively compact if and only if B is ϕ_F bounded and every linear functional bounded on B° is represented by some member of E.*

Proof. Necessity: if B is $\sigma(E, F)$ relatively compact then $x \in \hat{B} \Rightarrow \exists z \in E$ such that $\phi_F(x - z) \simeq 0$ i.e. for each $y \in F\, \langle x, y\rangle \simeq \langle z, y\rangle$. Thus $\langle x, y\rangle$

is finite. This holds for each $x \in \hat{B}$. Choosing an infinite number in $\hat{R}$ we can see that there is an $r \in \hat{R}$ such that $\forall x \in \hat{B}\ |\langle x, y\rangle| \leq r$. Transferring this to the standard structure we see that there is an $r_y \in R$ such that $\forall x \in B$ $|\langle x, y\rangle| \leq r_y$. Define $h \in R^F$ by $h(y) = r_y$. Then $x \in B \Rightarrow \phi_F(x) \leq h$. Thus B is ϕ_F bounded.

Suppose f is bounded by k on B^o. By Theorem 3.2.1 there is an $x \in \hat{B}$ such that for $y \in F\ f(y)/k \simeq \langle x, y\rangle$. But B is $\sigma(E, F)$ relatively compact so there is an $x_0 \in E$ such that $\phi_F(x - x_0) \simeq 0$. The $\sigma(F^*, F)$ topology on F^* is Hausdorff so clearly f is represented by $kx_0 \in E$.

Sufficiency: By hypothesis there is an $h \in R^F$ such that $\forall x \in B\ \phi_F(x) \leq h$. Transferred to the enlargement this shows that each x in $\hat{B}$ is ϕ_F bounded so the functional $\tilde{x}$ is well-defined. By definition $y \in B^o \Rightarrow \forall x \in B\ |\langle x, y\rangle| \leq 1$ so for $x \in \hat{B}$, $y \in B^o\ |\tilde{x}(y)| \leq 1$. Thus $\tilde{x}$ is a linear functional bounded on B^o. By hypothesis there is an $x_0 \in E$ such that for $y \in F\ \tilde{x}(y) = \langle x_0, y\rangle$, i.e. $\forall y \in F\ \langle x, y\rangle \simeq \langle x_0, y\rangle$, i.e. $\phi_F(x - x_0) \simeq 0$. Thus each $x \in \hat{B}$ is ϕ_F near-standard so B is $\sigma(E, F)$ relatively compact. q.e.d.

We now use our notion of bounded point to derive characterisations of two important classes of spaces–the semireflexive and the barrelled spaces–which we shall need later.

The *strong* topology on the dual of a locally convex topological vector space E is the topology of uniform convergence on the bounded subsets of E. The space of continuous linear functionals on E' with the strong topology is the bidual of E. E is *semireflexive* if it coincides with its bidual as a vector space.

3.2.5. THEOREM. *Let E be a locally convex topological vector space seminormed by $\phi: E \to R^\Delta$. E is semireflexive if and only if every x in $\hat{E}$ which is ϕ bounded is $\phi_{E'}$ near-standard.*

Proof. Necessity: If x is ϕ bounded then there is an $f \in R^\Delta$ such that $\phi(x) \leq f$. The set $S = \{z \in E \mid \phi(z) \leq f\}$ is bounded (Theorem 3.1.3) and so is bounded in the weaker $\sigma(E, E')$ topology. But $x \in \hat{S}$ so x is $\phi_{E'}$ bounded. The linear functional $\tilde{x}$ on E' is thus well-defined. S^o being the polar of a bounded set is a strong neighbourhood of 0. Also, for $y \in S^o$ we have that for $z \in E\ \phi(z) \leq f \Rightarrow |\langle z, y\rangle| \leq 1$. Interpreting this in the enlargement and applying it to x we have that for $y \in S^o$, $|\langle x, y\rangle| \leq 1$ since $\phi(x) \leq f$. That is, for $y \in S^o\ |\tilde{x}(y)| \leq 1$. Thus $\tilde{x}$ is bounded on a strong neighbourhood of 0 and so is continuous for the strong topology on E'. Thus $\tilde{x}$ belongs to the bidual of E. But E is semireflexive so $\tilde{x} \in E$. But for $y \in E'$ $\langle x, y\rangle \simeq \tilde{x}(y)$ so $\phi_{E'}(x - \tilde{x}) \simeq 0$ and x is $\phi_{E'}$ near-standard.

Sufficiency: let f be continuous on E' with the strong topology. Since $\subset$ directs the class of bounded subsets of E there is a bounded subset B of E such that

$$y \in B^{\circ} \Rightarrow |f(y)| \leq 1.$$

By Theorem 3.2.1 there is an $x \in \hat{A}$ (where A is the convex circled hull of B) such that for $y \in E'$, $f(y) \simeq \langle x, y\rangle$. As B is bounded there is on $h \in R^{\Delta}$ such that $x \in B \Rightarrow \phi(x) \leq h$. $S = \{x \in E |\, \phi(x) \leq h\}$ is a convex circled set containing B and therefore containing its convex circled hull A. Thus x is ϕ bounded. By hypothesis there is an $x_0 \in E$ such that $\phi_{E'}(x - x_0) \simeq 0$. Clearly f is represented by x_0. Thus E is semireflexive. q.e.d.

An immediate consequence is that a normed space is semireflexive (and therefore reflexive) if and only if the unit ball is $\sigma(E, E')$ compact.

The observation of Puritz [1972] that in a Hilbert space the norm-finite points are weakly near-standard follows since Hilbert spaces are reflexive.

A *barrel* is a closed convex circled radial set. A space is *barrelled* if every barrel is a neighbourhood of 0. We have the following characterisation.

3.2.6. THEOREM. *A locally convex topological vector space E is barrelled if and only if every ϕ_E bounded point in $\hat{E}'$ is in $\mu(0)^{\circ}$.*

Proof. Necessity: If $y \in \hat{E}'$ is ϕ_E bounded then there is an $f \in R^E$ such that $\phi_E(y) \leq f$. The set $S = \{z |\, \phi_E(z) \leq f\}$ is ϕ_E bounded so S° is radial. S° is also closed convex and circled so by hypothesis it is a neighbourhood of 0, i.e. $\hat{S}^{\circ} \supset \mu(0)$, i.e. $\hat{S} \subset \mu(0)^{\circ}$. Thus $y \in \mu(0)^{\circ}$.

Sufficiency: If B is a barrel then B° is ϕ_E bounded. By hypothesis every point in $\hat{B}^{\circ}$ is in $\mu(0)^{\circ}$: $\hat{B}^{\circ} \subset \mu(0)^{\circ}$. Therefore $\hat{B}^{\circ\circ} \supset \mu(0)^{\circ\circ} \supset \mu(0)$. As B is a barrel $\hat{B} = \hat{B}^{\circ\circ}$ (Theorem 3.2.8). Thus B is a neighbourhood of 0. q.e.d.

By Theorem 3.1.3 and Theorem 3.1.8 we can conclude that E is barrelled if and only if every ϕ_E bounded subset of E' is equicontinuous.

3.2.7. THEOREM. *If E is barrelled and y is a ϕ_E bounded point in $\hat{E}'$ then y is ϕ_E near-standard.*

Proof. There is an $f \in R^E$ *such that* $\phi_E(y) \leq f$.

Define a linear functional $\tilde{y}$ on E by $\tilde{y}(x) = \mathrm{st}(\langle x, y\rangle)$ for $x \in E$. Then for $x \in \{z |\, \phi(z) \leq f\}^{\circ}$ we have that $|\tilde{y}(x)| \leq 1$. As observed above $\{z |\, \phi_E(z) \leq f\}^{\circ}$

is a barrel and therefore a neighbourhood of 0 in E. Thus $\tilde{y}$ is continuous, i.e. $\tilde{y} \in E'$. But $\phi_E(\tilde{y} - y) \simeq 0$ so y is ϕ_E near-standard. q.e.d.

From Theorems 3.2.6, 3.2.7 it follows that the ϕ_E bounded, $\sigma(E', E)$ compact and the equicontinuous subsets of E' coincide.

The quasibarrelled, reflexive, Montel spaces etc. can be characterised in much the same vein and the usual theorems derived but the results are not particularly revealing.

Finally we derive within our theory a number of well known results which we call upon frequently.

3.2.8. THEOREM *(Bipolar Theorem). In the dual pair $\langle E, F\rangle$ the closed convex circled hull of a subset B of E is B^{oo}.*

Proof. Let A be the convex circled hull of B. Let $z \in B^{oo}$ so $y \in B^{o} \Rightarrow |\langle z, y\rangle| \leq 1$. By Theorem 3.2.1 there is an $x \in \hat{A}$ such that for all $y \in F$ $\langle x, y\rangle \simeq \langle z, y\rangle$, i.e. $\phi_F(x - z) \simeq 0$, i.e. z is in the weak closure of A. Thus B^{oo} is contained in the closed convex circled hull of B. The other inclusion holds since B^{oo} is a closed convex circled set containing B. q.e.d.

As an example of a useful technique we have:

3.2.9. THEOREM. *The closed convex circled hull of an equicontinuous set is equicontinuous.*

Proof. By Theorem 3.1.8 if B is equicontinuous then $\hat{B} \subset \mu(0)^{o}$. Therefore $\hat{B}^{oo} \subset \mu(0)^{ooo}$. But $\mu(0)^{ooo} \subset \mu(0)^{o}$. Thus B^{oo} is equicontinuous. q.e.d.

3.2.10. THEOREM. *Let E be a locally convex topological vector space. The topology on E is identical with the C topology in the dual pair $\langle E, E'\rangle$ where C is the class of closed convex circled equicontinuous subsets of E'.*

Proof. By Theorem 3.1.9 it suffices to show that $\mu(0) = \nu(C')^{o}$. By Theorem 3.1.8: $S \in C \Rightarrow S^{o} \supset \mu(0)$. Therefore

$$\nu(C)^{o} = \cap\{\hat{S}^{o} | S \in C\} \supset \mu(0).$$

As E is locally convex there is a base $\mathfrak{N}$ of closed convex circled neighbourhoods of 0 in E and

$$\mu(0) = \cap\{\hat{S} | S \in \mathfrak{N}\} = \cap\{\hat{S}^{oo} | S \in C\} \quad \text{by Theorem 3.2.8}$$
$$= [\cup\{\hat{S}^{o} | S \in C\}]^{o}.$$

But $S \in \mathfrak{N} \Rightarrow S^{o} \in C$ so $\mu(0) \supset \nu(C)^{o}$. Noting that $C' = C$ we now have the result. q.e.d.

3.3. The uniform structure. Given a dual pair of vector spaces $\langle E, F\rangle$ we consider the C uniformity on E where C is a class of subsets of F. This is the most general context in which to study the uniform structure of a locally convex topological vector space: any particular such space can always be paired with its dual and given the uniformity of uniform convergence on equicontinuous subsets of the dual.

We carry our non-standard duality theory a stage further for we shall proceed by developing a characterisation of the pre-near-standard points of $\hat{E}$ with the C uniformity which associates them with certain linear functionals on F. Even more happily the set of pre-near-standard points of $\hat{E}$ is identified as the polar of a certain external set of points in $\hat{F}$. The major standard results concerning completeness and precompactness follow swiftly and naturally.

Henceforth our enlargement is κ saturated where κ is chosen large enough to ensure that we can apply Theorem 1.1.1. Specifically κ is greater than the cardinality of $\mathscr{P}(\mathscr{P}(\mathscr{P}(F)))$ where F is the vector space from the dual pair we are considering and "$\mathscr{P}$" is the operation of taking power sets.

The key step in deriving our characterisation is found in the following:

3.3.1. THEOREM. *If A is a ϕ_E bounded closed convex circled subset of F then*

$$(\hat{A} \cap E^o)^o \subset \hat{A}^o + E.$$

Proof. If $x \in (\hat{A} \cap E^o)^o$ then $y \in \hat{A} \cap E^o \Rightarrow |\langle x, y\rangle| \leq 1$. (*)

Let $\mathfrak{F}$ be the filter of $\sigma(F, E)$ neighbourhoods of 0 in F and let Φ be the internal subset of $\hat{\mathfrak{F}}$ defined by

$$U \in \Phi \quad \text{iff} \quad y \in \hat{A} \cap U \Rightarrow |\langle x, y\rangle| \leq 1.$$

The monad of $\mathfrak{F}$ is precisely E^o and $U \subset E^o \Rightarrow U \in \Phi$ by (*).

By Theorem 1.1.1 there is an $S \in \mathfrak{F}$ such that $\hat{S} \in \Phi$–that is, there is a standard $\sigma(F, E)$ neighbourhood of 0 S such that

$$y \in \hat{A} \cap \hat{S} \Rightarrow |\langle x, y\rangle| \leq 1.$$

By the construction of the $\sigma(F, E)$ topology it follows that there exist $x_1, \ldots, x_n$ in E such that

$$y \in \hat{A} \quad \text{and} \quad |\langle x_i, y\rangle| \leq 1,\ i = 1, \ldots, n \Rightarrow |\langle x, y\rangle| \leq 1. \ (**)$$

Put $H = \{y \in F \mid \langle x_i, y\rangle = 0,\ i = 1, \ldots, n\}$ and recall (Theorem 3.1.1) that $\mathbf{A} = \cup\{\rho A : \rho > 0\}$ is a subspace of F seminormed by

$$g_A(z) = \inf\{\rho > 0 : z \in \rho A\}.$$

By definition of g_A

$$\forall z \in A \ \forall \alpha \in R : \alpha > g_A(z) \ \exists \omega \in A : z = \alpha\omega.$$

Transferred to the enlargement this implies that

$$\forall z \in \hat{A} \ \forall \alpha \in \hat{R} : \alpha > g_A(z) \ \exists \omega \in \hat{A} : |\langle x, z \rangle| = \alpha |\langle x, \omega \rangle|.$$

For $z \in \hat{H} \cap \hat{A}$ and $\alpha \in \hat{R} : \alpha > g_A(z)$ this allows us to choose a $\omega \in \hat{A}$ so that $\langle x_i, \omega \rangle = 0, i = 1, \ldots, n$. Then by (**) $|\langle x, \omega \rangle| \leq 1$, i.e. $|\langle x, z \rangle| \leq \alpha$. Thus for $z \in \hat{H} \cap \hat{A}$ we have that

$$\forall \alpha \in \hat{R} : \alpha > g_A(z) \Rightarrow |\langle x, z \rangle| \leq \alpha.$$

Transferring the appropriate sentence concerning the reals it follows that

$$|\langle x, z \rangle| \leq g_A(z) \quad \text{for} \quad z \in \hat{H} \cap \hat{A}.$$

$\hat{H} \cap \hat{A}$ is a subspace of $\hat{A}$ and the internal linear functional $\check{x}$ which maps z to $\langle x, z \rangle$ is bounded by the seminorm $g_A(z)$ which is defined on A. By the Hahn-Banach Theorem 3.1.4 transferred to the enlargement e therexists an internal linear functional φ on $\hat{A}$ such that

$$|\varphi(z)| \leq g_A(z) \quad \text{for} \quad z \in \hat{A}$$

which is an extension of $\check{x}$, i.e.

$$y \in \hat{H} \cap \hat{A} \Rightarrow (\varphi - \check{x})(y) = 0,$$

i.e. for $y \in \hat{A}$ if $\langle x_i, y \rangle = 0, i = 1, \ldots, n$ then $(\varphi - \check{x})(y) = 0$.

Transferring Theorem 3.1.7 to the enlargement we see that there exist $c_1, \ldots, c_n$ in $\hat{R}$ such that

$$(\phi - \check{x})(y) = \left\langle \sum_{i=1}^{n} c_i x_i, y \right\rangle \quad \text{for} \quad y \in \hat{A}. \quad (***)$$

We show how to reassemble the sum $\sum_{i=1}^{n} c_i x_i$ into a linear combination of a subset of the x_i's whose members are linearly independent as functionals over A. The coefficients of this new sum are then shown to be finite and taking their standard parts we construct the element of E which permits us to assert that $x \in \hat{A}^\circ + E$.

The reassembly takes place in n stages:

Put $d_1^1 = c_1$.

If for some $a_1^2 \in R$ $\langle x_2, y \rangle = \langle a_1^2 x_1, y \rangle$ for $y \in A$ then put $d_1^2 = d_1^1 + a_1^2 c_2$ and $d_2^2 = 0$. Otherwise put $d_1^2 = d_1^1$ and $d_2^2 = c_2$.

If for some $a_1^3 a_2^3 \in R$ $\langle x_3, y\rangle = \langle a_1^3 x_1 + a_2^3 x_2, y\rangle$ for $y \in \boldsymbol{A}$ then put $d_1^3 = d_1^2 + a_1^3 c_3$; $d_2^3 = d_2^3 + a_2^3 c_3$; $d_3^3 = 0$. Otherwise put $d_1^3 = d_1^2$; $d_2^3 = d_2^2$; $d_3^3 = c_3$.

Continue in this manner until x_n has been processed. If $d_i^i = 0$ then at any later jth stage it is always possible to rechoose the a's so that $a_i^j = 0$, ensuring that if $d_i^i = 0$ then $d_i^n = 0$.

We now have that

$$\sum_{i=1}^{n} c_i x_i = \sum_{i=1}^{n} d_i^n x_i$$

where these are considered as functionals over $\boldsymbol{A}$. Some of the d_i^n's may equal zero. We rewrite the sum as $\sum_{k=1}^{m} d_k \omega_k$ where the d_k's are merely the nonzero d_i^n's, and the ω_k's are the corresponding x_i's. In relabelling we make sure that if $i_1 < i_2$ and $\omega_{k_1} = x_{i_1}$, $\omega_{k_2} = x_{i_2}$ then $k_1 < k_2$. By construction the ω_k are linearly independent as functionals over $\boldsymbol{A}$.

By Theorem 3.1.7 for a given ω_j there is therefore a $z_j \in \boldsymbol{A}$ such that $\langle \omega_j, z_j\rangle \neq 0$ and $\langle \omega_k, z_j\rangle = 0$ for $k \neq j$. Now choose an $a \in R$ greater than the absolute values of all the coefficients which may have arisen in our reassembly process in expressing an x_i as a linear combination of preceding x_i's. If none arose put $a = 1$. Now choose $\gamma_j \in R$ such that

$$\gamma_j > \max\{g_A(z_j), a|\langle \omega_j, z_j\rangle|, |\langle \omega_j, z_j\rangle|\}.$$

As $g_A(z_j/\gamma_j) \leq 1$ we have that $z_j/\gamma_j \in \boldsymbol{A}$.

Also, $|\langle \omega_j, z_j/\gamma_j\rangle| \leq 1$. We have by choice of z_j that $\langle \omega_k, z_j/\gamma_j\rangle = 0$, $k \neq j$.

Now consider the x_i's of the original set which do not occur as one of the ω_k's. By construction such an x_i, considered as a functional over $\boldsymbol{A}$ can be expressed as a linear sum of the ω_k's say $x_i = \sum_{k=1}^{i} b_k \omega_k$.

As $z_j/\gamma_j \in \boldsymbol{A}$

$$\left\langle x_i, \frac{1}{\gamma_j} z_j \right\rangle = \left\langle \sum_{k=1}^{i} b_k \omega_k, \frac{1}{\gamma_j} z_j \right\rangle = \sum_{k=1}^{i} b_k \left\langle \omega_k, \frac{1}{\gamma_j} z_j \right\rangle.$$

All terms in this last sum not involving ω_j will be zero by the choice of z_j. If ω_j occurs in the sum then

$$\left|\left\langle x_i, \frac{1}{\gamma_j} z_j \right\rangle\right| = \left| b_j \left\langle \omega_j, \frac{1}{\gamma_j} z_j \right\rangle\right| \leq a \left|\left\langle \omega_j, \frac{1}{\gamma_j} z_j \right\rangle\right|$$

by the choice of a. Therefore by the choice of γ_j

$$\left|\left\langle x_i, \frac{1}{\gamma_j} z_j \right\rangle\right| \leq 1.$$

Thus for every x_i in the original set we now have

$$\left|\left\langle x_i, \frac{1}{\gamma_j} z_j\right\rangle\right| \leq 1.$$

We have observed that $z_j/\gamma_j \in A$. Therefore by (**)

$$\left|\left\langle x, \frac{1}{\gamma_j} z_j\right\rangle\right| \leq 1.$$

As $|\varphi(z_j/\gamma_j)| \leq g_A(z_j/\gamma_j) \leq 1$ we have by (***)

$$\left|\left\langle x + \sum_{k=1}^{m} d_k\omega_k, \frac{1}{\gamma_j} z_j\right\rangle\right| \leq 1.$$

That is,

$$\left|\left\langle x, \frac{1}{\gamma_j} z_j\right\rangle + d_j\left\langle x_j, \frac{1}{\gamma_j} z_j\right\rangle\right| \leq 1$$

as all other terms in the sum vanish by the choice of z_j. Therefore

$$\left|d_j\left\langle x_j, \frac{1}{\gamma_j} z_j\right\rangle\right| \leq 1 + \left|\left\langle x, \frac{1}{\gamma_j} z_j\right\rangle\right| \leq 2$$

so $|d_j| \leq 2/|\langle x_j, z_j/\gamma_j\rangle|$. Thus d_j is finite and we can take its standard part $\mathrm{st}(d_j)$. This is true of every d_k.

By (***)

$$\left|\left\langle x + \sum_{k=1}^{m} d_k\omega_k, y\right\rangle\right| \leq 1 \quad \text{for} \quad y \in \hat{A}.$$

But

$$\left|\left\langle x + \sum_{k=1}^{m} d_k\omega_k, y\right\rangle - \left\langle x + \sum_{k=1}^{m} \mathrm{st}(d_k)\omega_k, y\right\rangle\right| = \sum_{k=1}^{m} (d_k - \mathrm{st}(d_k))\langle\omega_k, y\rangle.$$

Now $\hat{A}$ is ϕ_E bounded and $\omega_k \in E$ so $\langle\omega_k, y\rangle$ is finite for $y \in \hat{A}$. Therefore the last expression is infinitesimal and

$$\left|\left\langle x + \sum_{k=1}^{m} \mathrm{st}(d_k)\omega_k, y\right\rangle\right| \leq 1 \quad \text{for} \quad y \in \hat{A}.$$

As $-\sum_{k=1}^{m} \mathrm{st}(d_k)\omega_k$ is a vector in E, we have that

$$x \in \hat{A}^{\circ} + E.$$

Thus we have shown that $(\hat{A} \cap E^{\circ})^{\circ} \subset \hat{A}^{\circ} + E$. q.e.d.

3.3.2. THEOREM. *In the dual pair of vector spaces* $\langle E, F\rangle$ *let* C *be a covering of* F *by* ϕ_E *bounded closed convex circled subsets. The following are equivalent for* $x \in \hat{E}$:

(1) x *is* ϕ_C *pre-near-standard,*

(2) x *is* ϕ_F *finite,* $\phi_C(x - \tilde{x}) \simeq 0$ *and* $\tilde{x}$ *is* $\sigma(F, E)$ *continuous on members of* C,

(3) $y \in v(C) \cap \mu_F(0) \Rightarrow \langle x, y\rangle \simeq 0$,

(4) $x \in [v(C') \cap \mu_F(0)]^\circ$.

Proof. 1⇒2: If x is ϕ_C pre-near-standard then by definition of the C uniformity on E and Theorem 1.1.16 for $S \in C$, $\varepsilon > 0$ there is an $x \in E$ such that $y \in \hat{S} \Rightarrow |\langle x - x_0, y\rangle| < \varepsilon$. As C is a *cover* of F this ensures that for every $y \in F$ $\langle x, y\rangle$ is finite, i.e. x is ϕ_F finite. We can therefore define the linear functional $\tilde{x}$ on F by

$$\tilde{x}(y) = \mathrm{st}(\langle x, y\rangle).$$

In F^* we clearly have $\phi_F(x - \tilde{x}) \simeq 0$. But x is ϕ_C pre-near-standard so by Theorem 2.9 we have $\phi_C(x - \tilde{x}) \simeq 0$ in F^*. Each $x \in E$ defines a linear functional on F which is $\sigma(F, E)$ continuous and therefore $\sigma(F, E)$ continuous on members of C. If $C(F, R)$ is the class of functions from F to R which are $\sigma(F, E)$ continuous on members of C we have $E \subset C(F, R)$. In the enlargement $\hat{E} \subset \hat{C}(F, R)$. But $x \in \hat{E}$ and $\phi_C(x - \tilde{x}) \simeq 0$ and by Theorem 2.1 $C(F, R)$ is a ϕ_C closed subset of the class of all functions from F to R. By Theorem 1.1.8 $\tilde{x} \in C(F, R)$, i.e. $\tilde{x}$ is $\sigma(F, E)$ continuous on members of C.

2⇒3: By hypothesis $y \in v(C) \cap \mu_F(0) \Rightarrow \tilde{x}(y) \simeq 0$. But $\phi_C(x - \tilde{x}) \simeq 0$ so

$$y \in v(C) \cap \mu_F(0) \Rightarrow \langle x, y\rangle \simeq 0.$$

3⇒4: If $z \in v(C') \cap \mu_F(0)$ then there is a standard $\varepsilon > 0$ such that $z/\varepsilon \in v(C) \cap \mu_F(0)$. By hypothesis $\langle x, z/\varepsilon\rangle \simeq 0$ so $\langle x, z\rangle \simeq 0$. Thus for $z \in v(C') \cap \mu_F(0)$ $|\langle x, z\rangle| \leq 1$ so $x \in [v(C') \cap \mu_F(0)]^\circ$.

4⇒1: $[v(C') \cap \mu_F(0)]^\circ = [\cup\{\hat{S} \mid S \in C'\} \cap E^\circ]^\circ = [\cup\{\hat{S} \cap E^\circ \mid S \in C'\}]^\circ = \cap\{(\hat{S} \cap E^\circ)^\circ \mid S \in C'\}$. But by Theorem 3.3.1 for $S \in C'$ we have $(\hat{S} \cap E^\circ)^\circ \subset \hat{S}^\circ + E$. Therefore

$$[v(C') \cap \mu_F(0)]^\circ \subset \cap\{\hat{S}^\circ + E \mid S \in C'\} = \cap\left\{\left(\frac{1}{\varepsilon}\hat{S}\right)^\circ + E \mid \varepsilon > 0, S \in C\right\}.$$

Therefore

$$x \in [v(C') \cap \mu_F(0)]^\circ \Rightarrow \forall\varepsilon > 0\, \forall S \in C\, \exists x_0 \in E : x - x_0 \in \left(\frac{1}{\varepsilon}\hat{S}\right)^\circ$$

$$\Rightarrow \forall\varepsilon > 0\, \forall S \in C\, \exists x_0 \in E\, \forall y \in \hat{S} \mid \langle x - x_0, y\rangle \mid \leq \varepsilon.$$

That is, for every vicinity V in the C uniformity there is a standard $x_0 \in E$ such that $x \in \hat{V}(x_0)$. By Theorem 1.1.16 x is ϕ_C pre-near-standard. q.e.d.

There is a simpler version for dual pairs $\langle E, E' \rangle$ where E is a normed space and E' is the space of continuous linear functionals on E under the norm defined by $\|y\|_{E'} = \sup\{|\langle x, y \rangle| \mid \|x\|_E \leq 1\}$. $S_{E'}$ is the closed unit ball of E'. Also, the norm on E can be extended in an obvious way to members of $(E')^*$ which are $\sigma(E', E)$ continuous on $S_{E'}$.

3.3.3. THEOREM. *The following conditions on* $x \in \hat{E}$ *are equivalent:*

(1) *x is norm pre-near-standard,*

(2) *x is norm finite,* $\|x - \tilde{x}\| \simeq 0$ *and* $\tilde{x}$ *is* $\sigma(E', E)$ *continuous on* $S_{E'}$,

(3) $y \in \hat{S}_{E'} \cap \mu_{E'}(0) \Rightarrow \langle x, y \rangle \simeq 0$.

Proof. $C = \{\varepsilon S_{E'} | \varepsilon > 0\}$ is a cover of E' by ϕ_E bounded closed convex circled sets which in fact is a co-base for the class of closed convex circled equicontinuous subsets of E'. Therefore by Theorem 3.2.10 the C topology on E is the original norm topology. In the resulting statement of Theorem 3.3.2 it is clear that "$v(C)$" can be replaced by "$\hat{S}_{E'}$" and "$\phi_{E'}$ finite" by "norm finite". This gives the result. q.e.d.

This simple form can be retained for barrelled spaces where we have:

3.3.4. THEOREM. *Let E be a barrelled locally convex space and E' its dual. Then* $x \in \hat{E}$ *is pre-near-standard if and only if for every* $y \in \mu_{E'}(0)$ *which is* ϕ_E *bounded,* $\langle x, y \rangle \simeq 0$.

Proof. This follows from the equivalence of (1) and (3) in Theorem 3.3.2 since the topology of E is the topology of uniform convergence on the class C of closed convex circled equicontinuous subsets of E' and we have noted after Theorem 3.2.6 that for barrelled spaces $v(C)$ consists of precisely the ϕ_E bounded points of E'. q.e.d.

Theorem 3.3.3 is due to Luxemburg [1969]. His proof contains an idea essential to the beginning of our proof of Theorem 3.3.1 but we are subsequently involved in a great deal more strife. The importation of some ideas from our theory of function spaces makes some of the steps in Theorem 3.3.2 rather clearer and we shall see that the introduction of polars from standard duality theory permits rather nonchalant derivations of important standard theorems.

The remainder of this section is concerned with the consequences of Theorem 3.3.2. These include a further development of our non-standard duality theory and a number of new characterisations of precompactness together with most known results concerning completeness and precompactness. However, we first genuflect toward the original definition of a pre-near-standard point as a point in the monad of a Cauchy filter by deriving a dual characterisation of Cauchy filters. Here, as throughout, E, F and C are as in Theorem 3.3.2.

Every subset A of E can be considered as a family of functions on F. For $S \subset F$ we write "A_S" for the family of restrictions of members of A to S. For a filter $\mathfrak{F}$ on E we put $\mathfrak{F}_S = \{A_S : A \in \mathfrak{F}\}$. Also note that if S is given the relative $\sigma(F, E)$ topology then the monad of 0 in S $\mu_S(0) = \hat{S} \cap \mu_F(0)$.

3.3.5. THEOREM. *A filter $\mathfrak{F}$ on E is ϕ_C Cauchy iff for every $S \in C$ there is an $A \in \mathfrak{F}$ such that A_S is an equicontinuous family on S with the relative $\sigma(F, E)$ topology.*

Proof. Necessity: If $\mathfrak{F}$ is ϕ_C Cauchy then every point in $\mu(\mathfrak{F})$ is pre-near-standard, i.e.

$$x \in \mu(\mathfrak{F}) \Rightarrow \forall y \in v(C) \cap \mu_F(0)\ \langle x, y\rangle \simeq 0$$
$$\Rightarrow \forall S \in C\ \forall y \in \hat{S} \cap \mu_F(0)\ \langle x, y\rangle \simeq 0,$$

i.e. for all $S \in C$ $\mu(\mathfrak{F}_S) \subset [\mu_S(0)]^{\circ}$. By Theorem 1.1.2 $\exists A \in \hat{\mathfrak{F}}_S : A \subset \mu(\mathfrak{F}_S)$ and if $\mathfrak{N}$ is the neighbourhood filter of 0 in S with the relative $\sigma(F, E)$ topology then $\exists B \in \mathfrak{N}$: $B \subset \mu_S(0)$, i.e. $B^{\circ} \supset [\mu_S(0)]^{\circ}$. We thus have: $\exists A \in \hat{\mathfrak{F}}_S\ \exists B \in \mathfrak{N} : A \subset B^{\circ}$. Transferring this sentence to the standard structure gives the result.

Sufficiency: From Theorem 3.1.8 the hypothesis implies that for every $S \in C$ there is a $B \in \mathfrak{F}$ such that $B_S \subset [\mu_S(0)]^{\circ}$. Therefore for $S \in C$, $y \in \hat{S} \cap \mu_F(0)$ we have that $\langle x, y\rangle \simeq 0$ for $x \in \mu(\mathfrak{F})$. That is, every x in $\mu(\mathfrak{F})$ is ϕ_C pre-near-standard so $\mathfrak{F}$ is ϕ_C Cauchy. q.e.d.

We now exploit the equivalence of (1), (2), (3) in Theorem 3.3.2 to further our non-standard duality theory by deriving explicit links between linear functionals on F and pre-near-standard points of $\hat{E}$. These should be compared with the remarks introducing the section on the weak topology.

3.3.6. THEOREM. *$x \in \hat{E}$ is ϕ_C pre-near-standard if and only if there is a linear functional f on E which is $\sigma(F, E)$ continuous on members of C such that $\phi_C(x - f) \simeq 0$.*

Proof. Necessity: By (2) in Theorem 3.3.2.

Sufficiency: The hypothesis implies that (3) in Theorem 3.3.2 is satisfied.

The movement in the other direction is not so obvious.

3.3.7. THEOREM. *A linear functional f on F is $\sigma(F, E)$ continuous on members of C if and only if there is a ϕ_C pre-near-standard point x in $\hat{E}$ such that $\phi_C(x - f) \simeq 0$.*

Proof. Necessity: consider the binary relation $R(A, x)$ which holds if $A \in C' = \{\varepsilon S | \varepsilon > 0, S \in C\}$, $x \in E$ and $f - x \in A^o$, the polar being taken in the dual pair $\langle F^*, F\rangle$. We show that R is concurrent in A. For any finite subclass $\{A_1, \ldots, A_n\}$ of C, f is $\sigma(F, E)$ continuous on each A_i and therefore on their union. It is an elementary observation that then f is $\sigma(F, E)$ continuous on the closed convex circled hull A of the union. Clearly A is ϕ_E bounded.

We have that $y \in \hat{A} \cap E^o \Rightarrow f(y) \simeq 0$. Therefore $f \in (\hat{A} \cap E^o)^o$ polars being taken in $\langle F^*, F\rangle$. By Theorem 3.3.1 $f \in \hat{A}^o + E$. That is, for some $x_0 \in E$, $f - x_0 \in \hat{A}^o$. But this may be expressed in a sentence containing only constants denoting standard entities so in the standard structure we have $f - x_0 \in A^o$. But $A^o \subset [A_1 \cup \ldots \cup A_n]^o = A_1^0 \cap \ldots \cap A_n^0$. Thus there is an $x_0 \in E$ such that $f - x_0 \in A_i^0$, $i = 1, \ldots, n$. Thus R is concurrent in A.

In the enlargement there is therefore an $x \in \hat{E}$ such that

$$f - x \in \cap\{(\varepsilon\hat{A})^o | \varepsilon > 0, A \in C\}.$$

By Theorem 3.1.9 this intersection is precisely the monad of 0 in E equipped with the C topology, i.e. $\phi_C(f - x) \simeq 0$. By Theorem 3.3.6 x is ϕ_C pre-near-standard.

Sufficiency: If x is ϕ_C pre-near-standard then by (3) of Theorem 3.3.2,

$$y \in \nu(C) \cap \mu_F(0) \Rightarrow \langle x, y\rangle \simeq 0.$$

But $\phi_C(f - x) \simeq 0$ so

$$y \in \nu(C) \cap \mu_F(0) \Rightarrow f(y) \simeq 0.$$

Thus f is $\sigma(F, E)$ continuous on members of C. q.e.d.

These results lead to the conclusion that a subset A of E is ϕ_C precompact iff for every $x \in \hat{A}$ there is some linear functional f on F which is $\sigma(F, E)$ continuous on members of C such that $\phi_C(f - x) \simeq 0$. This is intriguing since a closed set A is ϕ_C compact iff for every $x \in \hat{A}$ there is an $x_0 \in E$ such that $\phi_C(x_0 - x) \simeq 0$. That is, if and only if there is a linear functional f on F which is $\sigma(F, E)$ continuous on F such that $\phi_C(f - x) \simeq 0$ by Theorem 3.1.6. Light emerges when we recall that a set is precompact iff its *completion* is compact and that the completion of a subset of a complete space is merely its closure. The missing link is, of course, the completeness theorem of Grothendieck.

3.3.8. THEOREM *(Grothendieck Completeness Theorem). E endowed with the C uniformity is complete if and only if every linear functional on F which is $\sigma(F, E)$ continuous on members of C is $\sigma(F, E)$ continuous on F.*

Proof. Recall that a space is complete if and only if every pre-near-standard point is near-standard.

Necessity: If f is $\sigma(F, E)$ continuous on members of C then by Theorem 3.3.5 there is a ϕ_C pre-near-standard point $x \in \hat{E}$ such that $\phi_C(x - f) \simeq 0$. As E is complete there is some $x_0 \in E$ such that $\phi_C(x - x_0) \simeq 0$. But the C topology on F^* is Hausdorff so $f = x_0$ and so is $\sigma(F, E)$ continuous.

Sufficiency: Take a ϕ_C pre-near-standard $x \in \hat{E}$. By (2) of Theorem 3.3.2 $\phi_C(x - \tilde{x}) \simeq 0$ and $\tilde{x}$ is $\sigma(F, E)$ continuous on members of C. By hypothesis $\tilde{x}$ is $\sigma(F, E)$ continuous on F so $\tilde{x} = x_0$ for some $x_0 \in E$. Thus x is ϕ_C near-standard. q.e.d.

It is clear that the completion of E with the C uniformity can be identified with the space of linear functionals on F which are $\sigma(F, E)$ continuous on members of C. For, by Theorem 3.3.8 this space is complete and by Theorem 3.3.7 E is ϕ_C dense in it.

We can also infer the following simple result on completeness:

3.3.9. THEOREM. *Every weakly compact subset A of E is ϕ_C complete.*

Proof. For each ϕ_C pre-near-standard point x of $\hat{A}$, $\phi_C(x - \tilde{x}) \simeq 0$ by (2) of Theorem 3.3.2. As A is weakly compact there is an x_0 in A such that $\phi_F(x - x_0) \simeq 0$. Therefore $\tilde{x} = x_0$ and x is ϕ_C near-standard. q.e.d.

We can associate filters on a set with points of its extension in the enlargement and relations between particular filters will parallel relations between particular classes of points–such as those characterising the pre-near-standard points deriving from Theorem 3.3.2. Since a precompact set is characterised as having all points of its extension pre-near-standard we are able to derive a new characterisation of precompact sets by means of filters.

Specialising our results on function spaces we note that in the dual pair $\langle E, F\rangle$ with F considered as a space of functions from E to R, a point $y \in \hat{F}$ is in the monad of 0 in the topology of uniform convergence on a subset A of E if and only if for all $x \in \hat{A}$ $\langle x, y\rangle \simeq 0$. Further, a filter $\mathfrak{F}$ on F converges to 0 in this topology if and only if $\mu(\mathfrak{F})$ is contained in the monad of 0, i.e. if and only if $y \in \mu(\mathfrak{F}) \Rightarrow \langle x, y\rangle \simeq 0$ for all $x \in \hat{A}$.

3.3.10. THEOREM. *A subset A of E is precompact in the C topology if and only if every filter $\mathfrak{F}$ on F which contains a member of C and converges to 0 in $\sigma(F, E)$, converges to 0 in the topology of uniform convergence on A.*

Proof. Necessity: suppose A is precompact in the C topology and let $\mathfrak{F}$ be a filter which contains a member S of C and converges to 0 in $\sigma(F, E)$. Then $\mu(\mathfrak{F}) \subset \hat{S}$ and $\mu(\mathfrak{F}) \subset \mu_F(0)$ so $\mu(\mathfrak{F}) \subset \nu(C) \cap \mu_F(0)$. Since each $x \in \hat{A}$ is ϕ_C pre-near-standard we have by (3) of Theorem 3.3.2 that

$$y \in \mu(\mathfrak{F}) \Rightarrow \langle x, y\rangle \simeq 0 \quad \text{for} \quad x \in \hat{A}.$$

Thus $\mathfrak{F}$ converges to 0 in the topology of uniform convergence on A.

Sufficiency: let $y \in \nu(C) \cap \mu_F(0)$. We show that for every $x \in \hat{A}$, $\langle x, y\rangle \simeq 0$. Define $\mathfrak{F}_y = \{S \mid S \subset F \text{ and } y \in \hat{S}\}$. This is an ultrafilter on F with $y \in \mu(\mathfrak{F}_y)$. But $y \in \mu_F(0)$ so by Theorem 1.1.4 $\mu(\mathfrak{F}_y) \subset \mu_F(0)$ as $\mathfrak{F}_y$ is an ultrafilter. Also if $y \in \nu(C)$ then there is some $S \in C$ such that $y \in \hat{S}$. Then $S \in \mathfrak{F}_y$ by definition. Thus $\mathfrak{F}_y$ is a filter on F containing a member of C which converges to 0 in $\sigma(F, E)$. By hypothesis $\mathfrak{F}_y$ converges to 0 in the topology of uniform convergence on A:

$$x \in \hat{A},\ z \in \mu(\mathfrak{F}_y) \Rightarrow \langle x, z\rangle \simeq 0.$$

But $y \in \mu(\mathfrak{F}_y)$ so for each $x \in \hat{A}$, $\langle x, y\rangle \simeq 0$. This holds for every y in $\nu(C) \cap \mu_F(0)$. By (3) of Theorem 3.3.2 each $x \in \hat{A}$ is ϕ_C pre-near-standard, i.e. A is precompact. q.e.d.

For barrelled spaces this becomes the following generalisation of the Gelfand-Phillips compactness criterion in Banach spaces:

3.3.11. THEOREM. *Let E be a barrelled locally convex topological vector space and E′ its dual. A subset A of E is precompact if and only if every ϕ_E bounded filter on E′ which convergences to 0 in $\sigma(E', E)$ converges to 0 in the topology of uniform convergence on A.*

Proof. In the preceding theorem let $E' = F$ and let C be the class of closed convex circled equicontinuous subsets of E'. If a filter contains a member of C then it is ϕ_E bounded since equicontinuous sets of E' are ϕ_E bounded. If a filter contains a ϕ_E bounded set S then from Theorem 3.2.6 S is equicontinuous and so is its closed convex circled hull by Theorem 3.2.9. Thus the filter contains a member of C. This gives the result. q.e.d.

The result for normed spaces was derived from Theorem 3.3.3 by Luxemburg [1969]. We can give a further criterion for precompactness. We use the notation A_S as in Theorem 3.3.6.

3.3.12. THEOREM. *A subset A of E is ϕ_C precompact if and only if for every $S \in C$, the restrictions of the members of A to S form an equicontinuous family on S with the relative $\sigma(F, E)$ topology.*

Proof. By (3) of Theorem 3.3.2 A is precompact iff $\forall x \in \hat{A}\ \forall S \in C$ $y \in \hat{S} \cap \mu_F(0) \Rightarrow \langle x, y \rangle \simeq 0$. But $\hat{S} \cap \mu_F(0)$ is the monad of 0 in S with the relative $\sigma(F, E)$ topology. Theorem 2.3 now gives the result. q.e.d.

For normed spaces E this implies that $A \subset E$ is precompact if and only if its restriction to the unit ball $S_{E'}$ is equicontinuous with respect to the relative weak topology.

The condition in Theorem 3.3.12 is equivalent to requiring that $A^{\circ} \cap S$ be a relative $\sigma(F, E)$ neighbourhood of 0 on S for each S. But the sets A° as A ranges over the ϕ_C precompact subsets of A are the neighbourhoods of 0 in F for the topology of uniform convergence on the ϕ_C precompact subsets of E. Thus this topology coincides with $\sigma(F, E)$ on each member of C. We shall place this observation in a more general context after the next theorem.

3.3.13. THEOREM. *If $x \in \hat{E}$ is ϕ_F finite then x is ϕ_F pre-near-standard.*

Proof. Let C be the class of closed convex circled hulls of finite subsets of F so that the C topology on E is precisely $\sigma(F, E)$. Clearly $\nu(C)$ consists of *finite* sums $y = \sum_{i=1}^{n} \alpha_i y_i$ where $\alpha_i \in \hat{R}$, $\sum_{i=1}^{n} |\alpha_i| \leq 1$ and $y_i \in F$. y can be written as a sum with the y_i linearly independent as functionals over E.

If $y \in \nu(C) \cap \mu_F(0)$ then for $x \in E$ $\langle x, y \rangle \simeq 0$ and choosing appropriate $x_i \in E$ using Theorem 3.1.7 we can show that each α_i is infinitesimal. If $x \in \hat{E}$ is ϕ_F finite then $\langle x, y_i \rangle$ is finite for each $y_i \in F$ so $\langle x, y \rangle = \sum_{i=1}^{n} \alpha_i \langle x, y_i \rangle$ is infinitesimal. This holds for every y in $\nu(C) \cap \mu_F(0)$. By (3) of Theorem 3.3.2 x is ϕ_F pre-near-standard. q.e.d.

An immediate consequence, required for the next theorem, is that the ϕ_F bounded and ϕ_F precompact subsets of E coincide.

3.3.14. THEOREM. *Let $\langle E, F \rangle$ be a dual pair of vector spaces; $\mathfrak{M}$ a cover of E by ϕ_F bounded closed convex circled sets; $\mathfrak{N}$ a cover of F by ϕ_E bounded closed convex circled sets. The following are equivalent:*

1. *Each $M \in \mathfrak{M}$ is $\phi_{\mathfrak{N}}$ precompact.*
2. *The $\mathfrak{M}$ topology coincides with $\sigma(F, E)$ on each $N \in \mathfrak{N}$.*
3. *Each $N \in \mathfrak{N}$ is $\phi_{\mathfrak{M}}$ precompact.*
4. *The $\mathfrak{N}$ topology coincides with $\sigma(E, F)$ on each $M \in \mathfrak{M}$.*

In particular, in the dual pair $\langle E, E'\rangle$ where E is a locally convex topological vector space and E' its dual, the topology of uniform convergence on precompact subsets of E coincides with $\sigma(E', E)$ on equicontinuous subsets of E'.

Proof. 1 ⇒ 2: It is easy to see that the hypothesis implies that each member of $\mathfrak{M}' = \{\varepsilon M \mid \varepsilon > 0, M \in \mathfrak{M}\}$ is precompact. By (4) of Theorem 3.3.2:

$$v(\mathfrak{M}') \subset [v(\mathfrak{N}') \cap \mu_F(0)]^{\circ}.$$

Therefore

$$v(\mathfrak{M}')^{\circ} \supset [v(\mathfrak{N}') \cap \mu_F(0)]$$

i.e.

$$[v(\mathfrak{M}')^{\circ} \cap v(\mathfrak{N}')] \supset [v(\mathfrak{N}') \cap \mu_F(0)].$$

Also $\mathfrak{M}$ is a cover of E so $v(\mathfrak{M}') \supset E$ and $v(\mathfrak{M})^{\circ} \subset E^{\circ} = \mu_F(0)$. Therefore

$$[v(\mathfrak{M}')^{\circ} \cap v(\mathfrak{N}')] \subset [v(\mathfrak{N}') \cap \mu_F(0)].$$

These two inclusions give

$$[v(\mathfrak{M}')^{\circ} \cap v(\mathfrak{N})] = [\mu_F(0) \cap v(\mathfrak{N})].$$

But $v(\mathfrak{M}')^{\circ}$ is the monad of 0 in the $\mathfrak{M}$ topology. Therefore the $\mathfrak{M}$ topology coincides with $\sigma(F, E)$ on each $N \in \mathfrak{N}$.

2 ⇒ 3: each $N \in \mathfrak{N}$ is ϕ_E bounded so by Theorem 3.3.13 each $N \in \mathfrak{N}$ is ϕ_E precompact. The hypothesis is that the $\mathfrak{M}$ topology coincides with $\sigma(F, E)$ on each $N \in \mathfrak{N}$. Therefore each $N \in \mathfrak{N}$ is $\phi_{\mathfrak{M}}$ precompact.

3 ⇒ 4: similar to 1 ⇒ 2.

4 ⇒ 1: similar to 2 ⇒ 3.

For the last part of the theorem let $\mathfrak{N}$ be the class of closed convex circled equicontinuous subsets of E' so that $\phi_{\mathfrak{N}}$ is the initial topology on E and let $\mathfrak{M}$ be the class of closed convex circled precompact subsets of E, i.e. (1) of the theorem is satisfied. Our next theorem will show that every precompact subset of E is contained in a member of $\mathfrak{M}$ so the $\mathfrak{M}$ topology is the topology of uniform convergence on precompact subsets of E. The result now follows from (2) of the theorem recalling that every equicontinuous subset of E' is contained in a closed convex circled equicontinuous subset. q.e.d.

A yet more general version of this theorem is obtained in the following section (Theorem 3.4.1).

As a further application of (4) of Theorem 3.3.2 we have:

3.3.15. THEOREM. *If A is a ϕ_C precompact subset of E then its closed convex circled hull is also ϕ_C precompact.*

Proof. If A is ϕ_C precompact then $\hat{A}$ consists of ϕ_C pre-near-standard points, i.e. $\hat{A} \subset [\nu(C') \cap \mu_F(0)]^{\circ}$. Therefore $\hat{A}^{\circ\circ} \subset [\nu(C') \cap \mu_F(0)]^{\circ\circ\circ}$.

Now $[\nu(C') \cap \mu_F(0)] \subset [\nu(C') \cap \mu_F(0)]^{\circ\circ}$ so $[\nu(C') \cap \mu_F(0)]^{\circ\circ\circ} \subset [\nu(C') \cap \mu_F(0)]^{\circ}$. Thus $\hat{A}^{\circ\circ} \subset [\nu(C') \cap \mu_F(0)]^{\circ}$. Thus the closed convex circled hull $A^{\circ\circ}$ of A has an extension consisting of ϕ_C pre-near-standard points and so is ϕ_C precompact. q.e.d.

Comparison of this with the far from trivial standard proofs [e.g. Köthe [1969] p. 241] and also with the proof of the corresponding result for normed spaces in Luxemburg [1969] will point up the clarification which can arise from developing a general non-standard duality theory.

In fact were we grown so effete as to eschew Theorem 3.2.8 we could use the some procedure to show that the convex hull, the circled hull, the closure and the closed convex circled hull of a precompact set are precompact merely by noting that $A^{\circ\circ}$ is a closed convex circled set containing A and therefore containing the respective hulls.

Noting that a compact set is precompact we now have the following:

3.3.16. THEOREM. *The following conditions on the closed convex circled hull A of a ϕ_C compact subset of E are equivalent:*

(1) *A is ϕ_C complete.*

(2) *A is ϕ_C compact.*

(3) *A is $\sigma(E, F)$ compact.*

Proof. 1 $\Rightarrow$ 2: By Theorem 3.3.15 every $x \in \hat{A}$ is ϕ_C pre-near-standard. If A is ϕ_C complete then every $x \in \hat{A}$ is ϕ_C near-standard.

2 $\Rightarrow$ 3: trivial.

3 $\Rightarrow$ 1: By Theorem 3.3.9.

The last two theorems lead to the following observation: our characterisation of the pre-near standard points as the polar of an external set in the enlargement together with the characterisation of weak compactness by means of polars in Theorem 3.2.4 suggests that the weakly-near-standard points might be characterised as the polar of some external set. In fact much sweat was discharged in this endeavour.

It is now clear that such a characterisation is not possible since the method of proof of Theorem 3.3.15 together with Theorem 3.3.16 would lead to the conclusion that the closed convex circled hull of a relatively compact set is compact. Krein's Theorem asserts that this is the case if and only if the hull is complete in the Mackey topology.

Our next deduction from Theorem 3.3.2 is of interest if only because the result seems so remote from the writ of Non-Standard Analysis.

If $y \in E'$ then y is bounded on some neighbourhood V of 0 in E, i.e. $\exists k \in R : z \in V \Rightarrow |\langle z, y\rangle| \leq k$. If U is a precompact subset of E then for $x \in \hat{U}$ there is a standard $x_0 \in E$ such that $x - x_0 \in \hat{V}$. Transferring the above statement concerning V to the enlargement we see that $|\langle x - x_0, y\rangle| \leq k$. But $|\langle x, y\rangle| \leq |\langle x - x_0, y\rangle| + |\langle x_0, y\rangle|$ and $\langle x_0, y\rangle$ is standard so $\langle x, y\rangle$ is finite. This holds for any x in $\hat{U}$. Thus y would be bounded on U by any infinite number. Transferring the appropriate sentence back to the standard structure we see that if $y \in E'$ then y is bounded on any precompact set.

3.3.17. THEOREM. *If a locally convex topological vector space E is locally precompact then E is finite dimensional.*

Proof. Theorem 3.3.15 shows that the hypothesis implies that there is a circled neighbourhood U of 0 which is precompact. Suppose E is not finite dimensional, i.e. for any finite set of vectors $x_1, \ldots, x_n$ in E there is a $z \in E$ not linearly dependent on $x_1, \ldots, x_n$. Since E' separates points of E z is not linearly dependent on $z_1, \ldots, z_n$ when they are considered as linear functionals on E'. By Theorem 3.1.7 there is a $y \in E'$ such that $\langle x_i, y\rangle = 0$, $i = 1, \ldots, n$ but $\langle z, y\rangle \neq 0$.

We have seen above that y is bounded on the precompact set U. Also, U is radial, being a neighbourhood of 0. We can therefore choose new y', z' such that $y' \in U^\circ$, $z' \in U$, $\langle x_i, y\rangle = 0$, $i = 1, \ldots, n$ and $\langle z', y'\rangle = \frac{1}{2}$. Thus the relation $R(x, (z, y))$ which holds if $x \in E$, $z \in E$, $y \in E'$, $\langle x, y\rangle = 0$, $y \in U^\circ$, $z \in U$ and $\langle z, y\rangle = \frac{1}{2}$ is concurrent in x. In the enlargement there is a $y \in \hat{U}^\circ$, $z \in \hat{U}$ such that $\langle z, y\rangle = \frac{1}{2}$ and for $x \in E$ $\langle x, y\rangle = 0$. As U is pre-compact this z is pre-near-standard.

As U is a neighbourhood of 0, U° is equicontinuous. It is clearly closed convex and circled so the y we have found belongs to $v(C)$ where C is the class of closed convex circled equicontinuous subsets of E'. Also for $z \in E$, $\langle x, y\rangle = 0$ so $y \in E^\circ$. Thus $y \in v(C) \cap E^\circ$. But $\langle z, y\rangle = \frac{1}{2}$. By (3) of Theorem

3.3.2 z is not pre-near-standard. This is a contradiction. Thus E is finite dimensional. q.e.d.

3.4. Compact mappings. We apply the theory of the preceding sections to some preliminary results in the general theory of compact mappings–including two new characterisations.

Recall that given dual pairs $\langle E, F\rangle$; $\langle G, H\rangle$ and a linear map $T: E \to G$ which is continuous for the weak topologies we can define the adjoint T': $H \to F$ by

$$\langle x, T'(h)\rangle = \langle T(x), h\rangle \quad \text{for} \quad x \in E, h \in H.$$

The following theorem, a further application of Theorem 3.3.2 gives a generalisation of the Theorem of Schauder:

3.4.1. THEOREM. *Let* $\langle E, F\rangle$; $\langle G, H\rangle$ *be dual pairs of vector spaces*; C *a class of* ϕ_F *bounded closed convex circled sets covering* E; $\mathscr{D}$ *a class of* ϕ_G *bounded closed convex circled sets covering* H; $T: E \to G$ *a linear map which is continuous with respect to the weak topologies and* T' *its adjoint. Then the following are equivalent:*

(1) $\forall A \in C$ $T(A)$ *is precompact for the* $\mathscr{D}$ *topology on* G.

(2) $\forall S \in \mathscr{D}$ T' *restricted to* S *is a uniformly continuous map from* S *with the relative* $\sigma(H, G)$ *topology to* F *with the* C *topology.*

(3) $\forall S \in \mathscr{D}$ $T'(S)$ *is precompact for the* C *topology on* F.

(4) $\forall A \in C$ T *restricted to* A *is a uniformly continuous map from* A *with the relative* $\sigma(E, F)$ *topology to* G *with the* $\mathscr{D}$ *topology.*

Proof. 1 $\Rightarrow$ 2: By (4) of Theorem 3.3.2 the hypothesis implies that

$$T(\nu(C')) \subset [\nu(\mathscr{D}) \cap \mu_H(0)]^{\circ}.$$

Therefore

$$[T(\nu(C'))]^{\circ} \supset [\nu(\mathscr{D}) \cap \mu_H(0)],$$

i.e.

$$h \in \nu(\mathscr{D}) \cap \mu_H(0) \Rightarrow |\langle T(x), h\rangle| \leq 1 \quad \text{for} \quad x \in \nu(C').$$

By definition of T' this implies that

$$h \in \nu(\mathscr{D}) \cap \mu_H(0) \Rightarrow |\langle x, T'(h)\rangle| \leq 1 \quad \text{for} \quad x \in \nu(C'),$$

i.e.

$$T'(\nu(\mathscr{D}) \cap \mu_H(0)) \subset \nu(C')^{\circ}.$$

But by Theorem 3.1.9 $v(C')^{\circ}$ is the monad of 0 in F with the C topology. (2) now follows from Theorem 1.1.14 when we note that on convex circled subsets of a vector space two locally convex topologies induce the same uniform structure if they induce the same relative neighbourhoods of 0 so uniform continuity follows from continuity at 0.

$2 \Rightarrow 3$: Each $S \in \mathscr{D}$ is ϕ_H bounded and so is ϕ_H precompact by Theorem 3.3.13. The hypothesis then implies that $T(S)$ is ϕ_C precompact.

$3 \Rightarrow 4$: Similar to $1 \Rightarrow 2$.

$4 \Rightarrow 1$: Similar to $2 \Rightarrow 3$. q.e.d.

The case of greatest interest arises for pairs $\langle E, E' \rangle$; $\langle G, G' \rangle$ when C is the class of bounded closed convex circled subsets of E; G is quasibarrelled (so that strongly bounded subsets of G' are equicontinuous), $\mathscr{D}$ is the class of bounded closed convex circled equicontinuous subsets of G' and G' has the topology of uniform convergence on bounded sets of G (the strong topology). Then Theorem 3.4.1 asserts that T maps bounded sets to precompact sets if and only if T' maps bounded sets to precompact sets. The usual form of Schauder's Theorem for normed spaces now follows readily. But we prefer to approach this theorem through a new characterisation of compact mappings which generalises a result of Puritz [1972] on compact operators in Hilbert Space.

The norm on the normed vector space E will be denoted by "$\|\cdot\|_E$" and its closed unit ball by "S_E". The usual norm on the dual E' is given by $\|f\|_{E'} = \sup\{|f(x)| : \|x\|_E \leq 1\}$ and it is clear that $\|f\|_{E'} \simeq 0$ if and only if $f(x) \simeq 0$ for $x \in \hat{S}_E$.

A linear map between normed spaces $T: E \to F$ is *compact* if it maps norm bounded subsets of E to relatively compact subsets of F. Robinson [1966] has noted that this is equivalent to the requirement that T map norm finite points of $\hat{E}$ to norm near-standard points of $\hat{F}$. If F is complete then this is clearly equivalent to the requirement that T map points of $\hat{S}_E$ to norm pre-near-standard points of $\hat{F}$.

3.4.2. THEOREM. *Let E, F be normed spaces with F complete; E', F' their duals; $T: E \to F$ a linear map which is continuous with respect to the weak topologies. T is compact if and only if the adjoint T' maps points of $\hat{S}_{F'}$ in the weak monad $\mu_{F'}(0)$ to norm infinitesimal points of E'.*

Proof. By the last remark T is compact if and only if $T(\hat{S}_E)$ consists of norm pre-near-standard points. By (3) of Theorem 3.3.3 this is equivalent to the requirement that if $x \in \hat{S}_E$ then for $f \in \hat{S}_{F'} \cap \mu_{F'}(0)$, $\langle T(x), f \rangle \simeq 0$

i.e. $\langle x, T'(f)\rangle \simeq 0$. By the definition of $\| \ \|_{E'}$ this is equivalent to the requirement that if $f \in \hat{S}_{F'} \cap \mu_{F'}(0)$ then $\|T'(f)\|_{E'} \simeq 0$. q.e.d.

The Theorem of Schauder now follows

3.4.3. THEOREM. *Let E and F be normed spaces with F complete; E', F' their duals; T a weakly continuous linear map from E to F. T is compact if and only if T' is compact.*

Proof. Necessity: $S_{F'}$ is clearly a $\sigma(F', F)$ closed equicontinuous subset of F'. By Theorem 3.2.2 if $f \in \hat{S}_{F'}$ then there is a $g \in S_{F'}$ and an $h \in \mu_{F'}(0)$ such that $f = g + h$. Then

$$\|h\|_{F'} \leq \|f\|_{F'} + \|g\|_{F'} \leq 2$$

so $\frac{1}{2}h \in \hat{S}_{F'} \cap \mu_{F'}(0)$. By Theorem 3.4.2 $\|T'(h)\|_{E'} \simeq 0$. But $T'(g)$ is standard and $T'(f) = T'(g) + T'(h)$ so $T'(f)$ is norm near-standard. Thus T' maps points of $\hat{S}_{F'}$ to near-standard points of $\hat{E}$ so T' is compact.

Sufficiency: Suppose $f \in \hat{S}_{F'} \cap \mu_{F'}(0)$. The hypothesis implies that T' maps points of $\hat{S}_{F'}$ to near-standard points of $\hat{E}$ so there is an $h \in E'$ such that $\|T'(f) - h\|_E \simeq 0$. Clearly $T'(f) \in \mu_{E'}(h)$. But $f \in \mu_{F'}(0)$ and T is weakly continuous so $T'(f) \in \mu_{E'}(0)$. The $\sigma(E', E)$ topology is Hausdorff so $h = 0$. Therefore $\|T'(f)\|_{E'} \simeq 0$. Theorem 3.4.2 now gives the result. q.e.d.

With reflexive normed spaces we have a simpler characterisation of compact maps.

3.4.4. THEOREM. *Let E, F be normed spaces with E reflexive. If $T: E \to F$ maps points of $\hat{S}_E$ in the weak monad $\mu_E(0)$ to norm infinitesimal points then T is compact. If T is continuous with respect to the weak topologies then the condition is also necessary.*

Proof. By Theorem 3.2.5 the norm finite points of a reflexive space are weakly near-standard. Thus if $x \in \hat{S}_E$ then there is some standard $x_0 \in E$ and some $x_1 \in \mu_E(0)$: $x = x_1 + x_0$. As $\|x_1\|_E \leq \|x\|_E + \|x_0\|_E$ we have that $\frac{1}{2}x_1 \in \hat{S}_E \cap \mu_E(0)$. By hypothesis $\|T(x_1)\|_F \simeq 0$. But $T(x) = T(x_0) + T(x_1)$ and $T(x_0)$ is standard so $T(x)$ is near-standard. Thus T is compact.

Take $x \in \hat{S}_E \cap \mu_E(0)$. As T is compact there is a $y \in F$ such that $\|T(x) - y\|_F \simeq 0$. Clearly $T(x) \in \mu_F(y)$. But $x \in \mu_E(0)$ and T is continuous with respect to the weak topologies so $T(x) \in \mu_F(0)$. But the $\sigma(F, F')$ topology is Hausdorff so $y = 0$. Therefore $\|T(x)\|_F \simeq 0$. q.e.d.

This result is, of course, related to the original definition of compact maps as those mapping weakly convergent sequences to convergent sequences.

As an application of Theorem 3.4.4 we show that an important class of integral operator is compact. We can of course regard integration as a functional and transfer the properties of the functional to the enlargement. Let I be the closed unit interval and $K(x, t)$ a continuous function from $I \times I$ to R. On $L_2(I)$ the Hilbert space of continuous functions from I to R with the norm $\| \;\| : \varphi \to [\int |\varphi(t)|^2 \mathrm{d}t]^{\frac{1}{2}}$ define an operator T by

$$T(\phi) : x \mapsto \int_0^1 K(x, t)\phi(t)\mathrm{d}t.$$

We show that T is compact.

For each $x_0 \in I$ define a linear functional T_{x_0} on $L_2(I)$ by

$$T_{x_0} : \phi \mapsto \int_0^1 K(x_0, t)\varphi(t)\mathrm{d}t.$$

This is easily seen to be continuous, i.e. T_{x_0} is in the dual of $L_2(I)$. Therefore if $\varphi \in \hat{L}_2(I)$ is in the weak monad of 0 then $T_{x_0}(\phi) \simeq 0$, i.e.

$$\int_0^1 K(x_0, t)\varphi(t)\mathrm{d}t \simeq 0.$$

For each $x \in \hat{I}$ there is an $x_0 \in I$ such that $x \simeq x_0$ and as K is a continuous function in x we have for every $\varepsilon > 0$, $t \in I$

$$|K(x, t) - K(x_0, t)| < \varepsilon.$$

Let φ be in the extension of the unit ball of $L_2(I)$ so

$$\left[\int_0^1 |\varphi(t)|^2 \mathrm{d}t\right]^{\frac{1}{2}} \leq 1.$$

If $S = \{t \in I : |\varphi(t)| \leq 1\}$ then

$$\int_0^1 |\varphi(t)|\mathrm{d}t = \int_S |\varphi(t)|\mathrm{d}t + \int_{I-S} |\varphi(t)|\mathrm{d}t \leq 1 + \int_{I-S} |\varphi(t)|^2 \mathrm{d}t \leq 2.$$

For every $\varepsilon > 0$

$$\left| \int_0^1 [K(x,t) - K(x_0,t)]\varphi(t)\mathrm{d}t \right| < \varepsilon \int_0^1 |\varphi(t)|\mathrm{d}t \leq 2\varepsilon.$$

If φ is in the weak monad of 0 we have seen that

$$\int_0^1 K(x_0,t)\varphi(t)\mathrm{d}t \simeq 0.$$

Therefore for every $\varepsilon > 0$, every $x \in \hat{I}$

$$\left| \int_0^1 K(x,t)\varphi(t)\mathrm{d}t \right| < 2\varepsilon.$$

Transferring the appropriate statement about $L_2(I)$ we can infer that for every $\varepsilon > 0$ $\|T(\varphi)\| < 2\varepsilon$, i.e. $T(\varphi)$ is norm infinitesimal. Thus T maps points of the unit ball in the weak monad to norm infinitesimal points and so is compact.

References

Antonovskii, M. Ya., Boltyanskii, V. G. and Sarymsakov, T. A., 1966, An Outline of the Theory of Topological Semifields, *Russian Mathematical Surveys* 21, pp. 164-191.
Edwards, R. E., 1965, *Functional Analysis* (Holt, Rinehart and Winston).
Fischer, H. R., 1959, Limesräume, *Math. Annalen* 137, pp. 269–303.
Gillman, L. and Jerison, M., 1960, *Rings of Continuous Functions* (Van Nostrand).
Kelley, J. L., 1955, *General Topology* (Van Nostrand).
Kelley, J. L. and Namioka, I., 1963, *Linear Topological Spaces* (Van Nostrand).
Köthe, G., 1969, *Topological Vector Spaces* (Springer Verlag).
Luxemburg, W. A. J., 1969, A General Theory of Monads, in: *Applications of Model Theory to Algebra Analysis and Probability*, ed. W. A. J. Luxemburg (Holt, Rinehart and Winston) pp. 18–86.
Machover, M. and Hirschfeld, J., 1969, *Lectures in Non-Standard Analysis* (Springer Verlag).
Puritz, C. W., 1972, Almost Perpendicular Vectors, *this volume*.
Robertson, A. P. and Robertson, W., 1966, *Topological Vector Spaces* (Cambridge University Press).
Robinson, A., 1966, *Non-Standard Analysis* (North-Holland).
Schaefer, H. H., 1966, *Topological Vector Spaces* (Macmillan).

Received 14 January 1971

NON-STANDARD NOTES ON THE HYPERSPACE

I. JUHÁSZ
Budapest

The aim of the present note is to show how hyperspaces (i.e., the monads of their points) can be characterised in a non-standard fashion and then to give examples in which this is used to simplify the proofs of some known results concerning hyperspaces. We also mention two interesting open problems, whose solution might be more easily accessible using the non-standard approach.

1. The hyperspace.

1.1. The hyperspace $H(R)$ of a topological space R (cf. Michael [1951] Definition 1.7, p. 153) consists of all non-empty closed subsets of R, and its topology is determined by the following open basis $\mathfrak{B}$:

$$\mathfrak{B} = \{\langle O_1, \ldots, O_n\rangle : O_i \text{ is open in } R\},$$

where a closed non-empty set $A \subset R$ belongs to $\langle O_1, \ldots, O_n\rangle$ if and only if

(i) $A \subset \bigcup_{i=1}^{n} O_i$,

and

(ii) $A \cap O_i \neq \phi$ for each $i = 1, \ldots, n$.

1.2. We assume that the basic ideas of non-standard analysis are known to the reader. Suppose now that R as well as all objects to be mentioned throughout this paper belong to a fixed structure and an enlargement of this structure is given (cf. Luxemburg [1969], Machover and Hirschfeld [1969] or Robinson [1966]) where it is immaterial whether our approach is type-theoretic or set-theoretic. It will also be convenient for us to assume that this enlargement is saturated (cf. Luxemburg [1969] 2.6, p. 28). This will allow us to infer the existence of a standard member of a standard filter $\mathscr{F}$ in a given internal set I provided that every infinitesimal member of $\mathscr{F}$ belongs to I, and vice versa.

We shall denote by $\mu(p)$ and $\mu(S)$ the (neighbourhood) monads of a point $p \in R$ and a subset $S \subset R$ in the space $^*R$, respectively. If $A \in H(R)$, $\mu_H(A)$ denotes the monad of A as a point of the space $^*H(R)$. In what follows, R is always assumed to be a T_1 space.

1.3. LEMMA. *Let $A \in H(R)$ and $X \in {}^*H(R)$. Then $X \in \mu_H(A)$ if and only if*

(1) $X \subset \mu(A)$,

and

(2) *$p \in A$ implies $\mu(p) \cap X \neq \phi$.*

Proof. Let $X \in \mu_H(A)$ and

$$U = \langle O_1, \ldots, O_n \rangle$$

be an arbitrary basic neighbourhood of A in $H(R)$. Then $X \in {}^*U$, hence by transfering (i) to the enlargement,

$$X \subset {}^*\left(\bigcup_{i=1}^{n} O_i\right).$$

But it is obvious that for any open set G containing A we can choose U in such a way that $\bigcup_{i=1}^{n} O_i \subset G$, hence $X \subset {}^*G$, and thus we obtain (1).

To prove (2) let $p \in A$ and G be any open set containing p. If $A = \{p\}$, then $\langle G \rangle \in \mu_H(A)$, hence $X \subset {}^*G$, and this implies $\phi \neq X \subset \mu(p)$.

However, if $\{p\} \neq A$, then $\langle G, R \backslash \{p\} \rangle$ is a basic neighbourhood of A in $H(R)$, hence by (ii)

$$X \cap {}^*G \neq \phi.$$

Now those members of $^*\mathfrak{P}(R)$ (the * power set of R) which intersect X obviously form an internal set. Therefore, saturatedness implies the existence of an infinitesimal neighbourhood of p intersecting X. But this is contained in $\mu(p)$, hence

$$\mu(p) \cap X \neq \phi.$$

To prove the converse, assume $X \in {}^*H(R)$, (1) and (2), and let U be as above. We have to show $X \in {}^*U$. Now $X \subset {}^*(\bigcup_{i=1}^{n} O_i)$ is obvious, since

$$X \subset \mu(A) \subset {}^*\left(\bigcup_{i=1}^{n} O_i\right),$$

and this proves the transfer of (i). To show the same for (ii), let $1 \leq i \leq n$ and choose a $p \in O_i \cap A$. Then $\mu(p) \subset {}^*O_i$, and $\mu(p) \cap X \neq \phi$, hence

$$X \cap {}^*O_i \neq \phi;$$

the proof is complete.

2. Applications.

2.1. The above simple and intuitive non-standard characterisation of the topology of the hyperspace will now be put to use, by giving simple and intuitive proofs of three known theorems. Not surprisingly, they will be concerned with compactness and uniform structures, which are known to become extremely simple in a non-standard setting.

2.2. THEOREM *(cf. Kuratowski* [1966] *or Michael* [1951]*). If R is compact so is $H(R)$.*

Proof. We have to show that every $X \in {}^*H(R)$ is near-standard. So let

$$A = \{p \in R : \mu(p) \cap X \neq \phi\}.$$

By saturatedness, A is closed in R (see Luxemburg [1969] Theorem 3.4.2, p. 63), and $A \neq \phi$ because $\phi \neq X \subset {}^*R$ and R is compact, hence each point of ${}^*R$ is near-standard. We claim that

$$X \in \mu_H(A).$$

Condition (2) of Lemma 1.3 is automatically satisfied by the choice of A. To show (1), let G be an arbitrary standard open set containing A, and assume $X \not\subset {}^*G$. Then there is a $y \in X \cap {}^*(R \backslash G)$. Again, by the compactness of R, y is near-standard, hence there is a $q \in R$ with $y \in \mu(q)$. But this implies $\mu(q) \cap {}^*(R \backslash G) \neq \phi$, hence $q \in R \backslash G$, since $R \backslash G$ is closed, what contradicts $\mu(q) \cap X \neq \phi$, because it implies

$$q \in A \subset G.$$

Thus, indeed, $X \subset {}^*G$ and therefore $X \subset \mu(A)$, and the proof is completed.

2.3. THEOREM *(cf. Michael* [1951]*). If R is normal then $H(R)$ is completely regular.*

Proof. What we are going to show is actually that if R is normal then there exists a uniform structure on $H(R)$ compatible with its hyperspace topology. (For a non-standard treatment of uniform structures we refer to Luxemburg [1969] 3.9, p. 72 or Machover and Hirschfeld [1969] 7., p. 48).

As is known a uniform structure on a set T can be given by an equivalence relation on $^*T$ (i.e., a subset of $^*T \times {}^*T$), which is "nuclear", i.e., the monad of a standard filter on $T \times T$.

Thus we define an equivalence relation $\equiv$ on $^*H(R)$ as follows: If $X, Y \in {}^*H(R)$ then $X \equiv Y$ if and only if for any pair U, V of standard open sets in R such that $\bar{U} \subset V$,

(3) $X \subset {}^*U$ implies $Y \subset {}^*V$ and $Y \subset {}^*U$ implies $X \subset {}^*V$.

It is obvious that $\equiv$ is reflexive and symmetric, hence to show that it is an equivalence relation it suffices to prove its transitivity.

So assume $X \equiv Y \equiv Z$, and let U, V be open sets such that $\bar{U} \subset V$. Since R is normal, there is an open set W in R for which

$$\bar{U} \subset W \subset \overline{W} \subset V.$$

Now, if $X \subset {}^*U$, then $X \equiv Y$ implies $Y \subset {}^*W$, which together with $Y \equiv Z$ implies $Z \subset {}^*V$. Similarly we can show that $Z \subset {}^*U$ implies $X \subset {}^*V$, hence $X \equiv Z$.

To show that $\equiv$ is the monad of a filter on $H(R) \times H(R)$, it is obviously sufficient to show that if $X \not\equiv Y$ then there is a standard set $\mathscr{D} \subset H(R) \times H(R)$ such that

(4) $(X, Y) \notin {}^*\mathscr{D}$, but for any pair (X', Y') with $X' \equiv Y'$ we have $(X', Y') \in {}^*\mathscr{D}$.

If $X \not\equiv Y$ this means that for some U and V with $\bar{U} \subset V$ we have e.g. $X \subset {}^*U$ but $Y \not\subset {}^*V$. It is obvious then that

$$\mathscr{D} = \{(A, B) : A, B \in H(R) \wedge (A \subset U \Rightarrow B \subset V)\}$$

will satisfy (4).

Thus we see that $\equiv$ indeed determines a uniform structure on $H(R)$. We still have to prove that $\equiv$ is compatible with the topology of $H(R)$, which amounts to showing that the monad of a standard point $A \in H(R)$ coincides with the $\equiv$-equivalence class of $^*A$, to be denoted by $[^*A]$.

To see that $[^*A] \subset \mu_H(A)$, let $X \in [^*A]$ and choose a standard open set V for which $A \subset V$. The normality of R implies the existence of an open set U with

$$A \subset U \subset \bar{U} \subset V.$$

Thus from $X \equiv {}^*A$ and $A \subset U$ we have $X \subset {}^*V$, hence $X \subset \mu(A)$ and (1) is satisfied. To show (2), let $p \in A$ and assume

$$\mu(p) \cap X = \phi.$$

By saturatedness, this implies the existence of an open neighbourhood G of p such that ${}^*G \cap X = \phi$. Now let G_1 and G_2 be open neighbourhoods of p with

$$p \in G_1 \subset \bar{G}_1 \subset G_2 \subset \bar{G}_2 \subset G,$$

which exist because R is regular. Let us put

$$U = R \backslash \bar{G}_2 \quad \text{and} \quad V = R \backslash \bar{G}_1.$$

Then $U \subset R \backslash G_2$, hence $\bar{U} \subset R \backslash G_2$, because $R \backslash G_2$ is closed and therefore

$$\bar{U} \subset R \backslash G_2 \subset V.$$

Now we have $X \subset {}^*U$, since ${}^*\bar{G}_2 \cap X = \phi$, hence $X \equiv A$ implies ${}^*A \subset {}^*V$, hence $A \subset V$, which contradicts $p \in A \backslash V$. Thus (2) is also satisfied and $X \in \mu_H(A)$.

Let now $X \in \mu_H(A)$ and show $X \in [{}^*A]$, i.e., $X \equiv A$. Choose the open sets U, V such that $\bar{U} \subset V$ and assume first that ${}^*A \subset {}^*U$. Since $X \subset \mu(A)$, this implies $X \subset {}^*U \subset {}^*V$. On the other hand, if $X \subset {}^*U$ and $p \in A$ then $\mu(p) \cap X \neq \phi$, hence $\mu(p) \cap {}^*U \neq \phi$ which implies $p \in \bar{U}$ and we obtain $A \subset \bar{U}$, and consequently ${}^*A \subset {}^*\bar{U} \subset {}^*V$. This completes the proof of $X \equiv A$ and thus of the theorem.

2.4. In order to formulate our third theorem, we need some definitions. A subset $S \subset R$ is called relatively compact (in R) if $\bar{S}$ is a compact subspace of R. It is known (cf. Luxemburg [1969] Theorem 3.6.1, p. 65) that for a regular space R, S is relatively compact if and only if every $y \in {}^*S$ is near-standard in ${}^*R$.

Let α be an infinite cardinal number. We shall say that the space R is α-bounded if every subset $S \subset R$ of cardinality $\leq \alpha$ is relatively compact. Obviously, if R is regular, α-boundedness has the following non-standard characterisation:

(5) R is α-bounded if and only if for any (indexed) family $\{p_i : i \in I\}$ of points of R with $|I| \leq \alpha$, $j \in {}^*I \backslash I$ implies that p_j is near-standard in ${}^*R$.

2.4. Theorem. *If R is normal and α-bounded then $H(R)$ is also α-bounded.*

Proof. By 2.2, $H(R)$ is regular, hence it suffices to show that (5) holds in

$H(R)$. So let $\{A_i : i \in I\}$ be a family of non-empty closed subsets of R with $|I| \leq \alpha$ and let $j \in {}^*I \backslash I$.

Now we put

$$B = \{p \in R : \mu(p) \cap A_j \neq \phi\}.$$

Then, by saturatedness, B is closed in R similarly as in 2.2, because A_j is internal. Also, $B \neq \phi$, because choosing a $p_i \in A_i$ for each $i \in I$ and taking into consideration that R is regular and α-bounded we have by (5) $p_j \in A_j$ and p_j is near-standard in ${}^*R$, hence there is a $q \in R$ with $p_j \in \mu(q)$, which obviously implies $q \in B$.

We claim that $A_j \in \mu_H(B)$ and thus is near-standard in ${}^*H(R)$. Now condition (2) of 1.3 is obviously satisfied by the definition of B, and it remains to show (1), i.e., $A_j \subset \mu(B)$.

To see this let $G \supset B$ be a standard open set and put

$$I_1 = \{i \in I : A_i \subset G\} \quad \text{and} \quad I_2 = I \backslash I_1.$$

Then ${}^*I = {}^*I_1 \cup {}^*I_2$ and we claim that $j \in {}^*I_1$.

Suppose, on the contrary, $j \in {}^*I_2$. For each $i \in I_2$, $A_i \backslash G \neq \phi$, hence we can choose points $p_i \in A_i \backslash G$. Consider the family $\{p_i : i \in I_2\} \subset R$. Since $|I_2| \leq |I| \leq \alpha$ and R is α-bounded we have then, by transfer,

$$p_j \in A_j \backslash {}^*G$$

and p_j is near-standard in ${}^*R$. Thus there is a $q \in R$ with $p_j \in \mu(q)$, hence $q \in B$ and $\mu(q) \not\subset {}^*G$ which implies $q \notin G$. However, this contradicts $B \subset G$ and thus shows $j \in {}^*I_1$, i.e., $A_j \subset {}^*G$. The proof is completed.

Keesling [1970a] Theorem 5, p. 764 proved the above result for $\alpha = \omega$. The reader is advised to compare his standard proof with ours. He also raises the question whether normality could be reduced in this result. I think that this non-standard proof sheds some light on why the normality of R is needed. In fact, what we use of this is that $H(R)$ is regular, and as is known (cf. Kuratowski [1966] § 17, Theorem 5.4) the regularity of $H(R)$ implies the normality of R. We take this occasion to point out that Theorem 3.6.2 of Luxemburg [1969] p. 66, claiming that (5) also holds for Hausdorff spaces is false (cf. e.g., Machover and Hirschfeld [1969] 5.5.3, p. 31).

2.5. It is beyond any doubt by now that certain mathematical proofs and constructions become essentially simpler and more transparent when done in a non-standard way. I think, however, that the number of interesting new results obtained in this way is relatively very small. Of course, I do not take here into consideration results which concern the non-standard notions and means themselves.

That is why I find it important to draw attention to the following two open problems, whose solutions might be found more easily with the aid of non-standard methods.

Problem I (cf. Keesling [1970a or b]). Does the normality of $H(R)$ imply the compactness of R (and thus of $H(R)$)?

Keesling [1970b] gave an affirmative answer to this question, assuming the continuum hypothesis.

Problem II. Is the hyperspace of the interval [0, 1] homeomorphic to the Hilbert-cube?

Added in proof, Dec. 19, 1971. After this manuscript had been completed J. E. West and R. M. Schori gave an affirmative answer to Problem II.

References

Keesling, J., 1970a, Normality and Properties Related to Compactness in Hyperspaces, *Proc. Amer. Math. Soc.* 24, pp. 760–766.

Keesling, J., 1970b, On the Equivalence of Normality and Compactness in Hyperspaces, *Pacific J. Math.* 33, pp. 657–667.

Kuratowski, K., 1966, *Topology I* (Academic Press, New York).

Luxemburg, W. A. J., 1969, A General Theory of Monods, in: *Applications of Model Theory to Algebra, Analysis and Probability*, ed. W. A. J. Luxemburg (Holt, Rinehart and Winston).

Machover, M. and Hirschfeld, J., 1969, *Lectures on Non-Standard Analysis*, Springer Lecture Notes series, no. 94 (Heidelberg, New York).

Michael, E., 1951, Topologies on Spaces of Subsets, *Trans. Amer. Math. Soc.* 71, pp. 152–182.

Robinson, A., 1966, *Non-Standard Analysis*, Studies in Logic and the Foundations of Mathematics (North-Holland, Amsterdam).

Received 16 March 1971

NONSTANDARD-KOMPLETTIERUNG VON CAUCHY-ALGEBREN

Manfred WOLFF
Mathematischen Institut der Universität, Tübingen

Neben dem von einer Topologie abgeleiteten Grenzwertbegriff spielen in der Analysis noch weitere Konvergenzbegriffe eine Rolle, so die Konvergenz meßbarer Funktionen f.ü. bezüglich eines nicht atomaren Maßes und verschiedene Ordnungskonvergenzen in Verbandsgruppen, oder insbesondere auch die stetige Konvergenz in Funktionenräumen (stellvertretend für viele Arbeiten auf dem letzgenannten Gebiet s. Binz [1968]). Schon M. Fréchet, K. Kuratowsky und vor allem Kowalsky [1954] betrachteten sogenannte Limitierungen und Limesräume, Abstraktionen der oben genannten Konvergenzbegriffe. Fischer [1959] lieferte einen systematischen Aufbau dieser Theorie.

Genau wie Limesräume Verallgemeinerungen der topologischen Räume sind uniforme Konvergenzstrukturen Verallgemeinerungen der uniformen Räume. Diese wurden von Cook und Fischer [1965, 1967a] eingeführt, und eine ganze Reihe von Autoren beschäftigte sich mit einer Komplettierungstheorie für sie (z.B. Kowalsky [1954b], Kent [1967], Biesterfeldt [1966a], Ramaley und Wyler [1970a und b])[1]).

Nachdem in den vergangenen Jahren vor allem Robinson [1966] und– auf seiner Theorie aufbauend–gleichzeitig Machover und Hirschfeld [1969] und Luxemburg [1969] die Modelltheorie erfolgreich auf die Analysis, insbesondere auf die Topologie und Theorie der uniformen Räume anwandten, lag es nahe, dasselbe für Limesräume und uniforme Konvergenzstrukturen durchzuführen. Dies ist Gegenstand der vorliegenden Arbeit.

Der Vorteil der "Nonstandard-Analysis" tritt besonders bei der Komplettierung und Kompaktifizierung von uniformen Räumen in Erscheinung, wenn zusätzlich algebraische Strukturen vorliegen. Dieser Gedanke erscheint

1) Die Arbeit von H. J. Kowalsky lag 11 Jahre vor dem Erscheinen der ersten Arbeit von Cook und Fischer. In ihr werden die Cauchy-Filter axiomatisch eingeführt ohne Benutzung einer uniformen Konvergenzstruktur.

explizit bei Robinson [1969], der mit ihm bewies, daß ein positiver Satz einer Sprache erster Ordnung in der Bohrkompaktifizierung einer topologischen Gruppe (eines topologischen Ringes) gilt, wenn er in der ursprünglichen Struktur schon wahr ist. Es ist natürlich leicht zu sehen, daß aus analogen Gründen ein positiver Allsatz, der in einer topologischen Gruppe gilt, auch in ihrer Komplettierung bezüglich der beidseitig uniformen Struktur wahr sein muß, denn diese ist darstellbar als Quotientengruppe einer Untergruppe einer elementaren Erweiterung der ursprünglichen Gruppe.

Das Hauptanliegen dieser Arbeit ist, mit Hilfe der Nonstandard-Analysis zu einem gegebenen Raum mit einer uniformen Konvergenzstruktur und einer algebraischen Struktur eine Komplettierung zu konstruieren, die den folgenden Bedingungen genügt:

(i) Die Komplettierung trägt die gleiche algebraische Struktur wie der gegebene Raum.

(ii) Die Komplettierung genügt den üblichen kategorien-theoretischen Anforderungen.

(iii) Ist der ursprüngliche Raum "dicht" in einem "vollständigen" Raum, so ist dieser isomorph zu der konstruierten Komplettierung.

(iv) Im Falle eines uniformen Räume (i. Sinne von A. Weil, s. Bourbaki [1965]) stimmt die Komplettierung mit der "klassischen" überein.

Dabei beschränken wir uns zunächst der Einfachheit halber auf Ω-Algebren im Sinne der universellen Algebra; in Sektion 6 zeigen wir, wie man die Ergebnisse auf andere Fälle–etwa Vektorräume–übertragen kann.

Wir merken an, daß die Konstruktion von Kowalsky [1954b] (iii) nicht erfüllt; diejenigen Komplettierungen von Ramaley und Wyler [1970b] genügen i.a. nicht den Anforderungen (i), (iii) und (iv).

Es handelt sich bei unserer Konstruktion um eine weitgehende Analogie zum Vorgehen von Robinson [1966] und vor allem von Machover und Hirschfeld [1969]. Dagegen ist genau genommen die Methode von Luxemburg [1969] für unsere Zwecke weniger geeignet, da er Halbmetriken verwendet, deren Verallgemeinerung auf uniforme Konvergenzstrukturen eher hinderlich ist. Auch braucht man dann–im Gegensatz zum Verfahren von Machover und Hirschfeld [1969]–κ-saturierte Enlargements für eine gewisse Kardinalzahl κ.[1])

Neben Komplettierungen interessieren (gewissermaßen als Spezialfall) Kompaktifizierungen. Dabei wenden wir ein Verfahren von Holm [1964]

[1]) Dies halten wir jedoch für weniger gravierend, da man von solchen speziellen Modellen häufig sowieso wirkungsvolleren Gebrauch machen kann als von allgemeinen.

an, und erhalten ein dem Robinsonschen [1969] voll entsprechendes Resultat für sie.

Im einzelnen enthalten Sektion 0 Terminologisches und Sektion 1 Definitionen und grundlegende Sätze. In Sektion 2 behandeln wir Trennungsaxiome, in Sektion 3 stellen wir die zu topologischen Räumen analogen Sätze für Limesräume zusammen. Sektion 4 behandelt die Nonstandard-Komplettierung. Ihre wichtigsten Eigenschaften sind in Theorem 4.16 zusammengefaßt. Sektion 5 bringt Kompaktifizierungen und Sektion 6 verschiedene weitergehende Bemerkungen.

Den Teilnehmern der Nonstandard-Analysis-Tagung in Oberwolfach, vor allem den Herren Professoren A. Robinson und W. A. J. Luxemburg, möchte ich herzlich danken für das Interesse, das sie der Arbeit nach Anhören des Vortrags darüber entgegen brachten sowie für die vielen Anregungen in den Diskussionen. Besonderen Dank schulde ich auch den Herren Professoren H. H. Schaefer und E. Binz, die die Arbeit stets freundlichst förderten.

0. Terminologisches. Sei Ω disjunkte Vereinigung von Mengen $\Omega_n (n = 1, 2, \ldots$; Ω kann leer sein). Die Elemente von Ω_n heißen n-stellige Operationen (auch Operationssymbole). Eine Ω-Algebra $\mathfrak{A}$ ist eine Menge A, versehen mit Abbildungen $\Omega_n \to A^{(A^n)}$. Für die Operation und die durch sie bezeichnete Funktion von $A^n \to A$ verwenden wir wie üblich dasselbe Symbol. Polynome sind aus Operationen in kanonischer Weise induktiv aufgebaute Funktionssymbole. Eine Menge Γ von Gleichungen ist eine Menge von Paaren von Polynomen. $\mathfrak{A}$ heiße Ω-Γ-Algebra, wenn $\mathfrak{A}$ Ω-Algebra ist, in der für jedes Paar (p, q) aus Γ stets $p = q$ argumentweise gilt (Näheres hierüber s. Grätzer [1968]).

Sei jetzt A eine Menge. Wir bezeichnen mit $\mathfrak{P}(A)$ die Potenzmenge und mit $\mathscr{F}(A)$ den Verband der eigentlichen Filter auf A (mit der Inklusion als Ordnung). Ist $M \subset A$, so sei $\dot{M}$ der von M erzeugte Hauptfilter, statt $\{x\}^{\cdot}$ schreiben wir $\dot{x}$. Zur Vereinfachung der Schreibweise führen wir noch den uneigentlichen Filter $\boldsymbol{E}$ $(= \mathfrak{P}(A))$ ein. (Das Symbol $\boldsymbol{E}$ wird einheitlich benutzt, auch wenn es sich um verschiedene Mengen handelt.) Eine Menge $\mathscr{M} \subset \mathscr{F}(A)$ heißt solid, wenn aus $\boldsymbol{F} \in \mathscr{M}$ und $\boldsymbol{F} \subset \boldsymbol{G} \in \mathscr{F}(A)$ stets $\boldsymbol{G} \in \mathscr{M}$ folgt. Es ist nun klar, was man unter der soliden Hülle einer Menge von Filtern versteht. Ein $\cap$-Ideal $\mathfrak{F}$ in $\mathscr{F}(A)$ ist eine solide Menge mit der zusätzlichen Eigenschaft: sind $\boldsymbol{F}, \boldsymbol{G} \in \mathfrak{F}$, so ist auch $\boldsymbol{F} \cap \boldsymbol{G}$ in $\mathfrak{F}$. Sind A, A' Mengen, ist $f: A \to A'$ eine Abbildung und $\boldsymbol{F}$ aus $\mathscr{F}(A)$, so sei $f(\boldsymbol{F})$ der von $\{f(F) : F \in \boldsymbol{F}\}$ erzeugte Filter.

Für die Nonstandard-Analysis benutzen wir die Bezeichnungen von Luxemburg [1969] (mit der Ausnahme, daß weder Standardgrößen vom Typ 0 noch–im Falle von Ω-Algebren–Operationssymbole einen Stern erhalten). Insbesondere ist für eine Teilmenge $\boldsymbol{F}$ von $\mathfrak{P}(A)$ (A sei die Grundmenge) $\mu(\boldsymbol{F}) = \bigcap_{F \in \boldsymbol{F}} {}^*F$ und für eine (nicht notwendig interne) Teilmenge B des Enlargements

$$\mu_{\mathrm{d}}(B) = \bigcap_{\substack{F \subset A \\ B \subset {}^*F}} {}^*F.$$

Ist $B \neq \emptyset$, so ist $\boldsymbol{U}_B = \{F \subset A : B \subset {}^*F\}$ ein Filter mit $\mu_{\mathrm{d}}(B) = \mu(\boldsymbol{U}_B)$. Mit ${}^\circ B$ bezeichnen wir die Menge aller (Standard-)Elemente aus A, die in B liegen (dabei denken wir uns stets A in ${}^*A$ eingebettet). Für alle weiteren Fragen verweisen wir auf Luxemburg [1969], jedoch möchten wir einen häufig benutzten Schluß besonders herausstellen, der aus dem Fundamentaltheorem der Nonstandard-Analysis folgt (loc. cit. S. 24 u. 44): Sei $(\boldsymbol{F}_i)_{i \in I}$ ein System von Filtern auf A. Äquivalent sind (i) $\bigcap_{i \in I} \mu(\boldsymbol{F}_i) = \emptyset$ und (ii) $\vee_{i \in I} \boldsymbol{F}_i = \boldsymbol{E}$.

1. Cauchy-Algebren. Im folgenden sei $\mathfrak{A}$ eine feste Ω-Γ-Algebra mit nichtleerer Trägermenge A. $\mathscr{F}(A)$ wird zu einer Ω-Algebra, wenn man die n-stelligen Operationen in kanonischer Weise auf $(\mathscr{F}(A))^n$ fortsetzt (d.h. ist ω eine n-stellige Operation und sind $\boldsymbol{F}_1, \ldots, \boldsymbol{F}_n$ Filter, so sei $\omega(\boldsymbol{F}_1, \ldots, \boldsymbol{F}_n) := \omega(\boldsymbol{F}_1 \times \ldots \times \boldsymbol{F}_n)$).[1])

1.1. DEFINITION. *Sei γ eine Teilmenge von $\mathscr{F}(A)$. γ heißt Cauchy-Struktur und (A,γ) Ω-Γ-Cauchy-Algebra (kurz: Cauchy-Algebra), wenn folgende Axiome gelten:*

(i) *$a \in A$ impliziert stets $\dot{a} \in \gamma$,*

(ii) *$\boldsymbol{F}, \boldsymbol{G} \in \gamma$ und $\boldsymbol{F} \vee \boldsymbol{G} \neq \boldsymbol{E}$ impliziert $\boldsymbol{F} \cap \boldsymbol{G} \in \gamma$,*

(iii) *γ ist solid,*

(iv) *γ ist eine Ω-Unteralgebra von $\mathscr{F}(A)$.*

Die Elemente aus γ heißen Cauchy-Filter. Ist $\Omega = \emptyset$, so heißt (A, γ) Cauchy-Raum.

Bemerkungen: 1) Bis aus Axiom (iv) entspricht diese Definition derjenigen von Keller [1968]. Dort wird bewiesen, daß mindestens eine uniforme

[1]) Die Ausnutzung dieser Möglichkeit, mit Filtern zu rechnen, taucht zum ersten Mal explizit bei Kowalsky [1954a] auf. (iv) aus Def. 1.1 ist durch diese Arbeit angeregt.

Konvergenzstruktur $\mathfrak{F}$ (i.S. von Cook und Fischer [1965, 1967a]) existiert, so daß γ gleich der Menge der $\mathfrak{F}$-Cauchy-Filter wird. Wie wir später sehen werden, ist die Eigenschaft (iv) nicht immer an $\mathfrak{F}$ abzulesen. (iv) ist die axiomatische Forderung der gleichmäßigen Stetigkeit der algebraischen Operationen.

2) (A, γ) ist ein U_2-Raum i. S. von Ramaley und Wyler [1970a] und γ ein Cauchysches Ende i. S. von Kowalsky [1954b].

3) Sei ein System $\mathscr{D} \subset \mathfrak{P}(A)$ mit den Eigenschaften

(i) $\emptyset$ und $A \in \mathscr{D}$,

(ii) $\mathscr{D}$ ist stabil gegenüber endlichen Vereinigungen und endlichen Durchschnitten

gegeben (etwa das System aller Z-Mengen in einem vollständig regulären Raum). Dann kann man noch fordern:

Ist $\boldsymbol{F}$ aus γ, so existiert ein Filter $\boldsymbol{G}$ mit Basis in $\mathscr{D}$ und $\boldsymbol{F} \supset \boldsymbol{G} \in \gamma$.

Die hier dargelegte Theorie wird dann etwas komplizierter, ohne daß sich Wesentliches ändert. Wichtig scheint dieses Axiom bei speziellen Kompaktifizierungen zu werden (vergl. Stroyan [1970], von wo die Anregung zu diesem Axiom kommt).

1.2. DEFINITION. *Sei (A, γ) eine Cauchy-Algebra und $\boldsymbol{F} \in \gamma$. Wir sagen, $\boldsymbol{F}$ konvergiert gegen $x \in A$ (in Zeichen: $\boldsymbol{F} \to x$), wenn $\boldsymbol{F} \cap \dot{x} \in \gamma$ gilt.*

Die Zuordnung $\tau_\gamma : x \to \tau_\gamma x := \{\boldsymbol{F} \in \gamma : \boldsymbol{F} \cap \dot{x} \in \gamma\}$ ist eine Limitierung und (A, τ_γ) ein Limesraum i.S. von Fischer [1959].

1.3. DEFINITION. *(A, τ_γ) heißt die zu (A, γ) assoziierte Limes-Algebra.*[1]
(A, γ) heißt
vollständig, wenn jeder Cauchy-Filter konvergiert,
präkompakt, wenn γ alle Ultrafilter enthält,
kompakt, wenn (A, γ) vollständig und präkompakt ist.

Bemerkung. Sei (X, τ) ein T_2-Limesraum i.S. von Fischer [1959] und γ die Menge aller konvergenten Filter. Dann ist (X, γ) ein vollständiger Cauchy-Raum in unserem Sinn. Wir erhalten also durch Spezialisierung eine Nonstandard-Theorie der T_2-Limesräume.

[1]) Spezielle Limes-Algebren betrachteten bereits u.a. Fischer [1959] (Gruppen) und Binz und Keller [1966].

Sei nun (A, γ) eine Cauchy-Algebra, $\mathfrak{M}$ die volle Struktur höherer Ordnung über der Grundmenge A und $^*\mathfrak{M}$ ein fest gewähltes Enlargement. Wir definieren in Analogie zu Machover und Hirschfeld [1969] Def. 7.3.4, und Luxemburg [1969] S. 76:

1.4. Definition. *Ein Punkt* $a \in {}^*A$ *heißt Pränahstandard-Punkt, wenn ein* $\boldsymbol{F} \in \gamma$ *mit* $a \in \mu(\boldsymbol{F})$ *existiert. Die Menge der Pränahstandard-Punkte bezeichnen wir mit* $P({}^*A, \gamma)$ *(kurz: P). Ist außerdem* $\boldsymbol{F}$ *konvergent, so heißt a Nahstandard-Punkt; die Menge aller Nahstandard-Punkte sei* $N({}^*A, \gamma)$ *(kurz: N).*

Jeder Standard-Punkt ist nahstandard wegen (i) in 1.1.

Sei $(X, \boldsymbol{U})$ ein uniformer Raum (i.S. von A. Weil). Dann ist $\mu(\boldsymbol{U})$ der Graph einer Äquivalenzrelation auf $^*X$, die eng mit dem durch $\boldsymbol{U}$ induzierten Konvergenzbegriff auf X zusammenhängt (Luxemburg [1969] S. 72ff, Machover und Hirschfeld [1969] S. 50ff). Wir ersetzen diese Relation in naheliegender Weise. Axiom (iv) von 1.1 liefert aber noch mehr:

1.5. Proposition. $P({}^*A, \gamma)$ *ist eine* Ω*-Unteralgebra von* $^*A$ *und* $B({}^*A, \gamma) := \bigcup_{\boldsymbol{F}\in\gamma} (\mu(\boldsymbol{F}) \times \mu(\boldsymbol{F}))$ *ist der Graph einer Kongruenzrelation* $\sim_\gamma$ *auf* $P({}^*A, \gamma)$.

Vor dem Beweis führen wir einige Bezeichnungen ein: wir schreiben kurz B und $\sim$ statt $B({}^*A, \gamma)$ bzw. $\sim_\gamma$ und nennen "$\sim$" die durch γ (in P) induzierte Kongruenzrelation. Für $a \in P$ sei $[a]_\gamma := \{b \in P : b \sim a\}$ und für $M \subset {}^*A$ (intern oder extern) sei $[M]_\gamma := \bigcup_{a\in M\cap P} [a]_\gamma$. (Ist keine Unklarheit zu befürchten, lassen wir den Index γ fort.)

Beweis von 1.5. Ist ω eine nullstellige Operation und a_ω das durch ω in A bestimmte Element, so liegt $\dot{a}_\omega$ in γ, a_ω also in P.[1]) Sei ω eine n-stellige Operation ($n \neq 0$) und seien $a_1, \ldots, a_n \in P$. Dann existieren $\boldsymbol{F}_1, \ldots, \boldsymbol{F}_n \in \gamma$ mit $a_i \in \mu(\boldsymbol{F}_i)$, also

$$b := \omega(a_1, \ldots, a_n) \in \omega(\mu(\boldsymbol{F}_1) \times \ldots \times \mu(\boldsymbol{F}_n)) \subset \mu(\omega(\boldsymbol{F}_1 \times \ldots \times \boldsymbol{F}_n)).$$

Mit 1.1 (iv) ist $b \in P$, P also eine Ω-Unteralgebra von $^*A$.

Ganz analog beweist man, daß B eine Ω-Unteralgebra von $P \times P$ ist. Symmetrie und Reflexivität der Relation "$\sim$" sind evident. Sind (a, b), (b, c) aus B und $\boldsymbol{F}, \boldsymbol{G} \in \gamma$ mit $a, b \in \mu(\boldsymbol{F})$ und $b, c \in \mu(\boldsymbol{G})$, so ist $b \in \mu(\boldsymbol{F}) \cap \mu(\boldsymbol{G}) \neq \emptyset$. Also gilt $\boldsymbol{F} \vee \boldsymbol{G} \neq \boldsymbol{E}$ (s. Sektion 0) und damit nach 1.1 (ii) $\boldsymbol{F} \cap \boldsymbol{G} =:$

[1]) A is in $^*A$ eingebettet.

$\boldsymbol{H} \in \gamma$. Das ergibt $(a, c) \in \mu(\boldsymbol{H}) \times \mu(\boldsymbol{H}) \subset B$, d.i. die Transitivität von $\sim$.

q.e.d.

Aus 1.5 folgt, daß mit A auch $P/\sim$ eine Ω-Γ-Algebra ist. Dies wollen wir jedoch erst im Zusammenhang mit der Komplettierung erörtern.

1.6. Lemma. *Seien $a_1, \ldots, a_n \in P$ untereinander äquivalent (bezüglich $\sim$). Dann existiert ein Filter $\boldsymbol{G}_0$ mit $a_i \in \mu(\boldsymbol{G}_0)$ für $i = 1, \ldots, n$.*

Beweis. Für $k = 2$ ist die Behauptung klar. Sei sie schon für $k = n - 1$ bewiesen. Dann existieren Filter $\boldsymbol{F}$ und $\boldsymbol{G}$ aus γ mit $a_1, \ldots, a_{n-1} \in \mu(\boldsymbol{F})$ und $a_1, a_n \in \mu(\boldsymbol{G})$. Damit folgt $\mu(\boldsymbol{F}) \cap \mu(\boldsymbol{G}) \neq \emptyset$, also nach 1.1 (ii) $\boldsymbol{G}_0 = \boldsymbol{F} \cap \boldsymbol{G} \in \gamma$ und $a_1, \ldots, a_n \in \mu(\boldsymbol{G}_0)$.

Der Kongruenzrelation $\sim_\gamma$ entspricht eine Kongruenzrelation $\approx$ auf γ.

1.7. Proposition. *Es gelte $\boldsymbol{F} \approx \boldsymbol{G}$ genau dann, wenn $\boldsymbol{F} \cap \boldsymbol{G}$ aus γ ist. "$\approx$" ist eine Kongruenzrelation in der Ω-Algebra γ und "$\boldsymbol{F} \approx \boldsymbol{G}$" ist äquivalent zu "$[\mu(\boldsymbol{F})] = [\mu(\boldsymbol{G})]$".*

Beweis. Wir zeigen die letzte Behauptung. Der Rest folgt dann aus 1.5.

Ist $\boldsymbol{F} \cap \boldsymbol{G} =: \boldsymbol{H}$ aus γ, so gilt $\mu(\boldsymbol{F}) \cup \mu(\boldsymbol{G}) \subset \mu(\boldsymbol{H})$, also $[\mu(\boldsymbol{F})] = [\mu(\boldsymbol{G})]$. Es bestehe umgekehrt diese Beziehung. Sei $a \in \mu(\boldsymbol{F})$, $b \in \mu(\boldsymbol{G})$. Dann existiert ein $\boldsymbol{H} \in \gamma$ mit $a, b \in \mu(\boldsymbol{H})$, also sind (nach 1.1 (ii)) $\boldsymbol{F} \cap \boldsymbol{H}$ und $\boldsymbol{H} \cap \boldsymbol{G}$ in γ. Hieraus folgt wegen $\boldsymbol{E} \neq \boldsymbol{H} \subset (\boldsymbol{F} \cap \boldsymbol{H}) \vee (\boldsymbol{H} \cap \boldsymbol{G})$ die Beziehung $\gamma \in \boldsymbol{F} \cap \boldsymbol{H} \cap \boldsymbol{G} \subset \boldsymbol{F} \cap \boldsymbol{G}$, also $\boldsymbol{F} \cap \boldsymbol{G} \in \gamma$. q.e.d.

Dieser Satz zeigt nun den Weg, wie man die Komplettierung ohne Benutzung der Nonstandard-Analysis erhält (vergl. Sektion 4). Wir werden davon aber keinen Gebrauch machen.

1.8. Korollar. *Sei $\boldsymbol{F} \in \gamma$, $x \in A$. Folgende Aussagen sind äquivalent:*

(i) $\boldsymbol{F} \to x$,

(ii) $\mu(\boldsymbol{F}) \subset [x]$,

(iii) $[\mu(\boldsymbol{F})] = [x]$.

Beweis. klar.

Die Äquivalenzklasse $[x]$ entspricht also der Monade des Umgebungsfilters in der Nonstandard-Theorie der topologischen bzw. uniformen Räume (s. Robinson [1966], Machover und Hirschfeld [1969], Luxemburg [1969]). Insbesondere erhält man sofort folgendes Analogon:

1.9. Theorem. *Für eine Cauchy-Algebra* (A, γ) *sind folgende Aussagen äquivalent:*

(i) *A ist vollständig,*

(ii) $P(^*A, \gamma) = N(^*A, \gamma)$.

Beweis. klar.

Ebenso einfach ergibt sich

1.10. Theorem. *Sei* (A, γ) *eine Cauchy-Algebra und man betrachte die folgende Aussagen:*

(i) *A ist präkompakt,*

(ii) $P(^*A, \gamma) = {}^*A$,

(iii) *A ist kompakt,*

(iv) $N(^*A, \gamma) = {}^*A$.

Dann gilt (i) $\Leftrightarrow$ (ii) *und* (iii) $\Leftrightarrow$ (iv) $\Rightarrow$ (i).

Das folgende Beispiel zeigt, daß man mit der Nonstandard-Analysis von Cauchy-Algebren hauptsächlich das Konvergenzverhalten von Ultrafiltern erfaßt:

Sei $E = L^1(X, \Sigma, m)$, wobei (X, Σ, m) der Lebesguesche Maßraum über dem Einheitsintervall X sei. γ_1 sei die Menge aller Cauchy-Filter der durch die Norm induzierten uniformen Struktur. Es gelte $\mathbf{F} \in \gamma_2$ genau dann, wenn eine monoton fallende Folge $(u_n)_{n\in\mathbf{N}}$ mit $\inf_{n\in\mathbf{N}}(u_n) = 0$ existiert, so daß $\mathbf{F} - \mathbf{F}$ feiner ist als der von $\{\{x : |x| \leqslant u_n\} : n \in \mathbf{N}\}$ erzeugte Filter. Mit den Gruppen- und Verbandsoperationen sind (E, γ_i) vollständige Cauchy-Algebren mit $N(^*E, \gamma_1) = N(^*E, \gamma_2)$ und $B(^*E, \gamma_1) = B(^*E, \gamma_2)$, aber $\gamma_1 \neq \gamma_2$, da der Nullumgebungsfilter der Normtopologie zu γ_1 aber nicht zu γ_2 gehört.

Wir wollen noch kurz auf die Verallgemeinerungen bekannter topologischer Begriffe auf Limesräume und ihren Zusammenhang mit der bisher entwickelten Nonstandard-Analysis dieser Räume eingehen.

1.11. Definition (*Fischer* [1959], *vergl. Kowalsky* [1954b]): *Sei* (A, γ) *eine Cauchy-Algebra und* $F \subset A$. *Dann ist* $h(F) := \{x \in A$: *es exist.* $\mathbf{G} \in \gamma$ *mit* $\mathbf{G} \vee \dot{F} \neq \mathbf{E}$ *und* $\mathbf{G} \to x\}$. *h heißt Hüllenoperator.*

F heißt abgeschlossen, wenn $h(F) = F$ *gilt. F heißt offen wenn aus* $\mathbf{G} \in \gamma$ *und* $\mathbf{G} \to x \in F$ *stets* $F \in \mathbf{G}$ *folgt.*

Schließlich nennen wir F dicht in A, wenn $h(F) = A$ *gilt.*

h ist im allgemeinen nicht idempotent (Kowalsky [1954b]). Es ergibt sich nun (vergl. Robinson [1966] IV; Machover und Hirschfeld [1969] S. 25ff; Luxemburg [1969]3):

1.12. PROPOSITION
a) $h(F) = {}^\circ([{}^*F])$.
b) *F ist genau dann offen, wenn für jedes $x \in A$ aus $x \in F$ stets $[x] \subset {}^*F$ folgt.*
c) *F ist genau dann dicht in A, wenn $N({}^*A, \gamma) \subset [{}^*F]$ gilt.*
Beweis. klar.

2. Separationsaxiome. Neben den üblichen werden wir solche Separationsaxiome betrachten, die erst für die Komplettierung eine Rolle spielen. Hierzu definieren wir eine Relation v auf den Teilmengen einer Cauchy-Algebra (A, γ), die sich auf die Filter übertragen läßt.

2.1. DEFINITION. *Sei (A, γ) eine Cauchy-Algebra. Zwei Teilmengen F, $G \subset A$ heißen γ-verbunden (kurz: verbunden, in Zeichen $F \, v \, G$), wenn ein $\mathbf{H} \in \gamma$ existiert mit $\bar{F} \vee \mathbf{H} \neq \mathbf{E} \neq \bar{G} \vee \mathbf{H}$.*

Zwei Filter $\mathbf{F}$, $\mathbf{G}$ auf A heißen verbunden (in Zeichen: $\mathbf{F} \, v \, \mathbf{G}$), wenn alle Elemente von $\mathbf{F}$ mit allen von $\mathbf{G}$ verbunden sind.

Wir konstruieren nun zu jedem Filter $\mathbf{F}$ auf A zwei neue Filter $b(\mathbf{F})$ und $v(\mathbf{F})$ auf $\mathscr{F}(A)$ (also Elemente von $\mathscr{F}(\mathscr{F}(A))$): Sei zunächst F eine beliebige Teilmenge und $b(F) = \{\mathbf{H} \in \gamma$: es exist. $\mathbf{H}' \in \gamma$ mit $\mathbf{H}' \subset \mathbf{H}$ und $\mathbf{H}' \vee \dot{F} \neq \mathbf{E}\}$; $v(F) = \{\mathbf{H} \in \gamma : \mathbf{H} \, v \, \dot{F}\}$.

Für einen beliebigen Filter $\mathbf{F}$ auf A sei $b(\mathbf{F})$ (bzw. $v(\mathbf{F})$) der von $\{b(F): F \in \mathbf{F}\}$ (bzw. $\{v(F) : F \in \mathbf{F}\}$) erzeugte Filter auf $\mathscr{F}(A)$.

2.2. LEMMA. *Sei ${}^*\mathfrak{M}$ ein Enlargement der vollen Struktur $\mathfrak{M}$ über A. Für zwei Filter $\mathbf{F}$, $\mathbf{G}$ auf A sind folgende Aussagen äquivalent:*
(i) $\mathbf{F} \, v \, \mathbf{G}$.
(ii) *Für alle $F \in \mathbf{F}$, $G \in \mathbf{G}$ gilt $[{}^*F] \cap [{}^*G] \neq \emptyset$.*
(iii) $b(\mathbf{F}) \vee b(\mathbf{G}) \neq \mathbf{E}$.
Beweis. (i) $\Leftrightarrow$ (iii): klar.
(i) $\Leftrightarrow$ (ii): Man rechnet leicht mit Hilfe von 1.6 und 1.7 die Gültigkeit der folgenden Formel nach:

Für $M \subset A$ ist $b(M) = \{\mathbf{H} \in \gamma : \mu(\mathbf{H}) \subset [{}^*M]\}$.

Daraus ergibt sich dann die Behauptung.

Bei der Konstruktion unserer Komplettierung spielen die Filter $b(\boldsymbol{F})$ (für $\boldsymbol{F} \in \gamma$) eine wesentliche Rolle. Grob skizziert: $\gamma/\approx$ wird die der Komplettierung zugrunde liegende Punktmenge (über "$\approx$" s. 1.7) und die solide Hülle von $\{b(\boldsymbol{F}) : \boldsymbol{F} \in \gamma\}$ (mod. $\approx$) wird die Cauchy-Struktur. Für Feinheiten verweisen wir jedoch auf Sektion 4.

2.3. DEFINITION *(Separationsaxiome).*

s_2: *$a, b \in A$ und $\dot{a} \cap \dot{b} \in \gamma$ impliziert $a = b$.*
Gilt s_2, so heißt A separiert.

s_3: *Aus $\boldsymbol{F} \in \gamma$ folgt $h(\boldsymbol{F}) \in \gamma$. Dabei ist $h(\boldsymbol{F})$ der von $\{h(F) : F \in \boldsymbol{F}\}$ erzeugte Filter. Gilt s_3, so heißt A regulär.*

vs_2: *Sind $\boldsymbol{F}$, $\boldsymbol{G}$ aus γ und gilt $b(\boldsymbol{F}) \vee b(\boldsymbol{G}) \neq \boldsymbol{E}$, so folgt $\boldsymbol{F} \cap \boldsymbol{G} \in \gamma$. Gilt vs_2, so heißt A v-separiert.*

vs_3: *Zu jedem $\boldsymbol{F} \in \gamma$ existiert ein $\boldsymbol{G} \in \gamma$ mit $b(\boldsymbol{G}) \subset v(\boldsymbol{F})$. Ist vs_3 erfüllt, so heißt A v-regulär.*

Eine Cauchy-Algebra, die alle vier Axiome erfüllt, heißt stark separiert.

Bemerkung. s_2 wird im allgemeinen mit T_2 bezeichnet. s_3 ist ebenfalls bekannt. Der assoziierte Limesraum ist dann regulär i.S. von Cook und Fischer [1967b] (s. Biesterfeldt [1966b]). Die Axiome vs_2 und vs_3 sind neu und der vorgesehenen Art der Komplettierung angepaßt. Wir werden später (2.8) sehen, daß wichtige Klassen von Cauchy-Algebren stark separiert sind, ohne das Diagonallimitierungsaxiom (Kowalsky [1954b]) notwendig zu erfüllen. Die Nonstandard-Komplettierung einer stark separierten Cauchy-Algebra genügt den in der Einleitung genannten vier Anforderungen.

Wir wenden uns nun Nonstandard-Charakterisierungen der Separationsaxiome zu. Klar ist die Äquivalenz:

A ist genau dann separiert, wenn für je zwei verschiedene Standardpunkte x, y stets $[x] \cap [y] = \emptyset$ gilt.

2.4. PROPOSITION. *Sei (A, γ) eine Cauchy-Algebra und $^*\mathfrak{M}$ ein Enlargement der vollen Struktur $\mathfrak{M}$ über A. Man betrachte folgende Aussagen:*

(i) *A ist v-separiert.*

(ii) *Sind $\boldsymbol{F}$, $\boldsymbol{G}$ aus γ, so ist $[\mu(\boldsymbol{F})] = [\mu(\boldsymbol{G})]$ gleichwertig mit $[^*F] \cap [^*G] \neq \emptyset$ für alle $F \in \boldsymbol{F}$, $G \in \boldsymbol{G}$.*

(iii) *Ist $\boldsymbol{F} \in \gamma$, so ist $\bigcap_{F \in \boldsymbol{F}} [^*F] = [\mu(\boldsymbol{F})]$.*

Dann gilt (i) $\Leftrightarrow$ (ii) $\Rightarrow$ (iii).

Beweis. Zunächst gilt allgemein in Cauchy-Algebren: Ist $\mathbf{F} \in \gamma$, so ist $[\mu(\mathbf{F})]$ enthalten in $\bigcap_{F \in \mathbf{F}} [{}^*F]$.

Damit impliziert $[\mu(\mathbf{F})] = [\mu(\mathbf{G})]$ stets $\mathbf{F}\ v\ \mathbf{G}$, wie aus 2.2 folgt.

Es gelte nun (i). Ferner seien $\mathbf{F}, \mathbf{G}$ aus γ mit $\mathbf{F}\ v\ \mathbf{G}$. Wegen 2.2 ist $[{}^*F] \cap [{}^*G] \neq \emptyset$ für jedes $F \in \mathbf{F}$, $G \subset \mathbf{G}$. Da A v-separiert ist, ist $\mathbf{F} \cap \mathbf{G} \in \gamma$, also $[\mu(\mathbf{F})] = [\mu(\mathbf{G})]$. Damit ist (i) $\Rightarrow$ (ii) gezeigt. Die umgekehrte Richtung folgt aus 2.2 und 1.7. (i) $\Rightarrow$ (iii): Wir wissen schon, daß $[\mu(\mathbf{F})]$ in $\bigcap_{F \in \mathbf{F}} [{}^*F]$ enthalten ist. Ist x aus dieser rechts stehenden Menge und $\mathbf{U}_x$ der durch x bestimmte Ultrafilter (s. Sektion 0), so folgt $\mathbf{U}_x\ v\ \mathbf{F}$ aus 2.2. Dann ist aber $[\mu(\mathbf{U}_x)] = [\mu(\mathbf{F})]$ (s.o.), insbesondere also $x \in [\mu(\mathbf{F})]$.

2.5. Lemma. *Folgende Aussagen sind äquivalent:*

(i) *A ist* v-*regulär.*

(ii) *Zu jedem $\mathbf{F}$ aus γ existiert ein $\mathbf{G} \in \gamma$ und zu jedem G aus diesem $\mathbf{G}$ ein $F \in \mathbf{F}$ mit der Eigenschaft: Ist $\mathbf{H} \in \gamma$ und $\mathbf{H}\ v\ \dot{F}$, so liegt $\mu(\mathbf{H})$ in $[{}^*G]$.*

Beweis. Es gilt (s. Beweis zu 2.2):

$b(G) = \{\mathbf{H} \in \gamma: \mu(\mathbf{H}) \subset [{}^*G]\}$. Hieraus folgt die Behauptung.

An einfachen Beispielen kann man zeigen, daß i.a. keine der folgenden Implikationen gilt: $\mathrm{vs}_2 \Rightarrow \mathrm{s}_2$; $\mathrm{s}_2 \Rightarrow \mathrm{vs}_2$; $\mathrm{vs}_2 \Rightarrow \mathrm{vs}_3$; $\mathrm{vs}_3 \Rightarrow \mathrm{s}_2$; $\mathrm{vs}_3 \Rightarrow \mathrm{s}_3$. Über andere möglichen Zusammenhänge ist i.a. nichts bekannt (vergl. aber 2.8). Für vollständige Cauchy-Algebren gilt jedoch

2.6. Proposition. *Jede separierte, reguläre vollständige Cauchy-Algebra (A, γ) ist stark separiert.*

Beweis. a) A ist v-separiert: Seien $\mathbf{F}, \mathbf{G} \in \gamma$ mit $\mathbf{F}\ v\ \mathbf{G}$. Aus der Vollständigkeit folgt $h(F) \cap h(G) \neq \emptyset$ für alle $F \in \mathbf{F}$, $G \in \mathbf{G}$. Aus der Regularität und dem Axiom 1.1 (ii) erhalten wir $h(\mathbf{F}) \cap h(\mathbf{G}) \in \gamma$. Wegen $\mathbf{F} \cap \mathbf{G} \supset h(\mathbf{F}) \cap h(\mathbf{G})$ folgt hieraus die Behauptung.

b) A ist v-regulär: Sei $\mathbf{F} \in \gamma$ und $\mathbf{G} = h(\mathbf{F})$. Sei ferner $F \in \mathbf{F}$ und $\mathbf{H} \in v(F)$. Ist $H \in \mathbf{H}$, so existiert ein $\mathbf{V} \in \gamma$ mit $\mathbf{V} \vee \dot{H} \neq \mathbf{E}$ und $\mathbf{E} \neq \mathbf{V} \vee \dot{F}$. Da $\mathbf{V}$ konvergent ist, folgt $h(H) \cap h(F) \neq \emptyset$. Da $H \in \mathbf{H}$ beliebig war, erhält man $\mathbf{H} \supset h(\mathbf{H}) \in b(h(F))$, also gilt $v(F) \subset b(h(F))$, woraus $v(\mathbf{F}) \supset b(h(\mathbf{F}))$ folgt.

Wir bringen nun Beispiele zur Klärung der Abhängigkeiten der einzelnen Separationsaxiome zueinander.

2.7. *Beispiele.*

1) $s_2 \not\Rightarrow vs_2$: Sei $A = \mathbf{R} \cup \{-\infty, \infty\}$,[1]) $\Omega = \emptyset$ und γ_1 die Menge der in der gewöhnlichen Topologie konvergenten Filter. $\boldsymbol{H}$ sei der von $\{\{x \in \mathbf{R}: |x| > n\}: n \in \mathbf{N}\}$ erzeugte Filter und $\boldsymbol{F} = (\boldsymbol{H} \vee \dot{\mathbf{Q}}) \cap \{-\infty\}$, $\boldsymbol{G} = (\boldsymbol{H} \vee (\mathbf{R}\backslash\mathbf{Q})^{\cdot}) \cap \{+\infty\}$. Sei γ die solide Hülle von $\gamma_1 \cup \{\boldsymbol{F}, \boldsymbol{G}\}$. (A, γ) ist ein vollständiger Cauchyraum. Es gilt s_2, aber wegen $\boldsymbol{F} \not\vee \boldsymbol{G}$ und $\boldsymbol{F} \cap \boldsymbol{G} \notin \gamma$ nicht vs_2.

2) $vs_2 \not\Rightarrow s_3$: Hierzu sei A ein topologischer T_2-raum, der nicht T_3 ist, und γ das System aller konvergenten Filter. (A, γ) ist v-separiert, aber nicht regulär.

3) $vs_3 \not\Rightarrow s_3$: Sei $A = \mathbf{R}$ und für $x \in \mathbf{R}$ sei $V(x) = (\boldsymbol{U}(x) \vee \dot{\mathbf{Q}}) \cap \dot{x}$, wobei $\boldsymbol{U}(x)$ dem Umgebungsfilter von x in der gewöhnlichen Topologie bezeichnet. Sei γ die solide Hülle von $\{V(x): x \in \mathbf{R}\}$. (A, γ) ist vollständig, aber nicht regulär. Mit Hilfe von 2.5(ii) rechnet man leicht die v-Regularität nach (ist $\boldsymbol{F} \supset V(x)$, so wähle $\boldsymbol{G} = V(x)$).

Die Gegenbeispiele gegen die anderen auf S. 20 genannten Implikationen sind trivial.

Wir geben nun als Beispiel die Limesgruppen (Kowalsky [1954b], Fischer [1959]).

2.8. *Limesgruppen.* Sei A eine Gruppe mit neutralem Element e.[2]) Sei ferner τe ein $\cap$-Ideal in $\mathscr{F}(A)$ mit den Eigenschaften

(i) $\dot{e} \in \tau e$,

(ii) $x \in A$ impliziert $\dot{x}\boldsymbol{F}\dot{x}^{-1} \in \tau e$ für alle $\boldsymbol{F} \in \tau e$,

(iii) τe ist eine Ω-Unteralgebra von $\mathscr{F}(A)$.

Durch $x \to \tau x := \{\dot{x}\boldsymbol{F} : \boldsymbol{F} \in \tau e\}$ wird eine "zulässige" (Fischer [1959]) Limitierung auf A definiert; (A, τ) heißt Limesgruppe. Sei $\gamma_\tau = \{\boldsymbol{G} \in \mathscr{F}(A): \boldsymbol{G}\boldsymbol{F}\boldsymbol{G}^{-1} \cap \boldsymbol{G}^{-1}\boldsymbol{F}\boldsymbol{G} \in \tau e$ für alle $\boldsymbol{F} \in \tau e\}$.[3]) (A, γ_τ) ist eine Cauchy-Gruppe und die assoziierte Limesgruppe ist die ursprünglich gegebene (A, τ).

Sei umgekehrt (A, γ) eine Cauchy-Gruppe. Dann ist die hierzu assoziierte Limesgruppe (A, τ_γ) eine Limesgruppe i.S. von Fischer [1959] (s. Def. 1.3). Es gilt stets $\gamma \subset \gamma_{\tau_\gamma}$ (s.o.). Im allgemeinen gilt jedoch nicht die Gleichheit. (Ein Gegenbeispiel liefert schon $(\mathbf{Q}, +)$, wenn man für γ die Menge aller in der gewöhnlichen Topologie konvergenten Filter nimmt. Es gibt sogar

[1]) $\mathbf{R}$: Körper der reellen Zahlen, $\mathbf{Q}$: Körper der rationalen Zahlen, $\mathbf{N}$ und $\mathbf{Z}$ wie üblich.

[2]) ω_2: Multiplikation, ω_1: Inversenbildung, $\Omega = \{\omega_2, \omega_1, e\}$.

[3]) $\boldsymbol{G}^{-1} = \omega_1(\boldsymbol{G})$. Für topologische bzw. abelsche Limesgruppen ist $\gamma_\tau = \{\boldsymbol{G} \in \mathscr{F}(A): \boldsymbol{G}\boldsymbol{G}^{-1} \cap \boldsymbol{G}^{-1}\boldsymbol{G} \in \tau e\}$. Ob dies allgemein gilt, ist unbekannt.

eine uniforme Struktur i.S. von Weil auf **Q**, so daß γ die Menge von deren Cauchy-Filtern ist.)

Wir nennen Cauchy-Gruppen mit $\gamma = \gamma_{\tau_\gamma}$ *natürlich.*

Es gilt allgemein der

SATZ. *Jede reguläre natürliche Cauchy-Gruppe* (A, γ) *ist* v-*separiert.*

Beweis. Seien $\boldsymbol{F}, \boldsymbol{G} \in \gamma$ mit $b(\boldsymbol{F}) \vee b(\boldsymbol{G}) \neq E$. Wir müssen $(\boldsymbol{F} \cap \boldsymbol{G})\boldsymbol{H}(\boldsymbol{F} \cap \boldsymbol{G})^{-1} \in \tau_\gamma e$ für alle $\boldsymbol{H} \in \tau_\gamma e$ zeigen. Nach kurzer Rechnung sieht man, daß es genügt, $\boldsymbol{F}\boldsymbol{G}^{-1} \in \tau_\gamma e$ zu beweisen. Wir zeigen für $F \in \boldsymbol{F}$, $G \in \boldsymbol{G}$ die Formel $FG^{-1} \subset h(FF^{-1}GG^{-1})$. Daraus erhält man $\boldsymbol{F}\boldsymbol{G}^{-1} \supset h(\boldsymbol{F}\boldsymbol{F}^{-1}\ \boldsymbol{G}\boldsymbol{G}^{-1}) \in \tau_\gamma e$ und der Satz ist bewiesen.

Sei $^*\mathfrak{M}$ ein Enlargement der vollen Struktur $\mathfrak{M}$ über A. Ferner seien $x \in F$, $y \in G$ ($F \in \boldsymbol{F}$, $G \in \boldsymbol{G}$ fest). Nach 2.2 ist $[{}^*F] \cap [{}^*G] \neq \emptyset$. Sei z aus dieser Menge. Wir erhalten

$$xy^{-1} = xz^{-1}zy^{-1} \in F[{}^*F]^{-1}[{}^*G](P \cap {}^*G)^{-1}$$
$$\subset [{}^*(FF^{-1})][{}^*(GG^{-1})] \subset [{}^*(FF^{-1}GG^{-1})].$$

Nach 1.12a bedeutet dies $xy^{-1} \in h(FF^{-1}GG^{-1})$. q.e.d.

Beispiel. Sei A eine archimedische Verbandsgruppe.[1]) Ein Filter $\boldsymbol{F}$ konvergiere gegen 0 (wir schreiben die Gruppe additiv), wenn eine monoton gegen Null fallende Folge $(u_n)_{n \in \mathbf{N}}$ existiert, so daß $\boldsymbol{F}$ feiner ist als der von den Intervallen $[-u_n, u_n]$ $(:= \{x : -u_n \leqslant x \leqslant u_n\})$ erzeugte Filter.

Sei $\tau 0$ die Menge aller dieser Filter und γ_τ die oben angegebene Cauchy-Struktur. Dann ist (A, γ_τ) eine Cauchy-Verbandsgruppe. In ihr sind die Intervalle abgeschlossen, und die Differenz zweier Intervalle J_1, J_2 ist wieder ein Intervall. Ist $\boldsymbol{F}$ ein beliebiger Filter aus γ_τ, so existiert also eine monoton gegen Null fallende Folge $(u_n)_{n \in \mathbf{N}}$ und zu jedem n ein $F_n \in \boldsymbol{F}$ mit $F_n - F_n \subset [-u_n, u_n]$. Wir bestimmen aus jedem F_n ein x_n. Dann liegt F_n ganz in $x_n + [-u_n, u_n]$, also bildet $\{x_n + [-u_n, u_n] : n \in \mathbf{N}\}$ eine Filterbasis eines Filters $\boldsymbol{G}$. Es gilt $\boldsymbol{G} \in \gamma_\tau$ und $v(\boldsymbol{F}) \supset b(\boldsymbol{G})$. Da (A, γ_τ) offenbar regulär und separiert ist, ist (A, γ_τ) ein nichttriviales Beispiel einer stark separierten Cauchy-Algebra.[2])

Man kann dieses Beispiel verallgemeinern: Sei (A, τ) eine separierte

[1]) A ist kommutativ, s. Birkhoff [1967] S. 312ff. Die angegebene Konvergenz heißt manchmal Folgen-Ordnungskonvergenz. Mit geringen Modifikationen bleibt das folgende richtig, wenn mann absteigend filtrierende Netze benutzt.

[2]) (A, γ_τ) wurde bereits ausführlich bei Papangelou [1964] behandelt und dort (im Grunde genommen auf dieselbe Weise wie hier) komplettiert.

Limesgruppe. $\mathscr{M} \subset \tau e$ sei eine Teilmenge, deren solide Hülle τe ist. Jeder Filter $\boldsymbol{F}$ aus $\mathscr{M}$ besitze eine Basis aus speziellen abgeschlossenen Mengen; sind B_1, B_2 zwei solcher Mengen, ferner b_1, $b_2 \in A$ beliebig und ist $b_1 B_1 \cap b_2 B_2 = \emptyset$, so gelte $e \notin h(b_1 B_1 B_2^{-1} b_2^{-1})$. Dann ist (A, γ_τ) stark separiert.

Im Zusammenhang mit dem Beispiel von Limesgruppen zeigen wir, daß selbst im Fall einer topologischen Gruppe A die Eigenschaft (iv) von Def. 1.1 für Cauchy-Filter nicht am Filterideal $\mathfrak{F} = \{\boldsymbol{F} \in \mathscr{F}(A \times A) : \boldsymbol{F} \supset \boldsymbol{U}\}$ unmittelbar abzulesen ist; dabei bezeichne $\boldsymbol{U}$ den Nachbarschaftsfilter der beidseitig uniformen Struktur.

Genauer wollen wir damit sagen, das $\mathfrak{F}$ nicht notwendig eine Ω-Unteralgebra von $\mathscr{F}(A \times A)$ ist. Die Filtermonade $\mu(\boldsymbol{U})$ in einem Enlargement ist Graph einer Äquivalenzrelation (Luxemburg [1969], Machover und Hirschfeld [1969]). Wäre $\mathfrak{F}$ eine Ω-Unteralgebra, so wäre $\mu(\boldsymbol{U})$ gleichzeitig eine Ω-Algebra in $^*A \times {}^*A$ und damit $[e]_\gamma$ ein Normalteiler in $^*A$. Daß dies nicht der Fall zu sein braucht, zeigte Parikh [1969].

3. Einige Verallgemeinerungen topologischer Begriffe. Sei $\mathfrak{A}$ eine feste Ω-Γ-Algebra mit Trägermenge A. Berücksichtigen wir die algebraische Struktur nicht, so schreiben wir A_0. Die Cauchy-Strukturen auf A_0 bilden mit der Inklusion als Ordnung ebenso wie die Cauchy-Strukturen auf A einen ordnungsvollständigen Verband. Infima sind in beiden Verbänden die mengentheoretischen Durchschnitte. Ist γ enthalten in γ', so nennen wir γ feiner als γ' (γ' gröber als γ).

Eine *uniforme Konvergenzstruktur* (kurz: UKS) (Cook und Fischer [1965, 1967a]) ist ein $\cap$-Ideal $\mathfrak{F}$ von $\mathscr{F}(A \times A)$ mit den Eigenschaften:

(i) Der von der Diagonalen Δ erzeugte Hauptfilter ist in $\mathfrak{F}$.

(ii) $\boldsymbol{F} \in \mathfrak{F}$ impliziert $\boldsymbol{F}^- := \{\{(y, x) : (x, y) \in F\} : F \in \boldsymbol{F}\} \in \mathfrak{F}$.

(iii) $\boldsymbol{F}, \boldsymbol{G} \in \mathfrak{F}$ und $\boldsymbol{F} \circ \boldsymbol{G} \neq \boldsymbol{E}$ implizier $\boldsymbol{F} \circ \boldsymbol{G} \in \mathfrak{F}$.[1])

Ist $\mathfrak{F}$ ein Hauptideal, d.h. $\mathfrak{F} = \{\boldsymbol{F} \in \mathscr{F}(A \times A) : \boldsymbol{F} \supset \boldsymbol{U}\}$, so ist $\boldsymbol{U}$ ein Nachbarschaftsfilter i.S. von A. Weil (Cook und Fischer [1967a]). $C_{\mathfrak{F}} = \{\boldsymbol{F} \in \mathscr{F}(A) : \boldsymbol{F} \times \boldsymbol{F} \in \mathfrak{F}\}$ heißt die Menge der $\mathfrak{F}$-Cauchy-Filter. Ist $\mathfrak{F}$ ein Hauptideal mit Nachbarschaftsfilter $\boldsymbol{U}$, so schreiben wir $C_{\boldsymbol{U}}$ statt $C_{\mathfrak{F}}$.

$(A_0, C_{\mathfrak{F}})$ ist ein Cauchy-Raum in unserem Sinne. Umgekehrt existiert zu jeder Cauchy-Struktur γ auf A_0 eine UKS $\mathfrak{F}$ mit $C_{\mathfrak{F}} = \gamma$ (Keller [1968] s.a. Sektion 1). Im allgemeinen ist diese nicht eindeutig bestimmt.

[1]) $F \circ G = \{(x, y)$: es existiert $z \in A$ mit $(x, z) \in F$, $(z, y) \in G\}$. $\boldsymbol{F} \circ \boldsymbol{G}$ ist der von allen $F \circ G$ ($F \in \boldsymbol{F}$, $G \in \boldsymbol{G}$) erzeugte Filter.

3.1. DEFINITION. *Eine Cauchy-Struktur γ auf A heißt Weil-Struktur und (A, γ) Weil-Algebra, wenn ein Nachbarschaftsfilter $\boldsymbol{U}$ mit $\gamma = C_{\boldsymbol{U}}$ existiert.*

Die Menge der Weil-Strukturen auf A_0 (bzw. A) bildet wieder mit der Inklusion als Ordnung einen ordnungsvollständigen Verband.

Sei $^*\mathfrak{M}$ ein Enlargement der vollen Struktur über A. Ist $\mathfrak{F}$ eine UKS, so ist $G(\mathfrak{F}) := \bigcup_{F \in \mathfrak{F}} \mu(\boldsymbol{F})$ Graph einer Äquivalenzrelation auf $^*A$ und d-gesättigt.[1]) Ist umgekehrt G Graph einer Äquivalenzrelation auf $^*A$ und d-gesättigt, so ist $\mathfrak{F}(G) := \{\boldsymbol{F} \in \mathscr{F}(A \times A) : \mu(\boldsymbol{F}) \subset G\}$ eine UKS. Es gilt $G(\mathfrak{F}(G)) = G$ (im allgemeinen jedoch $\mathfrak{F}(G(\mathfrak{F})) \neq \mathfrak{F}$). Dies ist das Analogon zur Theorie der uniformen Räume (Luxemburg [1969], Machover und Hirschfeld [1969]).

Das folgende Lemma ist rein technischer Art.

3.2. LEMMA. *Sei $\mathscr{M}$ eine Ω-Unteralgebra von $\mathscr{F}(A)$ und zu jedem $a \in A$ existiere ein $\boldsymbol{F} \in \mathscr{M}$ mit $\boldsymbol{F} \subset \dot{a}$. Sei γ die feinste Cauchy-Struktur auf A, in der $\mathscr{M}$ enthalten ist. Dann existieren zu jedem $\boldsymbol{G} \in \gamma$ endlich viele Filter $\boldsymbol{F}_1, \ldots, \boldsymbol{F}_n \in \mathscr{M}$ mit $\boldsymbol{G} \supset \bigcap_{i=1}^n \boldsymbol{F}_i$ und $\bigcap_{i=1}^n \boldsymbol{F}_i \in \gamma$.*

Beweis. Da wir Abbildungen und Monadenbildung vertauschen wollen, benutzen wir ausnahmsweise ein κ-saturiertes Enlargement, wo κ größer als die Mächtigkeit von $\mathfrak{P}(\mathfrak{P}(A))$ sei (vergl. Puritz [1972]).

Sei γ' die Menge aller Filter $\boldsymbol{G}$ aus $\mathscr{F}(A)$, zu denen endlich viele Filter $\boldsymbol{F}_1, \ldots, \boldsymbol{F}_n \in \mathscr{M}$ existieren mit $\boldsymbol{G} \supset \bigcap_{i=1}^n \boldsymbol{F}_i$ und $\bigcap_{i=1}^n \boldsymbol{F}_i \in \gamma$. γ' liegt in γ und erfüllt (i), (ii) und (iii) aus 1.1. Wir zeigen, daß γ' eine Ω-Algebra ist. Dann ist $\gamma' = \gamma$ und damit ist alles gezeigt.

γ' ist abgeschlossen bezüglich nullstelliger Operationen (klar). Sei also ω eine n-stellige Operation ($n \neq 0$) und seien $\boldsymbol{G}_1, \ldots, \boldsymbol{G}_n \in \gamma'$. Dann existieren Filter $\boldsymbol{F}_{ij}$ ($i = 1, \ldots, n; j = 1, \ldots, r_i$) aus $\mathscr{M}$ mit $\boldsymbol{G}_i \supset \bigcap_{j=1}^{r_i} \boldsymbol{F}_{ij}$ und (nach 1.7) $[\mu(\boldsymbol{F}_{ij})]_\gamma = [\mu(\boldsymbol{F}_{i1})]_\gamma$ für alle i, j.

Seien $a_i \in \mu(\boldsymbol{F}_{i1})$ fest gewählt ($i = 1, \ldots, n$). Dann erhalten wir wegen der speziellen Wahl des Enlargements

$$\begin{aligned}
\mu(\omega(\boldsymbol{G}_1 \times \ldots \times \boldsymbol{G}_n)) &= \omega(\mu(\boldsymbol{G}_1) \times \cdots \times \mu(\boldsymbol{G}_n)) \\
&\subset \bigcup_{\substack{i=1,\ldots,n \\ k_i = 1,\ldots,r_i}} \omega(\mu(\boldsymbol{F}_{1k_1}) \times \cdots \times \mu(\boldsymbol{F}_{nk_n})) \\
&= \bigcup_{\substack{i=1,\ldots,n \\ k_i = 1,\ldots,r_i}} \mu(\omega(\boldsymbol{F}_{1k_1} \times \cdots \times \boldsymbol{F}_{nk_n})) \\
&\subset [\omega(a_1, \ldots, a_n)]_\gamma
\end{aligned}$$

[1]) d.h. mit $x \in G(\mathfrak{F})$ ist $\mu_d(x)$ enthalten in $G(\mathfrak{F})$.

wobei die letzte Relation gilt, weil die durch γ auf $P(^*A, \gamma)$ induzierte Äquivalenzrelation eine Kongruenzrelation ist. Da $\mathscr{M}$ selbst eine Unteralgebra von $\mathscr{F}(A)$ ist, ist $\omega(\boldsymbol{F}_{1k_1} \times \cdots \times \boldsymbol{F}_{nk_n})$ aus $\mathscr{M}$. Aus 1.7 folgt daher

$$\bigcap_{\substack{i=1,\ldots,n\\ k_i=1,\ldots,r_i}} \omega(\boldsymbol{F}_{1k_1} \times \cdots \times \boldsymbol{F}_{nk_n}) \in \gamma.$$

Daraus ergibt sich $\omega(\boldsymbol{G}_1 \times \ldots \times \boldsymbol{G}_n) \in \gamma'$. q.e.d.

Wir werden das oben stehende Lemma bei der Konstruktion der Komplettierung benutzen; daneben ist es der Schlüssel zum Beweis der Vollständigkeit des induktiven Limes vollständiger Cauchy-Algebren (s.u.).

Zunächst beweisen wir jedoch, daß jede Weil-Algebra v-separiert, regulär und v-regulär ist. Dies ist wichtig für den Nachweis, daß die von uns konstruierte Komplettierung in diesem Fall mit der aus der Topologie bekannten zusammenfällt.

3.3. Proposition. *Jede Weil-Algebra* (A, γ) *ist* v-*separiert, regulär und* v-*regulär.*

Beweis. Wir benutzen ein festes Enlargement $^*\mathfrak{M}$ der vollen Struktur $\mathfrak{M}$ über A.

Sei $\boldsymbol{U}$ ein Nachbarschaftsfilter mit $\gamma = C_{\boldsymbol{U}}$. Ist $M \subset A$, so sei $U(M) = \{y \in A$: es existiert ein $x \in M$ mit $(x, y) \in U\}$.

Ist $\boldsymbol{F} \in \gamma$, so ist der durch $\{U(F): U \in \boldsymbol{U}, F \in \boldsymbol{F}\}$ erzeugte Filter $\boldsymbol{U}(\boldsymbol{F})$ ein minimaler Cauchy-Filter und daher $[\mu(\boldsymbol{F})] = \mu(\boldsymbol{U}(\boldsymbol{F}))$.

Allgemein gilt für eine Teilmenge $M \subset A$

(I): $[^*M] \subset \mu(\boldsymbol{U})(^*M) := \{y \in {}^*A$: es existiert $x \in {}^*M$ mit $(x, y) \in \mu(\boldsymbol{U})\}$. Denn ist $z \in [^*M]$, so existiert ein $\boldsymbol{H} \in \gamma$ mit $z \in \mu(\boldsymbol{H})$ und $\mu(\boldsymbol{H}) \cap {}^*M \neq \emptyset$. Wegen $\mu(\boldsymbol{H}) \times \mu(\boldsymbol{H}) \subset \mu(\boldsymbol{U})$ folgt $z \in \mu(\boldsymbol{U})(^*M)$.

Nach diesen Vorbemerkungen läßt sich der Satz nun einfach beweisen.

a) vs_2 (vergl. 2.4(ii)). Seien $\boldsymbol{F}_1, \boldsymbol{F}_2 \in \gamma$ mit $[\mu(\boldsymbol{F}_1)] \cap [\mu(\boldsymbol{F}_2)] = \emptyset$. Dann gilt (s.o.) $\mu(\boldsymbol{U}(\boldsymbol{F}_1)) \cap \mu(\boldsymbol{U}(\boldsymbol{F}_2)) = \emptyset$. Damit existiert aber ein $U \in \boldsymbol{U}$ und $F_i \in \boldsymbol{F}_i$ $(i = 1, 2)$ mit $^*(U(F_1)) \cap {}^*(U(F_2)) = \emptyset$. Mit (I) erhält man $[^*F_1] \cap [^*F_2] = \emptyset$, also nach 2.4(ii) die Behauptung.

b) s_3: Aus 1.12a und (I) folgt $\boldsymbol{U}(\boldsymbol{F}) \subset h(\boldsymbol{F})$.

c) vs_3: Sei $\boldsymbol{F} \in \gamma$. Wir zeigen $b(\boldsymbol{U}(\boldsymbol{F})) \subset v(\boldsymbol{F})$.

Sei $F \in \boldsymbol{F}$, $\boldsymbol{H} \in \gamma$ und $\boldsymbol{H} \mathrel{v} \bar{F}$. Zu jedem $H \in \boldsymbol{H}$ existiert also ein $\boldsymbol{D} \in \gamma$ mit $\boldsymbol{D} \vee \dot{H} \neq \boldsymbol{E} \neq \boldsymbol{D} \vee \dot{F}$, d.h. $\mu(\boldsymbol{D}) \cap {}^*H \neq \emptyset \neq \mu(\boldsymbol{D}) \cap {}^*F$. Sei $x \in \mu(\boldsymbol{D}) \cap {}^*H$. Wegen $\mu(\boldsymbol{U}) \supset \mu(\boldsymbol{D}) \times \mu(\boldsymbol{D})$ folgt hieraus $x \in \mu(\boldsymbol{U})(^*F) \subset {}^*(U(F))$ für jedes beliebige Standard-Element U aus $\boldsymbol{U}$. Das bedeutet $^*H \cap {}^*(U(F)) \neq \emptyset$, also nach dem Fundamentaltheorem der Nonstandard-Analysis (Luxemburg [1969] S. 24) $H \cap U(F) \neq \emptyset$. Hieraus folgt leicht die Behauptung.

In einer Theorie von Cauchy-Räumen unerläßlich ist ein passender Stetigkeitsbegriff für Abbildungen.

3.4. DEFINITION. *Seien* (A_i, γ_i) $(i = 1, 2)$ *Cauchy-Algebren mit gleichem Operationenbereich* Ω *und* φ *eine Abbildung von* A_1 *in* A_2. φ *heißt*

(a) C-*stetig, wenn* $\varphi(\boldsymbol{F}) \in \gamma_2$ *für alle* $\boldsymbol{F} \in \gamma_1$ *gilt;*

(b) C-*offen, wenn zu jedem* $\boldsymbol{G} \in \gamma_2$ *ein* $\boldsymbol{F} \in \gamma_1$ *mit* $\varphi(\boldsymbol{F}) \subset \boldsymbol{G}$ *existiert;*

(c) *bedingt* C-*offen, wenn zu jedem Ultrafilter* $\boldsymbol{U} \in \gamma_2$ *ein* $\boldsymbol{F} \in \gamma_1$ *mit* $\varphi(\boldsymbol{F}) \subset \boldsymbol{U}$ *existiert.*

Ist φ C-*stetig und ein* Ω-*Homomorphismus, so heißt* φ *Cauchy-Morphismus (kurz:* C-*Morphismus). Ist* φ *ein injektiver, surjektiver (bedingt)* C-*offener* C-*Morphismus, so heißt* φ *(bedingter) Cauchy-Isomorphismus (kurz:* C-*Isomorphismus).*

Die Klasse aller Cauchy-Algebren mit gemeinsamem Operationenbereich bildet zusammen mit den C-Morphismen eine Kategorie. Die Notwendigkeit für den Begriff "bedingt offen" liegt bei uniformen Räumen (also Weil-Algebren) nicht vor. Das im Anschluß an Theorem 1.10 gegebene Beispiel zeigt, daß die Identität auf E ein bedingter C-Isomorphismus, aber kein C-Isomorphismus von (E, γ_2) auf (E, γ_1) ist. Vollständigkeit wird schon durch C-stetige, bedingt C-offene Abbildungen übertragen (s.u.).

Die aus Definition 3.4 resultierenden Nonstandard-Charakterisierungen von Stetigkeit bzw. Offenheit wollen wir nicht in aller Ausführlichkeit bringen. Es wird davon ganz zwanglos Gebrauch gemacht. Beispielhaft führen wir an:

3.5. PROPOSITION (*Vergl. Machover und Hirschfeld* [1969] 9.1.2). *Sei* $\varphi: (A_1, \gamma_1) \to (A_2, \gamma_2)$ *stetig und* $^*\mathfrak{M}$ *ein Enlargement der vollen Struktur über* $A_1 \cup A_2$. *Dann liegt* $^*\varphi(P(^*A_1, \gamma_1))$ *in* $P(^*A_2, \gamma_2)$ *und* $^*(\varphi \times \varphi)\ (B(^*A_1, \gamma_1))$ *in* $B(^*A_2, \gamma_2)$.

Die Umkehrung braucht nicht zu gelten, wie die identische Abbildung von (E, γ_1) auf (E, γ_2) (s.o.) zeigt.

Die i.S. von Cook und Fischer [1965, 1967a] uniform stetigen Abbildungen von $(A_1, \mathfrak{F}_1)$ in $(A_2, \mathfrak{F}_2)$ ($\mathfrak{F}_k$: UKS für $k = 1, 2$) sind C-stetig für $(A_1, C_{\mathfrak{F}_1})$ und $(A_2, C_{\mathfrak{F}_2})$. Sind (A_i, γ_i) Cauchy-Räume, $\mathfrak{F}_1$ UKS mit $\gamma_i = C_{\mathfrak{F}_i}$ $(i = 1, 2)$

und ist $\varphi: A_1 \to A_2$ C-stetig, so muß φ nicht uniform stetig sein. Es gibt jedoch immer "passende" UKS $\mathfrak{F}'_1$, $\mathfrak{F}'_2$ mit $\gamma_i = C_{\mathfrak{F}_i'}$, so daß φ uniform stetig ist von $(A_1, \mathfrak{F}'_1)$ in $(A_2, \mathfrak{F}'_2)$.

3.6. KOROLLAR. *Seien (A_i, γ_i) Cauchy-Algebren ($i = 1, 2$) und $\varphi: A_1 \to A_2$ eine beliebige Abbildung. Dann gilt:*

(i) *Ist (A_1, γ_1) vollständig und φ C-stetig und bedingt C-offen, so ist (A_2, γ_2) ebenfalls vollständig.*

(ii) *Ist (A_1, γ_1) (prä-) kompakt und φ surjektiv und C-stetig, so ist φ bedingt C-offen und (A_2, γ_2) ist ebenfalls (prä-) kompakt.*

Der Beweis folgt aus 3.5 und 1.9 bzw. 1.10.

Wir wollen uns auch nicht in Einzelheiten verlieren bei Bildung neuer Räume durch Systeme von Abbildungen und geben nur den für die Komplettierung wichtigsten Begriff an:

3.7. DEFINITION. *Sei (A', γ') eine Cauchy-Algebra mit Operationenbereich Ω, $A \subset A'$ eine Teilmenge und $\varphi: A \to A'$ die Einbettungsabbildung. Ist γ die gröbste Cauchy-Struktur auf A,*[1]*) für die φ stetig ist, so heißt (A, γ) (Cauchy-) Unterraum.*

Bemerkungen. 1) Ist A eine Ω-Unteralgebra, so ist (A, γ) automatisch eine Cauchy-Algebra; wir nennen dann (A, γ) Cauchy-Unteralgebra.

2) Mit (A', γ') ist auch (A, γ) v-separiert (bzw. regulär, v-regulär).

3.8. PROPOSITION. *Sei (A', γ') eine Cauchy-Algebra und (A, γ) ein Cauchy-Unterraum. Dann gilt:*

(a) *Ist (A, γ) vollständig und (A', γ') separiert, so ist A abgeschlossen in A'. Ist umgekehrt A' vollständig und A abgeschlossen in A', so ist (A, γ) vollständig.*

(b) *(A, γ) ist genau dann präkompakt (bzw. kompakt), wenn $^*A$ enthalten ist in $P(^*(A'), \gamma')$ (bzw. in $N(^*(A'), \gamma')$ und A abgeschlossen ist).*

Beweis. Wir benutzen ein Enlargement der vollen Struktur über A'. Dies enthält in kanonischer Weise ein solches der vollen Struktur über A. Dann folgen mit 1.9, 1.10 und 1.12(a) leicht die Behauptungen.

[1]) Auf A betrachten wir zunächst keine Operationen, γ muß also nur (i)–(iii) aus 1.1 erfüllen.

Teil (b) ist das Analogon zu Nonstandard-Analysis der entsprechenden Begriffe der Topologie (s. Robinson [1966], Luxemburg [1969], Machover und Hirschfeld [1969]).

Es ergibt sich sofort, wann ein T_2-Limesraum X lokalkompakt ist (d.h. wann jeder konvergente Filter eine kompakte Teilmenge als Element enthält). Hierzu sei γ die Menge aller konvergenten Filter. (X, γ) ist dann in unserer Terminologie ein vollständiger Cauchy-Raum und wir haben (vergl. Machover und Hirschfeld [1969], Luxemburg [1969] für den topologischen Fall): *(X, γ) ist genau dann lokalkompakt, wenn* $N({}^*X, \gamma) = \bigcup_{C \in \mathfrak{C}} {}^*C$ *ist, wo* $\mathfrak{C}$ *das System der kompakten Mengen bezeichnet.*

Die bisher entwickelte Theorie scheint gut geeignet zur Erörterung von Fragen, die mit der stetigen Konvergenz zu tun haben (für dieses Thema s. beispielsweise Binz [1968]). Wir werden dies in einer anderen Arbeit darstellen.

Es ist klar, wie man Produkte, projektive und induktive Limites definiert. Ein Produkt ist genau dann vollständig (bzw. kompakt), wenn dies für jeden Faktor zutrifft. Dies ist weniger überraschend als der folgende Satz:

3.9. Proposition. *Der induktive Limes vollständiger Cauchy-Algebren in der Kategorie der Cauchy-Algebren mit gleichem Operationenbereich Ω ist eine vollständige Cauchy-Algebra.*

Der Satz folgt aus 3.2. Einen entsprechenden Satz für Limesvektorräume bewies Wloka [1963]. Wir müssen jedoch darauf hinweisen, daß hier verschiedene Erfordernisse sich gegenseitig durchkreuzen. In der Theorie der Limesvektorräume wird Vollständigkeit grundsätzlich nur bezüglich der "natürlichen" Cauchy-Struktur definiert (s. 2.8). Der induktive Limes natürlicher Cauchy-Gruppen ist natürlich, wenn es sich um Untergruppen und Einbettungsabbildungen handelt. Dies ist die Voraussetzung des Wlokaschen Satzes; er folgt mit dieser Bemerkung sofort aus 3.9.[1]) Das ist nicht überraschend, da 3.2 eine Verallgemeinerung des wesentlichen Beweisschrittes im Satz von J. Wloka ist.

4. Komplettierung. Wir haben in 1.11 definiert, wann eine Teilmenge C einer Cauchy-Algebra (A, γ) dicht in A heißen soll. Bei Komplettierungsfragen

[1]) Daß es sich um Vektorräume handelt, die sich nicht ohne weiteres in die Theorie der Ω-Algebren einfügen, ist weniger wesentlich (s. Sektion 6).

spielt die Dichtheit eine besondere Rolle für die Fortsetzbarkeit von C-stetigen Abbildungen. Es zeigt sich, daß man hierfür einen schärferen Begriff benötigt, der im Fall des uniformen Raumes (Weil-Raumes in unserer Terminologie) mit dem obigen übereinstimmt.

4.1. Definition. *Eine Teilmenge C einer Cauchy-Algebra* (A, γ) *heißt uniform dicht in A, wenn zu jedem* $\mathbf{F} \in \gamma$ *ein* $\mathbf{G}$ *aus* γ *existiert mit* $C \in \mathbf{G}$ *und* $h(\mathbf{G}) \subset \mathbf{F}$.

Jede uniform dichte Teilmenge ist dicht (aus $a \in A$ folgt $\dot{a} \in \gamma$, also existiert ein $\mathbf{G} \in \gamma$ mit $C \in \mathbf{G}$ und $h(\mathbf{G}) \subset \dot{a}$, daraus folgt $a \in h(C)$). Die Umkehrung gilt nicht: sei $A = \mathbf{R}$, $\Omega = \emptyset$ und für $x \in \mathbf{R}$ sei $\mathbf{U}(x)$ der Umgebungsfilter in der gewöhnlichen Topologie. Sei z eine irrationale Zahl und $\mathbf{F}$ der Abschnittsfilter der Folge $(n + z)_{n \in \mathbf{N}}$. Wir setzen

$$\mathbf{V}(x) = \begin{cases} \mathbf{U}(x) & : x \neq 0, \\ \mathbf{U}(0) \cap \mathbf{F} & : x = 0. \end{cases}$$

Ist γ die solide Hülle von $\{\mathbf{V}(x) : x \in \mathbf{R}\}$, so ist $\mathbf{Q}$ dicht, aber nicht uniform dicht in $(\mathbf{R}, \gamma)$.

Wir erklären jetzt den grundlegenden Begriff:

4.2. Definition. *Sei* (A, γ) *ein Cauchy-Raum.*[1]) *Ein vollständiger Cauchy-Raum* (A', γ') *heißt Komplettierung von* (A, γ), *wenn die beiden folgenden Bedingungen erfüllt sind:*

(i) *Es existiert eine* C-*stetige Abbildung T von A auf einen uniform dichten Unterraum von* (A', γ').

(ii) *Ist* (A'', γ'') *ein separierter, regulärer, vollständiger Cauchy-Raum und U eine* C-*stetige Abbildung von* (A, γ) *in* (A'', γ''), *so existiert eine* C-*stetige Abbildung S von* (A', γ') *in* (A'', γ'') *mit* $U = ST$.

Wir konstruieren nun die "Nonstandard-Komplettierung", von der wir in Einzelschritten die Eigenschaften (i) und (ii) einer Komplettierung nachweisen. Wir betonen, daß wir in der Einleitung strengere Anforderungen an eine Komplettierung gestellt haben, die die Nonstandard-Komplettierung von stark separierten Cauchy-Algebren erfüllen wird.

4.3. *Konstruktion der Nonstandard-Komplettierung*. Sei (A, γ) eine Ω-Γ-

[1]) Wir lassen also bewußt eventuelle Operationen auf A zunächst außer acht.

Cauchy-Algebra und $^*\mathfrak{M}$ ein Enlargement der vollen Struktur $\mathfrak{M}$ über A.[1]) Mit A_v bezeichnen wir die Quotientenalgebra aller Äquivalenzklassen in $P(^*A, \gamma)$ bezüglich der Kongruenzrelation $\sim_\gamma$ (s. 1.5). Die Restklassenabbildung bezeichnen wir mit q und die Elemente von A_v kennzeichnen wir durch ein "^", wogegen wir nach wie vor $[a]$ (bzw. $[a]_\gamma$) für die Äquivalenzklasse, aufgefaßt als Teilmenge von $P(^*A, \gamma)$, schreiben.

Sei $M \subset A$. Dann setzen wir $M_v = q(^*M \cap P)$ $(P := P(^*A, \gamma))$. Es gilt $q^{-1}(M_v) = [^*M]$. Ist $\boldsymbol{F}$ ein beliebiger Filter auf A, so bezeichnen wir mit $\boldsymbol{F}_v$ den von $\{F_v : F \in \boldsymbol{F}\}$ erzeugten Filter. Sei $\mathcal{M}$ die solide Hülle von $\{\boldsymbol{F}_v : \boldsymbol{F} \in \gamma\}$ und γ_v die feinste Cauchy-Struktur auf A_v, in der $\mathcal{M}$ enthalten ist.[2]) Wir fassen (wie bisher) A als Teilmenge von P auf und bezeichnen mit T die Einschränkung von q auf A. (A_v, γ_v) wird die gewünschte Komplettierung sein, wie wir im folgenden in Einzelschritten nachweisen werden. Die wichtigsten Eigenschaften dieser Komplettierung fassen wir dann in 4.16 zusammen.

4.4. Lemma. a) *(A_v, γ_v) ist eine vollständige Cauchy-Algebra (mit demselben Operationenbereich wie A).*

b) *$T: A \to A_v$ ist ein Cauchy-Morphismus und $T(A)$ ist uniform dicht in A_v.*

Beweis. a) Wir zeigen zunächst, daß das obige $\mathcal{M}$ (s. 4.3) die Voraussetzungen von 3.2 erfüllt.

Ist $\hat{a} \in A_v$, so existiert ein $\boldsymbol{F} \in \gamma$ mit $q(\mu(\boldsymbol{F})) = \{\hat{a}\}$. Damit ist $\dot{\hat{a}} \in \mathcal{M}$.

Sei ω eine n-stellige Operation (oBdA $n \neq 0$) und seien $\boldsymbol{G}^1, \ldots, \boldsymbol{G}^n \in \mathcal{M}$. Dann existieren $\boldsymbol{F}^i \in \gamma$ mit $\boldsymbol{F}^i_v \subset \boldsymbol{G}^i$ $(i = 1, \ldots, n)$. Wir zeigen $(\omega(\boldsymbol{F}^1 \times \cdots \times \boldsymbol{F}^n))_v \subset \omega(\boldsymbol{F}^1_v \cdots \boldsymbol{F}^n_v)$. Daraus folgt dann, daß $\mathcal{M}$ eine Ω-Algebra ist.

Seien $F^i \in \boldsymbol{F}^i$ beliebig $(i = 1, \ldots, n)$ und $\hat{z} \in \omega(F^1_v \ldots F^n_v)$.

Dann existieren $x_i \in {}^*F^i \cap P$ mit
$$\begin{aligned} \hat{z} &= \omega(q(x_1), \ldots, q(x_n)) \\ &= q(\omega(x_1, \ldots, x_n)) \\ &\in q(\omega(^*F^1 \times \cdots \times {}^*F^n) \cap P) \\ &= q(^*(\omega(F^1 \times \cdots \times F^n)) \cap P) \\ &= (\omega(F^1 \times \ldots \times F^n))_v. \end{aligned}$$
Da $\hat{z}$ beliebig und $F^i \in \boldsymbol{F}^i$ ebenfalls willkürlich waren, folgt die Behauptung über $\mathcal{M}$.

Wir können also 3.2 anwenden. Wegen 1.7 und 1.8 genügt es zu zeigen,

[1]) Wir betonen, daß wir (genau wie Machover und Hirschfeld [1969]) keine Saturiertheit von $^*\mathfrak{M}$ verlangen.

[2]) Nach Konstruktion ist A_v eine Ω-Algebra; wir verlangen also von γ_v die Eigenschaften (i)–(iv) von Def. 1.1.

daß jeder Filter F_v ($F \in \gamma$) konvergiert. Ist $F \in \gamma$ und $a \in \mu(F)$, so ist $F_v \subset \dot{\hat{a}}$, also F_v konvergent. Damit ist a) bewiesen.

b) Für $F \in \gamma$ liegt F_v in $T(F)$. Daraus folgt die C-Stetigkeit von T. T ist selbstverständlich ein Ω-Homomorphismus. Sei $T(A) =: C$ und $G \in \gamma_v$. Dann existieren nach 3.2 (s. unter a)) Filter $G^1, \ldots, G^n \in \gamma$ mit $\bigcap_{i=1}^n G_v^i \subset G$ und $\bigcap_{i=1}^n G_v^i \in \gamma_v$.

Sei h der Hüllenoperator in A_v. Wir zeigen

$$D_i := \bar{C} \vee G_v^i \neq E \text{ und } \bigcap_{i=1}^n G_v^i \supset h(\bigcap_{i=1}^n D_i).$$

Nun ist $h(\bigcap D_i) = \bigcap h(D_i)$; so genügt es, die folgende Behauptung zu beweisen: Ist $G \in \gamma$, so ist $D := \dot{C} \vee G_v \neq E$ und $h(D) \subset G_v$.

Sei schließlich $G \in G$. Dann ist G Teilmenge von $*G \cap P$, woraus $C \cap G_v \supset T(G) \cap G_v \neq \emptyset$ folgt. Das ergibt $D \neq E$.

Für beliebiges $G \in G$ zeigen wir $G_v \subset h(C \cap G_v)$. Daraus folgt dann $h(D) \subset G_v$.

Ist $a \in *G \cap P$, so existiert ein $H \in \gamma$ mit $a \in \mu(H)$, also $H_v \subset q(a)^{\cdot}$. Außerdem gilt $H \vee \dot{G} \neq E$ wegen $\mu(H) \cap *G \neq \emptyset$. Hieraus folgt $C \cap G_v \cap H_v \neq \emptyset$ für jedes $H \in H$, also

$$H \vee (C \cap G_v)^{\cdot} \neq E; \quad \text{das bedeutet } q(a) \in h(C \cap G_v). \qquad \text{q.e.d.}$$

4.5. Lemma. *Sei (A, γ) eine Cauchy-Algebra und $\mathfrak{M}$ die volle Struktur höherer Ordnung über A. Seien ferner $*\mathfrak{M}$ und $'\mathfrak{M}$ zwei Enlargements von $\mathfrak{M}$. Ist (A_{v1}, γ_{v1}) mit Hilfe von $*\mathfrak{M}$, (A_{v2}, γ_{v2}) mit Hilfe von $'\mathfrak{M}$ konstruiert und sind T_i die entsprechenden Abbildungen von $A \to A_{vi}$ ($i = 1, 2$), so existiert ein C-Isomorphismus U von A_{v1} auf A_{v2} mit $UT_1 = T_2$.*

Beweis. (Buchstaben mit 1 als Index beziehen sich auf $*\mathfrak{M}$, solche mit 2 auf $'\mathfrak{M}$.)

Wir betrachten die Unteralgebra $G = \bigcap_{F \in \gamma} (\mu_1(F) \times \mu_2(F))$ von $*A \times 'A$, und auf ihr die Relation ρ, definiert durch $(a, b)\rho(a', b') \Leftrightarrow (a, a') \in B_1$ und $(b, b') \in B_2$.

ρ ist offensichtlich eine Kongruenzrelation auf G. Sei $H := G/\rho$. Nun ist $P_1 = \{a \in *A$: es existiert $b \in 'A$ mit $(a, b) \in G\}$ und $P_2 = \{b, \in 'A$: es existiert $a \in *A$ mit $(a, b) \in G\}$. Also ist die Quotientenabbildung $Q: G \to H$ durch $Q(a, b) = (q_1(a), q_2(b))$ gegeben, und es gilt

$$A_{v1} = \{\hat{a} \in A_{v1}: \text{es existiert } \hat{b} \in A_{v2} \text{ mit } (\hat{a}, \hat{b}) \in H\}$$

sowie die analoge Formel für A_{v2}.

Sind $(\hat{a}, \hat{b}), (\hat{a}, \hat{c}) \in H$, so existieren $a \in *A$, $b, c \in 'A$ mit (a, b) und (a, c)

aus G. Dann gibt es also Filter $\boldsymbol{F}, \boldsymbol{G} \in \gamma$ mit $(a, b) \in \mu_1(\boldsymbol{F}) \times \mu_2(\boldsymbol{F})$, $(a, c) \in \mu_1(\boldsymbol{G}) \times \mu_2(\boldsymbol{G})$. Wegen $a \in \mu_1(\boldsymbol{F}) \cap \mu_1(\boldsymbol{G}) \neq \emptyset$ folgt $\boldsymbol{F} \cap \boldsymbol{G} \in \gamma$, also $\hat{b} = \hat{c}$. Ebenso leicht beweist man: $(\hat{b}, \hat{a})$ und $(\hat{c}, \hat{a}) \in H$ impliziert $\hat{b} = \hat{c}$.

Damit ist H Graph eines Ω-Isomorphismus U: $A_{v1} \to A_{v2}$. Die Gleichung $UT_1 = T_2$ ergibt sich nach Konstruktion. Ist $\boldsymbol{F} \in \gamma$, so wird $U(\boldsymbol{F}_{v1})$ erzeugt von $\{Uq_1(^*F \cap P_1) : F \in \boldsymbol{F}\} = \{q_2('F \cap P_2) : F \in \boldsymbol{F}\}$. Also ist $U(\boldsymbol{F}_{v1}) = \boldsymbol{F}_{v2}$. Hieraus folgt nun leicht Stetigkeit und Offenheit von U.

Damit ist also die Konstruktion von (A_v, γ_v) vom speziell benutzten Enlargement unabhängig. Wir benutzen die Symbole A_v, γ_v q, T etc. stets im oben angegebenen Sinn, wobei wir uns immer ein Enlargement gegeben denken.

4.6. Lemma. a) *Ist A* v-*separiert, so ist γ_v die solide Hülle von* $\{\boldsymbol{F}_v : \boldsymbol{F} \in \gamma\} =: \mathscr{M}_1$.
b) *Ist umgekehrt γ_v die solide Hülle von $\mathscr{M}_1$ und A regulär, so ist A* v-*separiert.*

Beweis. a) Es genügt zu zeigen, daß $\mathscr{M}$ die Bedingung (ii) von Definition 1.1 erfüllt (vergl. 4.3). Seien $\boldsymbol{D}_1, \boldsymbol{D}_2 \in \mathscr{M}$. Dann existieren $\boldsymbol{F}, \boldsymbol{G} \in \gamma$ mit $\boldsymbol{F}_v \subset \boldsymbol{D}_1$, $\boldsymbol{G}_v \subset \boldsymbol{D}_2$. Mit $\boldsymbol{D}_1 \vee \boldsymbol{D}_2 \neq \boldsymbol{E}$ gilt dasselbe auch für $\boldsymbol{F}_v$, $\boldsymbol{G}_v$. Dies bedeutet $[^*F] \cap [^*G] \neq \emptyset$ für alle $F \in \boldsymbol{F}$, $G \in \boldsymbol{G}$. Aus 2.2 und 1.7 erhalten wir wegen der Voraussetzung $\boldsymbol{F} \cap \boldsymbol{G} \in \gamma$, also $\boldsymbol{F}_v \cap \boldsymbol{G}_v = (\boldsymbol{F} \cap \boldsymbol{G})_v \in \mathscr{M}$.
b) Seien $\boldsymbol{F}, \boldsymbol{G} \in \gamma$ mit $\boldsymbol{F} \, v \, \boldsymbol{G}$. Aus 2.2 folgt $\boldsymbol{F}_v \vee \boldsymbol{G}_v \neq \boldsymbol{E}$. Nach Voraussetzung existiert also ein $\boldsymbol{H} \in \gamma$ mit $\boldsymbol{H}_v \subset \boldsymbol{F}_v \cap \boldsymbol{G}_v$. Zu jedem $H \in \boldsymbol{H}$ gibt es also ein $F \in \boldsymbol{F}$, $G \in \boldsymbol{G}$ mit $F_v \cup G_v \subset H_v$. Das bedeutet $[^*F] \cup [^*G] \subset [^*H]$, woraus mit 1.12(a) $F \cup G \subset h(H)$ folgt. Also erhalten wir $\boldsymbol{F} \cap \boldsymbol{G} \supset h(\boldsymbol{H}) \in \gamma$ und damit die Behauptung.

4.7. Proposition. a) *(A_v, γ_v) ist genau dann separiert, wenn (A, γ)* v-*separiert ist.*
b) *Ist (A, γ)* v-*separiert, so ist (A_v, γ_v) genau dann regulär wenn (A, γ)* v-*regulär ist.*

Beweis. a) Sei A v-separiert und $a, b \in P(^*A, \gamma)$ mit $\{q(a), q(b)\}^{\cdot} \in \gamma_v$. Nach 4.6 existiert ein $\boldsymbol{F} \in \gamma$ mit $\boldsymbol{F}_v \subset \{q(a), q(b)\}^{\cdot}$. Das bedeutet $a, b \in [^*F]$ für alle $F \in \boldsymbol{F}$. Aus 2.4(iii) folgt $q(a) = q(b)$.

Sei umgekehrt A_v separiert und seien $\boldsymbol{F}, \boldsymbol{G} \in \gamma$ verbunden. Aus 2.2 und 2.4 folgt $\boldsymbol{F}_v \vee \boldsymbol{G}_v \neq \boldsymbol{E}$, also $\boldsymbol{H} := \boldsymbol{F}_v \cap \boldsymbol{G}_v \in \gamma_v$. Sei $a \in \mu(\boldsymbol{F})$, $b \in \mu(\boldsymbol{G})$. Dann konvergiert $\boldsymbol{H}$ offenbar gegen $q(a)$ und $q(b)$; daraus folgt $q(a) = q(b)$, also

$[\mu(\boldsymbol{F})] = [\mu(\boldsymbol{G})]$, da a und b beliebig waren. Aus 2.4(ii) ergibt sich die Behauptung.

b) Sei (A, γ) v-separiert.

(i) Sei A v-regulär. Wegen 4.6 genügt es, für alle $\boldsymbol{F} \in \gamma$ $h(\boldsymbol{F}_v) \in \gamma_v$ zu beweisen. Seien $\boldsymbol{F} \in \gamma$ und $\boldsymbol{G} \in \gamma$ und $\boldsymbol{G}$ erfülle die in 2.5(ii) genannte Eigenschaft. Zu $G \in \boldsymbol{G}$ existiert also ein $F \in \boldsymbol{F}$, so daß für alle $\boldsymbol{H} \in \gamma$ aus $\boldsymbol{H} \curlyvee \dot{F}$ stets $\mu(\boldsymbol{H}) \subset [{}^*G]$ folgt. Sei $q(a) \in h(F_v)$. Dann existiert ein $\boldsymbol{H} \in \gamma$ mit $\boldsymbol{H}_v \subset q(a)^{\cdot}$ und $\boldsymbol{H}_v \vee \dot{F}_v \neq \boldsymbol{E}$. A_v ist separiert nach a). Also kann $a \in \mu(\boldsymbol{H})$ angenommen werden. Aus $H_v \cap F_v \neq \emptyset$ für jedes $H \in \boldsymbol{H}$ folgt nun $[{}^*H] \cap [{}^*F] \neq \emptyset$, also $\boldsymbol{H} \curlyvee \dot{F}$. Dann gilt $\mu(\boldsymbol{H}) \subset [{}^*G]$ also $q(a) \in G_v$. Das beweist $h(F_v) \subset G_v$, und daraus folgt $h(\boldsymbol{F}_v) \supset \boldsymbol{G}_v$, d.h. $h(\boldsymbol{F}_v) \in \gamma_v$.

(ii) Sei A_v regulär und $\boldsymbol{F} \in \gamma$. Dann existiert nach 4.6 ein $\boldsymbol{G} \in \gamma$ mit $h(\boldsymbol{F}_v) \supset \boldsymbol{G}_v$. Mit 2.5(ii) erhält man unter Verwendung ähnlicher Schlüsse wie unter (i) die Relation $v(\boldsymbol{F}) \supset b(\boldsymbol{G})$. q.e.d.

4.8. Proposition *(Eigenschaften von T).*

a) *T ist genau dann injektiv, wenn A separiert ist.*

b) *T ist genau dann surjektiv, wenn A vollständig ist.*

c) *Sei* (A, γ) *eine separierte,* v-*separierte Cauchy-Algebra und sei* $T(A) =: C$ *versehen mit der Unterraum-Cauchy-Struktur* γ_C *(vergl.* 3.7). *T ist genau dann ein* C-*Isomorphismus von* (A, γ) *auf* (C, γ_C), *wenn A regulär ist.*

Beweis. a): klar.

b): folgt aus 1.9.

c): T ist C-stetig (4.4) und injektiv nach a). Da A v-separiert ist, ist $\gamma_v = \mathcal{M}$ (4.6). Es genügt also, Filter $\boldsymbol{F}_v \vee \dot{C}$ für $\boldsymbol{F} \in \gamma$ zu betrachten. Es wird $T^{-1}(\boldsymbol{F}_v \vee \dot{C})$ erzeugt von Mengen der Form $T^{-1}(F_v \cap C)(F \in \boldsymbol{F})$. Nun liegt a in $T^{-1}(F_v \cap C)$ genau dann, wenn $[a] \cap [{}^*F] \neq \emptyset$ gilt. Nach 1.12 ist dies genau dann der Fall, wenn a aus $h(F)$ ist. Also ergibt sich $T^{-1}(\boldsymbol{F}_v \vee \dot{C}) = h(F)$ und damit der Satz.

4.9. Korollar. *Sei* (A, γ) *separiert und vollständig.* $T: (A, \gamma) \to (A_v, \gamma_v)$ *ist genau dann ein* C-*Isomorphismus, wenn A regulär ist.*

Wir sind nun in der Lage zu zeigen, daß (A_v, γ_v) eine Komplettierung i.S. von 4.2 ist. Dazu müssen wir nur noch die dort geforderte Faktorisierungseigenschaft (ii) beweisen. Es gilt allgemeiner:

4.10. Proposition. *Seien* (A_i, γ_i) *Cauchy-Algebren* $(i = 1, 2)$ *mit gleichem Operationenbereich,* $T_i: A_i \to A_{iv}$ *wie in* 4.3 *und* $S: A_1 \to A_2$ *eine* C-*stetige*

Abbildung. Dann existiert eine C-stetige Abbildung $S':A_{1v} \to A_{2v}$ *mit*

(I) $$S'T_1 = T_2S.$$

Ist A_2 v-*separiert, so ist* S' *durch* (I) *eindeutig bestimmt. Mit* S *ist auch* S' *ein* C-*Morphismus.*

Beweis. Wir betrachten jetzt ein Enlargement der vollen Struktur höherer Ordnung über der Grundmenge $A_1 \cup A_2$. Sei $*S:*A_1 \to A_2$ die S entsprechende Abbildung im Enlargement und S'' die Einschränkung von $*S$ auf $P(*A_1, \gamma_1) =: P_1$. Durch $q_2S'' = S'q_1$ wird wegen 3.5 eine Abbildung $S':A_{1v} \to A_{2v}$ definiert (q_i: s. unter 4.3), die nach Definition von T_i die Beziehung (I) erfüllt. Sei $\boldsymbol{F}$ aus γ_1. Dann ist $S(\boldsymbol{F})$ aus γ_2. Für $F \in \boldsymbol{F}$ gilt

$$S'q_1(*F \cap P_1) = q_2(S''(*F \cap P_1)) \subset q_2(*(S(F)) \cap P_2),$$

also $S'(\boldsymbol{F}_v) \supset (S(\boldsymbol{F}))_v$. Hieraus folgt die Stetigkeit von S'. Ist A_2 v-separiert, so ist A_{2v} separiert (4.7). Ist U eine weitere C-stetige Abbildung von A_{1v} in A_{2v} mit $UT_1 = T_1S$, so stimmen S' und U auf der dichten Untermenge $T_1(A_1)$ überein. Wie üblich schließt man hieraus $S' = U$.

Mit S ist auch $*S$ und damit auch S' ein Ω-Homomorphismus. Damit ist der Satz bewiesen.

4.11. Theorem. (A_v, γ_v) *ist eine Komplettierung von* (A, γ).
Der Beweis ergibt sich sofort aus 4.4, 4.9 und 4.10.

4.12. Definition. (A_v, γ_v) *heißt die Nonstandard-Komplettierung von* (A, γ).

Man kann sich leicht andere Komplettierungen konstruieren, die nicht zur Nonstandard-Komplettierung isomorph sind. Diese erfüllen jedoch nicht die nun in 4.13 beschriebene Eigenschaft, die ihrerseits eine Präzisierung der in der Einleitung genannten Anforderung (iii) an eine Komplettierung darstellt.

4.13. Proposition. *Sei* A *eine uniform dichte Unteralgebra einer vollständigen, separierten, regulären Cauchy-Algebra* (A', γ'), γ *die Unterraum-Cauchy-Struktur auf* A *und* φ *die Einbettungsabbildung von* A *in* A'. *Dann existiert ein* C-*Isomorphismus* φ_v *von* A_v *auf* A' *mit* $\varphi_v T = \varphi$, *wobei* T *die kanonische Abbildung von* A *in* A_v *gemäß* 4.3 *ist.*

Anders ausgedrückt: (A', γ') *ist die Nonstandard-Komplettierung von* (A, γ).

Der Satz wird falsch, wenn man die Bedingung "uniform dicht" durch die schwächere "dicht" ersetzt, wie das im Anschluß an 4.1 gegebene Beispiel zeigt.

Beweis von 4.13. Nach 2.6 und der Bemerkung 2 im Anschluß an 3.7 ist (A, γ) stark separiert, (A_v, γ_v) also nach 4.7 und 4.4 eine separierte, reguläre vollständige Cauchy-Algebra. Sei $T': A' \to A'_v$ die zu A' gemäß 4.3 gehörige Abbildung. T' ist nach 4.9 ein C-Isomorphismus. Es genügt also, einen Isomorphismus φ' von A_v auf A'_v mit $\varphi' T = T'\varphi$ zu finden. Wir benutzen ein Enlargement der vollen Struktur über A'. Dies enthält ein Enlargement der vollen Struktur über A. Somit gilt

(i) $P := P(^*A, \gamma) = P(^*(A'), \gamma') \cap {}^*A$

(ii) $B := B(^*A, \gamma) = B(^*(A'), \gamma') \cap {}^*(A \times A)$

nach Definition der Unterraum-Struktur.

Wir setzen noch $P' := P(^*(A'), \gamma')$. Sei $\bar{\varphi}$ die Einschränkung von $^*\varphi$ auf P und q, q' seien die Quotientenabbildungen aus 4.3, die zu P bzw. P' gehören. Wir beweisen, daß die durch $\varphi' q = q'\bar{\varphi}$ definierte Abbildung φ' ein C-Isomorphismus ist (vergl. den Beweis zu 4.10). Der Rest des Satzes ist dann klar. Aus $\varphi'(q(a)) = \varphi'(q(b))$ folgt $q'(\bar{\varphi}(a)) = q'(\bar{\varphi}(b))$ und damit wegen (i) und (ii) $q(a) = q(b)$. Also ist φ' injektiv. Sei $\hat{a}$ aus A'_v und $a \in A'$ mit $T'(a) = \hat{a}$. Dann existiert ein Filter $\boldsymbol{F} \in \gamma'$ mit $\boldsymbol{F} \vee \dot{A} \neq \boldsymbol{E}$ und $\boldsymbol{F} \to a$. Also ist $\boldsymbol{G} = \varphi^{-1}(\boldsymbol{F} \vee \dot{A})$ aus γ und $\mu(\boldsymbol{G}) \subset \mu(\boldsymbol{F})$, woraus für $b \in \mu(\boldsymbol{G})$ sofort $\varphi'(q(b)) = \hat{a}$ folgt. φ' ist also surjektiv.

φ' ist C-stetig (vergl. den Beweis zu 4.10). Sei $\boldsymbol{F} \in \gamma'$. Dann existiert nach Voraussetzung ein $\boldsymbol{G} \in \gamma'$ mit $A \in \boldsymbol{G}$ und $h(\boldsymbol{G}) \subset \boldsymbol{F}$. Zu $G \in \boldsymbol{G}$ (oBdA $G \subset A$) existiert also stets ein $F \in \boldsymbol{F}$ mit $F \subset h(G)$, woraus $q'(^*F \cap P') \subset q'(^*G \cap P')$ folgt. Es ist $\varphi'(q(^*G \cap P)) = q'(\bar{\varphi}(^*G \cap P))$ und dies ist wegen (i) und (ii) gleich $q'(^*G \cap P')$. Hieraus folgt $\boldsymbol{F}_v \supset \varphi'(\boldsymbol{G}_v)$, also ist φ' C-offen. Damit ist der Satz bewiesen.

4.14. Korollar. *Sei (A, γ) eine uniform dichte Unteralgebra der regulären, separierten, vollständigen Cauchy-Algebra (A', γ'). Dann läßt sich jede C-stetige Abbildung S von A in eine stark separierte Cauchy-Algebra (A_1, γ_1) eindeutig zu einer C-stetigen Abbildung von A' in die Nonstandard-Komplettierung von A_1 fortsetzen.*

Der Beweis folgt aus 4.13 und 4.10.

Bemerkung. Man überlegt sich leicht mit Hilfe von 4.13, daß die Komplettierung eines uniformen Raumes im Sinn von A. Weil Cauchy-isomorph ist zur Nonstandard-Komplettierung dieses Raumes. Man hat dabei nur 4.13 und 3.3 zu benutzen. Damit ist auch die Forderung (iv) der Einleitung erfüllt.

Wir wissen schon, daß A_v eine Cauchy-Algebra mit gleichem Operationenbereich wie die Ausgangsalgebra ist. Wir machen uns nun das von Robinson [1969] für Kompaktifizierungen angegebene Verfahren zunutze, um zu zeigen, daß A_v eine Ω-Γ-Algebra ist. Das Verfahren beruht auf dem bekannten Theorem von R. Lyndon (s. Grätzer [1968] S. 280), daß alle positiven Sätze, die in einer Ω-Algebra gelten, auch in jeder Quotientenalgebra von ihr wahr sind. Hierzu muß offensichtlich die Sprache präzisiert werden, in der die positiven Sätze formuliert sind. Das erwähnte Theorem von Lyndon gilt für eine Sprache L erster Ordnung mit Gleichheit. Die algebraischen Operationen sind nicht durch Konstanten, sondern durch Operationssymbole repräsentiert.

Zur Beschreibung von Strukturen höherer Ordnung bedienen sich Robinson [1966] bzw. Luxemburg [1969] einer Sprache L′ höherer Ordnung, die nur ein bzw. zwei Relationssymbole für jeden Typ besitzt. Die algebraischen Operationen werden durch Konstanten repräsentiert ebenso wie die Gleichheitsrelationen. So lassen sich Sachverhalte, die in L mit einem positiven Satz beschrieben werden können, in L′ nicht mehr durch einen solchen ausdrücken (ein einfaches Beispiel ist das Kommutativgesetz für Halbgruppen).

Die angedeutete Schwierigkeit ist aber metamathematischer Natur und läßt sich einfach so umgehen: Sei $\mathfrak{A}$ eine algebraische Struktur über der Grundmenge A. Dem Gleichheitssymbol und jedem Operations- und Relationssymbol in L, das in $\mathfrak{A}$ interpretierbar ist, ordnen wir die dadurch bestimmte Konstante in L′ zu und setzen diese Abbildung in naheliegender Weise auf die Formeln von L (durch Induktion nach dem Aufbau) fort. Ein in $\mathfrak{A}$ interpretierbarer Satz aus L ist in $\mathfrak{A}$ genau dann wahr, wenn dies für sein Bild zutrifft. Für die Formulierung algebraischer Sachverhalte ist L häufig bequemer.

Für das folgende benutzen wir also L.

Wir nennen eine offene Formel Q arithmetisch, wenn sie aufgebaut ist aus $\vee$, $\wedge$ und $(p = q)$ für beliebige Terme p, q (Grätzer [1968] S. 225f, nennt Terme Polynomsymbole)[1]). Ein Satz heiße *arithmetisch*, wenn er

[1]) Q enthält also keine Negation und kein Relationssymbol außer der Gleichheit.

äquivalent ist zu einem Satz in pränexer Normalform mit arithmetischer Matrix. Enthält der äquivalente Satz außerdem nur All-Quantoren, so nennen wir den gegebenen Satz einen arithmetischen Allsatz.

4.15. THEOREM. *Sei* (A, γ) *eine Cauchy-Algebra mit* Ω *als Operationenbereich und* Σ *ein arithmetischer Allsatz in* L. *Gilt* Σ *in* A, *so auch in* A_v.

Beweis. Es gelte Σ in A. Dann ist Σ auch in der elementaren Erweiterung $^*A$, also auch in der Unteralgebra $P(^*A, \gamma)$ wahr. Nach dem erwähnten Satz von Lyndon gilt Σ schließlich auch in $A_v = q(P(^*A, \gamma))$ (s. 4.3).

Speziell ist mit A auch A_v ein Ring, eine (kommutative) Gruppe etc.

Mit A ist auch $^*A$ ein Körper.[1]) Ist (A, γ) gleichzeitig ein Cauchy-Ring, so kann man die dargestellte Theorie zur Entscheidung heranziehen, wann A_v ein Körper ist. A_v ist der Quotient von $P(^*A, \gamma)$ nach dem Ringideal $[0]_\gamma$. A_v ist also genau dann ein Körper, wenn $[0]_\gamma$ ein maximales Ideal in $P(^*A, \gamma)$ ist. Dies läßt sich leicht in die Sprache der Cauchy-Filter übersetzen. Man erhält zu den Sätzen über topologische Körper ganz analoge Sätze, auf deren Formulierung wir nicht näher eingehen wollen.

Wir fassen die wichtigsten Ergebnisse über die Nonstandard-Komplettierung zusammen:

4.16. *Eigenschaften der Nonstandard-Komplettierung.* Sei (A, γ) eine Cauchy-Algebra mit Ω als Operationenbereich und Γ die Menge aller in A geltenden Gleichungen; sei ferner (A_v, γ_v) die in 4.3 konstruierte Nonstandard-Komplettierung und $T: A \to A_v$ der dort angegebene C-Morphismus. Es gilt:

a) (A_v, γ_v) ist eine vollständige Ω-Γ-Cauchy-Algebra und eine Komplettierung von (A, γ) i.S. von Def. 4.2.

b) Ist A präkompakt, so ist A_v kompakt.[2])

Für die weiteren Abschnitte sei A stark separiert.

c) T ist ein C-Isomorphismus; A kann also mit einer uniform dichten Cauchy-Unteralgebra identifiziert werden.

d) Jede C-stetige Abbildung S von A in eine separierte, reguläre, vollständige Cauchy-Algebra (A_1, γ_1) besitzt eine eindeutig bestimmte Fortsetzung zu einer C-stetigen Abbildung S_1 von (A_v, γ_v) in (A_1, γ_1). Mit S ist auch S_1 ein C-Morphismus.

[1]) Körper sind bekanntlich nur partielle Ω-Strukturen; es gibt kein nur aus arithmetischen Sätzen bestehendes Axiomensystem für sie. Wir betrachten nur kommutative Körper.

[2]) Dieses Ergebnis wird hier vorweggenommen. Der Beweis folgt in 5.5.

e) Ist (A, γ) eine uniform dichte Cauchy-Unteralgebra einer separierten, regulären, vollständigen Cauchy-Algebra (A', γ') so ist diese C-isomorph zu (A_v, γ_v).

Ist Cau(Ω, Γ) die Kategorie aller stark separierten Cauchy-Algebren mit Ω als Operationenbereich, in denen alle Gleichungen aus Γ gelten, so ist nach diesem Paragraphen die Unterkategorie der vollständigen stark separierten Algebren reflexiv und der zum Einbettungsfunktor linksadjungierte Funktor ordnet jedem Objekt aus Cau(Ω, Γ) seine Nonstandard-Komplettierung und jedem C-Morphismus seine Fortsetzung gemäß 4.14 zu.

5. Kompaktheit. Bei Kowalsky [1955] findet man den folgenden "mengentheoretischen Kern" der Beweise der üblichen Überdeckungssätze für kompakte Räume:

5.1. Proposition. *Sei $\mathfrak{B}$ eine Überdeckung einer Menge A, und jeder Ultrafilter auf A enthalte ein Element aus $\mathfrak{B}$. Dann existiert eine endliche Teilmenge von $\mathfrak{B}$, die A überdeckt.*

Beweis. klar.

Wir definieren nun spezielle Überdeckungssysteme:

5.2. Definition. *Sei (A, γ) eine Cauchy-Algebra.*

a) *Eine Überdeckung $\mathfrak{B}$ von A heißt* C*-Überdeckung, wenn für jedes $\mathbf{F} \in \gamma$ stets $\bigcap_{B \in \mathfrak{B}} (\mathbf{F} \vee \dot{B}) \neq \mathbf{E}$ gilt.*

b) *Eine Menge $\mathfrak{U}$ von* C*-Überdeckungen heißt* C*-Basis, wenn zu jedem Ultrafilter $\mathbf{H}$ auf A, der nicht in γ liegt, eine Überdeckung $\mathfrak{B} \in \mathfrak{U}$ existiert, so daß $\{A \backslash B : B \in \mathfrak{B}\}$ Subbasis eines Filters $\mathbf{G} \subset \mathbf{H}$ ist.*[1])

Mit 5.1 erhalten wir sofort den Überdeckungssatz:

5.3. Proposition. *Für eine Cauchy-Algebra (A, γ) sind folgende Aussagen äquivalent:*

(i) *(A, γ) ist präkompakt.*

(ii) *Jede* C*-Überdeckung enthält eine endliche* C*-Überdeckung.*

(iii) *Es existiert eine* C*-Basis $\mathfrak{U}$, so daß jede* C*-Überdeckung aus $\mathfrak{U}$ eine endliche* C*-Überdeckung enthält.*

[1]) $A \setminus B := \{x \in A : x \notin B\}$.

Dieser Satz liefert u.a. eine Vereinheitlichung der bekannten Charakterisierungen für kompakte topologische und präkompakte uniforme Räume. Im ersten Fall wähle man für $\mathfrak{U}$ das System aller offenen Überdeckungen (γ ist hier das System aller konvergenten Filter), im zweiten Fall das System aller Familien $\mathfrak{B}(V) := \{V(x) : x \in A\}$, wo V eine Nachbarschaft und $V(x) := \{y \in A : (x, y) \in V\}$ ist (γ ist hier das System aller Cauchy-Filter).

Wir müssen nun noch ein rein technisches Lemma beweisen. Dazu sei (A, γ) eine Cauchy-Algebra und $\mathfrak{T}$ eine Teilmenge von γ derart, daß zu jedem $\boldsymbol{F} \in \gamma$ endlich viele Elemente $\boldsymbol{G}_1, \ldots, \boldsymbol{G}_n$ aus $\mathfrak{T}$ existieren mit $\bigcap_{i=1}^n \boldsymbol{G}_i \in \gamma$ und $\bigcap_{i=1}^n \boldsymbol{G}_i \subset \boldsymbol{F}$. Für jedes $\boldsymbol{G}$ sei $B(\boldsymbol{G})$ eine festgewählte Filterbasis. Mit Ψ bezeichnen wir die Menge aller Abbildungen ψ von $\mathfrak{T}$ in $\mathfrak{P}(A)$ mit $\psi(\boldsymbol{G}) \in B(\boldsymbol{G})$ für alle $\boldsymbol{G} \in \mathfrak{T}$. Für jedes $\psi \in \Psi$ ist $\psi(\mathfrak{T})$ eine C-Überdeckung.

5.4. Lemma. $\mathfrak{U} := \{\psi(\mathfrak{T}) : \psi \in \Psi\}$ *ist eine* C-*Basis.*

Beweis. Sei $^*\mathfrak{M}$ ein Enlargement der vollen Struktur $\mathfrak{M}$ über A Dann gilt

$$P(^*A, \gamma) = \bigcup_{\boldsymbol{G}\in\mathfrak{T}} \mu(\boldsymbol{G}) = \bigcup_{\boldsymbol{G}\in\mathfrak{T}} \Big(\bigcap_{G\in\boldsymbol{G}} {}^*G\Big) = \bigcap_{\psi\in\Psi} \Big(\bigcup_{\boldsymbol{G}\in\mathfrak{T}} {}^*(\psi(\boldsymbol{G}))\Big).$$

Sei $x \in {}^*A$, aber nicht aus $P(^*A, \gamma)$. Dann existiert ein $\psi \in \Psi$ mit $x \notin \bigcup_{\boldsymbol{G}\in\mathfrak{T}} {}^*(\psi(\boldsymbol{G}))$.

$\mathscr{A} := \{\psi(\boldsymbol{G}) : \boldsymbol{G} \in \mathfrak{T}\}$ ist eine C-Überdeckung und es gilt $x \in \bigcap_{i=1}^n {}^*(A \backslash \psi(\boldsymbol{G}_i))$ für je endlich viele $\boldsymbol{G}_i \in \mathfrak{T}$.

$\{A \backslash \psi(\boldsymbol{G}) : \boldsymbol{G} \in \mathfrak{T}\}$ ist also Subbasis eines nichttrivialen Filters $\boldsymbol{H}$, der gröber ist als der durch x bestimmte Ultrafilter $\boldsymbol{U}_x$, der seinerseits wegen $x \notin P(^*A, \gamma)$ nicht in γ liegen kann. q.e.d.

5.5. Theorem. *Die Nonstandard-Komplettierung* (A_v, γ_v) *einer präkompakten Cauchy-Algebra* (A, γ) *ist kompakt.*

Beweis. Nach 4.4 ist (A_v, γ_v) vollständig. Es genügt also, die Präkompaktheit zu zeigen.

Sei $\mathfrak{T} = \{\boldsymbol{F}_v : \boldsymbol{F} \in \gamma\}$. Aus 4.3 folgt, das $\mathfrak{T}$ den Voraussetzungen von 5.4 genügt. Wir wählen also die C-Basis $\mathfrak{U}$ aus 5.4, die wir gewinnen, wenn wir $B(\boldsymbol{F}_v) = \{F_v : F \in \boldsymbol{F}\}$ setzen.

Sei für jedes $\boldsymbol{F} \in \gamma$ jetzt $\psi(\boldsymbol{F}_v) \in B(\boldsymbol{F}_v)$ beliebig gewählt. Wir nehmen dann für jedes $\boldsymbol{F}$ ein $F =: \varphi(\boldsymbol{F}) \in \boldsymbol{F}$ mit $\psi(\boldsymbol{F}_v) = (\varphi(\boldsymbol{F}))_v$. $\{\varphi(\boldsymbol{F}) : \boldsymbol{F} \in \gamma\}$ ist eine C-Überdeckung von A. Da A jedoch präkompakt ist, gibt es endlich viele $\boldsymbol{F}_1, \ldots, \boldsymbol{F}_n$ mit $A = \bigcup_{i=1}^n \varphi(\boldsymbol{F}_i)$. Also folgt (s. 1.10)

$^*A = \bigcup_{i=1}^n {}^*(\varphi(\boldsymbol{F}_i)) = P(^*A, \gamma)$ und damit

$A_v = \bigcup_{i=1}^n \psi(\boldsymbol{F}_{iv})$. Aus 5.3 folgt der Satz.

Für topologische Ω-Algebren wurde der folgende Gedanke bereits von Holm [1964] verwendet:

Sei (A, γ) eine Cauchy-Algebra und γ_c die feinste Cauchy-Struktur, in der γ und die Menge aller Ultrafilter enthalten sind. (A, γ_c) ist präkompakt.[1])

5.6. DEFINITION. *Die Nonstandard-Komplettierung von* (A, γ_c) *heißt Cauchy-Kompaktifizierung von* (A, γ); *sie wird mit* $\gamma(A)$ *bezeichnet.*

Nach 4.3 ist $\gamma(A)$ homomorphes Bild von $^*A$; diesen Homomorphismus bezeichnen wir mit q_γ und seine Einschränkung auf A mit T_γ.

5.7. THEOREM. *Sei* (A, γ) *eine Cauchy-Algebra. Für die Cauchy-Kompaktifizierung* $\gamma(A)$ *gilt dann:*

a) T_γ *ist ein C-Morphismus und* $T_\gamma(A)$ *ist dicht in* $\gamma(A)$.

b) *Ist* (A', γ') *eine separierte, reguläre kompakte Cauchy-Algebra und* $S: A \to A'$ *ein* C-*Morphismus, so existiert ein eindeutig bestimmter* C-*Morphismus* S' *von* $\gamma(A)$ *in* A' *mit* $S = S'T_\gamma$. *Ist* $S(A)$ *dicht in* A', *so ist* S' *surjektiv und bedingt offen.*

Beweis. Aus $\gamma \subset \gamma_c$ und 4.4 folgt, daß T_γ ein C-Morphismus ist. Sei $^*\mathfrak{M}$ ein Enlargement der vollen Struktur $\mathfrak{M}$ über A und $\hat{a} \in \gamma(A)$, $a \in q_\gamma^{-1}(\hat{a})$. a bestimmt einen Ultrafilter $\boldsymbol{U}_a$ (s. Sektion 0). Dann ist $T_\gamma(\boldsymbol{U}_a)$ feiner als der durch $\{q_\gamma(^*U): U \in \boldsymbol{U}_a\}$ gegebene Filter U', der in $\hat{a}$ enthalten ist, also gegen $\hat{a}$ konvergiert. Damit konvergiert auch $T_\gamma(\boldsymbol{U}_a)$ gegen $\hat{a}$; daraus folgt a).

b) Um 4.10 anwenden zu können, müssen wir zeigen, daß S auch stetig ist für γ_c. Da A' kompakt ist, enthält die gröbste Cauchy-Struktur, für die S stetig ist, γ und alle Ultrafilter, also auch γ_c. Aus 4.9 und 4.10 folgt die Existenz eines eindeutig bestimmten C-Morphismus S' von $\gamma(A)$ in A' mit $S = S'T_\gamma$. Sei $S(A)$ dicht und $a' \in A'$. Dann existiert ein $\boldsymbol{G} \in \gamma'$ mit $\boldsymbol{G} \vee S(A)^{\cdot} \neq \boldsymbol{E}$ und $\boldsymbol{G} \to a'$. Sei $\boldsymbol{U}$ ein Ultrafilter, der feiner als $S^{-1}(\boldsymbol{G} \vee S(A)^{\cdot})$ ist, $T_\gamma(\boldsymbol{U})$ konvergiert in $\gamma(A)$ gegen ein Element $\hat{a}$. Man erhält $S'\hat{a} = a'$. Der Rest folgt aus 3.6(ii).

Mit dem Schluß von Robinson [1969] erhalten wir für Cauchy-Kompaktifizierungen eine Verschärfung von 4.15 (wir benutzen die vor 4.15 erklärten Begriffe).

[1]) Die Menge aller Cauchy-Strukturen, die γ und alle Ultrafilter enthalten, ist nicht leer, da $\mathfrak{P}(A)$ in ihr liegt.

5.8. THEOREM. *Sei* (A, γ) *eine Cauchy-Algebra mit Operationenbereich* Ω *und* Σ *ein arithmetischer Satz in der Sprache* L, *der in* A *gilt. Dann gilt* Σ *in der Cauchy-Kompaktifizierung* $\gamma(A)$ *und darüber hinaus in jeder kompakten regulären separierten Cauchy-Algebra mit dem gleichen Operationenbereich, die ein dichtes* C-*homomorphes Bild von* A *enthält.*

Beweis. Σ gilt auch in $^*A$, also in dem homomorphen Bild $\gamma(A)$ von $^*A$. Der Rest folgt aus 5.7(b).

Hiermit erhält man leicht, daß die Cauchy-Kompaktifizierung einer dividierbaren Limesgruppe wieder dividierbar ist.

Sei (A, γ) eine Cauchy-Algebra. Dann gibt es eine feinste Weil-Struktur auf A (s. Def. 3.1), die γ und alle Ultrafilter und damit auch γ_c enthält. Deren Nonstandard-Komplettierung ist ein kompakter, separierter topologischer Raum (vergl. 3.3 und die Bemerkung im Anschluß an 4.14). Man kann diese Kompaktifizierung nach Bohr benennen. Sie ist wegen 5.7 stets bedingt C-isomorphes Bild der Cauchy-Kompaktifizierung. Als Beispiel wähle man $A = \mathbf{R}$, $\Omega = \emptyset$ und γ als die Menge aller in der gewöhnlichen Topologie konvergenten Filter. Die "Bohr-Kompaktifizierung" ist die Stone-Čech-Kompaktifizierung $\beta(\mathbf{R})$. Man überlegt sich leicht die Beziehung $\gamma(\mathbf{R}) \neq \beta(\mathbf{R})$.

6. Einige weitere Bemerkungen.

I. Die bisherigen Ausführungen galten für Ω-Algebren. Wendet man die Theorie auf Vektorräume über einem Körper $\mathbf{K}$ an, so erhält man nur die Stetigkeit der Multiplikation mit festen Skalaren. Diese Schwierigkeit läßt sich jedoch folgendermaßen umgehen:

Sei (L, γ_L) eine feste Ω_L-Γ_L-Cauchy-Algebra.[1]) Sei ferner $\mathscr{A}$ eine Klasse von Algebren mit Operationenbereich Ω' und zu jeder Algebra A aus $\mathscr{A}$ existiere eine Abbildung $U_A : L \times A \to A$. Wir führen zu jedem $x \in L$ eine einstellige Operation ω_x ein, definiert durch $\omega_x(a) = U_A(x, a)$ (für alle $a \in A$). Sei $\Omega = \Omega' \cup \{\omega_x : x \in L\}$. Dann ist $\mathscr{A}$ eine Klasse von Ω-Algebren. Sei Γ ein System von Gleichungen zwischen Polynomen, aufgebaut aus Ω. Wir betrachten nun die Unterklasse $\mathscr{A}_L$ aller Ω-Γ-Algebren (von der wir annehmen, daß sie nicht leer sei). Sei A aus $\mathscr{A}_L$. Eine Cauchy-Struktur γ auf A heiße L-verträglich, wenn $U_A : L \times A \to A$ C-stetig vom Produkt in (A, γ) ist.

[1]) Ω_L sei ein spezieller Operationenbereich und Γ_L eine feste Menge von Gleichungen, die in L gelten.

Sei (L, γ_L) regulär, separiert und vollständig und (A, γ) eine Ω-Γ-Algebra mit L-verträglicher Cauchy-Struktur γ. *Ist* (A, γ) *stark separiert, so ist* (A_v, γ_v) *eine* Ω-Γ-*Algebra und* γ_v *ist* L-*verträglich.*

Dies folgt sofort mit den in Sektion 4 gezeigten Methoden. Den exakten Beweis möchten wir nicht mehr bringen.

Damit ordnen sich insbesondere Cauchy-Vektorräume über vollständigen regulären, separierten Körpern in unsere Theorie ein, ebenso wie archimedisch geordnete Vektorverbände über **R** etc.

II. Wie schon in der Einleitung angemerkt, umfaßt die Klasse von Räumen, die mit dieser Komplettierungstheorie behandelt wird, diejenige von Kowalsky [1954b], wenn man nur separierte Räume betrachtet. Ein konkretes Beispiel, das nicht von Kowalsky [1954b] erfaßt wird, ist die archimedisch geordnete Verbandsgruppe (bzw. nach I der archimedisch geordnete Vektorverband über **R**) mit der Folgen-Ordnungskonvergenz (s. 2.8), die im Allgemeinen nicht das Diagonallimitierungsaxiom erfüllt.

Um unsere Komplettierung mit derjenigen von Ramaley und Wyler [1970b] zu vergleichen, kann man dort nur den Fall des biregulären Raumes mit der Regularisierenden p und nur uniformisierbare Cauchy-Strukturen heranziehen. Die dort konstruierte Komplettierung ist nicht separiert (selbst im topologischen Fall nicht). Rechnet man den genannten Spezialfall durch und vergleicht ihn mit unserer Komplettierung, so stellt man–abgesehen von der fehlenden Separiertheit–fest, daß in der dortigen Komplettierung die konvergenten Filter im allgemeinen feiner sind als bei uns; insbesondere gilt 4.14 nicht, und über die Gültigkeit von 4.15 läßt sich nur schwer etwas aussagen, da die Autoren keine algebraischen Strukturen betrachten.

III. Als letzte Anwendung der Nonstandard-Theorie möchten wir ein bekanntes Vollständigkeitskriterium für uniforme Räume auf Cauchy-Algebren verallgemeinern (vergl. Bourbaki [1965] S. 202f.).

Sei (A, γ) eine Cauchy-Algebra. Eine C-Basis $\mathfrak{U}$ heißt strikt, wenn gilt:

Ist $\boldsymbol{U}$ ein Ultrafilter aus γ und $\boldsymbol{V}$ der feinste in $\boldsymbol{U}$ enthaltene Filter, der aus Elementen von Überdeckungen aus $\mathfrak{U}$ bildbar ist, so sind alle Ultrafilter, die feiner sind als $\boldsymbol{V}$, äquivalent zu $\boldsymbol{U}$ i. Sinn von 1.7.

Wählen wir ein Enlargement, so läßt sich dies so ausdrücken: Für jedes

$$a \in P({}^*A, \gamma) \text{ ist } \bigcap_{\mathfrak{B} \in \mathfrak{U}} \Big(\bigcap_{\substack{B \in \mathfrak{B} \\ a \in {}^*B}} {}^*B \Big)$$

enthalten in $[a]_\gamma$. Ein Beispiel hierfür ist die in 5.4 gewählte C-Basis $\mathfrak{U}$. Wir erhalten mit diesen Festsetzungen:

Sei (A, γ) ein Cauchy-Raum, γ' eine weitere Cauchy-Struktur und $\mathfrak{U}$ eine strikte C-Basis, deren Überdeckungsfamilien aus in γ' vollständigen Mengen bestehen. Dann ist (A, γ) vollständig.

Eine typische Anwendung des erwähnten Satzes von Bourbaki findet man in den meisten Lehrbüchern über topologische Vektorräume (s. z.B. Schaefer [1971] I1.6). Die oben gezeigte Verallgemeinerung gestattet die Anwendung auf Cauchy-Vektorräume (vergl. Yosida [1967] Prop. 1 auf S. 369):

Sei E ein Vektorverband über $\mathbf{R}$ und $\mathfrak{T}$ eine separierte Vektorraum-Topologie mit der Eigenschaft: Ist $\inf_\alpha (x_\alpha) = 0$ so konvergiert das Netz (x_α) bezüglich $\mathfrak{T}$ gegen 0. Ist zusätzlich jedes Null enthaltende Ordnungsintervall $[a, b] = \{x \in E : a \leqslant x \leqslant b\}$ $\mathfrak{T}$-vollständig, so ist E ordnungsvollständig.

Man betrachtet hier die in 2.8 angedeutete Ordnungskonvergenz für Netze. Die geeignete strikte C-Basis besteht hier aus Überdeckungsfamilien, deren Elemente Verschobene solcher Ordnungsintervalle sind.

Literaturverzeichnis

Biesterfeldt, H. J., 1966a, Completion of a Class of Uniform Convergence Spaces, *Indag. Math.* 28, pp. 602–604.

Biesterfeldt, H. J., 1966b, Regular Convergence Spaces, *Indag. Math.* 28, pp. 605–607.

Binz, E., 1968, Bemerkungen zu limitierten Funktionenalgebren, *Mathem. Ann.* 175, pp. 169–184.

Binz, E. und Keller, H. H., 1966, Funktionenräume in der Kategorie der Limesräume, *Annales Acad. sci. Fenn. Ser.* AI, No. 383.

Birkhoff, G., 1967, *Lattice Theory*, 3rd ed., American Mathem. Soc. Colloquium Publications, Vol. XXV.

Bourbaki, N., 1965, *Eléments de Mathématique;* Livre III, Topologie Générale; chap. 2, Structures uniformes (Herman, Paris, 4ième éd.).

Cook, C. H. und Fischer, H. R., 1965, On Equicontinuity and Continuous Convergence, *Math. Ann.* 159, pp. 94–104.

Cook, C. H. und Fischer, H. R., 1967a, Uniform Convergence Spaces, *Math. Ann.* 173, pp. 290–306.

Cook, C. H. und Fischer, H. R., 1967b, Regular Convergence Spaces, *Math. Ann.* 174, pp. 1–7.

Fischer, H. R., 1959, Limesräume, *Math. Ann.* 137, pp. 269–303.

Grätzer, G., 1968, *Universal Algebra* (D. van Nostrand Comp., Princeton, N.J.).

Holm, P., 1964, On the Bohr Compactification, *Math. Ann.* 156, pp. 34–46.

Keller, H. H., 1968, Die Limes-Uniformisierbarkeit der Limesräume, *Math. Ann.* 176, pp. 334–341.

Kent, D. C., 1967, On Convergence Groups and Convergence Uniformities, *Fundamenta Math.* 60, pp. 213–222.

Kowalsky, H. J., 1954a, Beiträge zur topologischen Algebra, *Math. Nachr.* 11, pp. 143–185.

Kowalsky, H. J., 1954b, Limes-Räume und Komplettierung, *Math. Nachr.* 12, pp. 301–340.

Kowalsky, H. J., 1955, Stonesche Körper und ein Überdeckungssatz, *Math. Nachr.* 14, pp. 57–64.

Luxemburg, W. A. J., 1969, A General Theory of Monads, in: *Applications of Model Theory to Algebra, Analysis, and Probability*, ed. W. A. J. Luxemburg (Holt, Rinehart and Winston, New York) S. 18–86.

Machover, M. und Hirschfeld, J., 1969, *Lectures on Nonstandard Analysis*, Lecture Notes in Mathematics 94 (Springer, Berlin-Heidelberg-New York).

Papangelou, F., 1964, Order Convergence and Topological Completion of Commutative Lattice-Groups, *Math. Ann.* 155, pp. 81–107.

Parikh, R., 1969, A Nonstandard Theory of Topological Groups, in: *Applications of Model Theory to Algebra, Analysis, and Probability*, ed. W. A. J. Luxemburg (Holt, Rinehart and Winston, New York) S. 279–284.

Puritz, Chr., 1972, Skies, Constellations and Monads, *dieser Ausgabe*.

Ramaley, J. F. und Wyler, O., 1970a, Cauchy Spaces I. Structure and Uniformization Theorems, *Math. Ann.* 187, pp. 175–186.

Ramaley, J. F. und Wyler, O., 1970b, Cauchy Spaces II. Regular Completions and Compactifications, *Math. Ann.* 187, pp. 187–199.

Robinson, A., 1966, *Nonstandard Analysis*, Studies in Logic and the Foundations of Mathematics (North-Holland, Amsterdam).

Robinson, A., 1969, Compactifications of Groups and Rings and Nonstandard Analysis, *J. Symbolic Logic* 34, 576–587.

Schaefer, H. H., 1971, *Topological Vector Spaces* (3rd printing, Springer, Berlin-Heidelberg-New York).

Stroyan, K. D., 1970, Additional Remark on the Theory of Monads: Compactifications and Monadic Closure Operators, Vortrag, gehalten auf der *Nonstandard-Analysis-Tagung* in Oberwolfach.

Wloka, J., 1963, Limesräume und Distributionen, *Math. Ann.* 152, pp. 352–409.

Yosida, K., 1967, *Functional Analysis* (2nd ed., Springer, Berlin-Heidelberg-New York).

Received 22 April 1971

SKIES, CONSTELLATIONS AND MONADS[1])

Christian W. PURITZ
University of Glasgow

The division into skies and constellations of $*N - N$, the set of infinite numbers in a nonstandard model of arithmetic, was described in Puritz [1971][2]), of which this paper is partly a continuation. The key results of [1971] connected the sky structure of an ultrapower $N^N/\mathscr{U}$ with a classification of ultrafilters studied, in a completely different context, by Choquet [1968a and b]. They are summarised here in section 1, so that this paper is self-contained.

The notion of a filter monad, due to Luxemburg [1969] and independently to Machover and Hirschfeld [1969], is defined in section 2 and forms a staple ingredient in most of the following work. We first ask: What conditions ensure that a filter $\mathfrak{F}$ on a set X has a non-empty monad in every proper extension $*X$ of X? A sufficient condition is that $\mathfrak{F}$ should be *ample*, i.e. have a countably based refinement. Conversely, the statement (AN) that ampleness is necessary when X has power $\leqslant c$ is deduced from the Continuum Hypothesis (CH), and we also find that AN itself implies the existence of δ-stable filters (P-points in $\beta N - N$). Conditions are then obtained for the image of a monad under a standard mapping to be again a monad. That these conditions may fail to hold even in an enlargement is demonstrated in section 3, which is concerned with monads in $*N$ (and in $*N \times *N$), in particular with the distribution of a monad among the skies of $*N$. In a suitably saturated model a condition slightly weaker than ampleness is necessary and sufficient for a filter monad to meet every sky.

In section 4 a function $p: *N \to *N$ is defined to be *accessible* on a set $A \subseteq *N$ if, for all $a \in A$, $p(a)$ is not in a higher sky than a. We obtain a result relating this idea to that of p being dominated on A by a standard function.

[1]) Most of the research presented here forms part of the author's Ph.D. thesis, and was supported by a scholarship from the University of Glasgow.
[2]) From now on referred to as [1971].

If X is any infinite set, a point $a \in {}^*X$ is called *serial* if there is a 1–1 sequence $(a_n : n \in N)$ of elements of X and a number $\nu \in {}^*N$ such that $a = a_\nu$. For a given a, ν can vary throughout a constellation of ${}^*N$. The theory of skies and constellations is thus seen to have a scope wider than the particular set ${}^*N$.

This is illustrated in section 5 by expressions obtained for the topological monads of a serial point and of a σ-compact set in a metric space, followed by a generalisation to uniform spaces. (In passing Theorem 5.12 characterises the finest uniformity compatible with the usual topology on the reals.) The section concludes with a look at the weak topology of Hilbert space, which is uniformisable.

1. Skies and constellations.

1.1. In what follows M denotes the full structure on N, ${}^*M$ is any non-standard model of M, and N' denotes the set ${}^*N - N$ of infinite natural numbers in ${}^*M$. A *basic ultrapower* or *basic model* is an ultrapower $N^N/\mathscr{U}$ where $\mathscr{U}$ is any free ultrafilter (fuf) on N. F will denote the set of all functions: $N \to N$, and F_0 the set of all $f : N \to N$ such that $f(n) \to \infty$ as $n \to \infty$, i.e. such that $f^{-1}[n]$ is finite for all n. Each $f \in F$ extends in ${}^*M$ to a standard function ${}^*f$ (which I shall normally denote just by f).

The relations $\nearrow$, $\ll$, $\sim$, $\leftrightarrow$ are defined on N' as follows:

$$\begin{aligned}
&a \nearrow b && \text{if there exists } f \in F \text{ such that } \quad f(a) \geqslant b.\\
&a \ll b && \text{if } \quad f(a) < b \quad \text{for all} \quad f \in F.\\
&a \sim b && \text{if } \quad a \nearrow b \quad \text{and} \quad b \nearrow a.\\
&a \leftrightarrow b && \text{if, for some} \quad f, g \in F, \quad f(a) = b \quad \text{and} \quad g(b) = a.
\end{aligned}$$

The *sky*, *constellation* and *exact range* of a number $a \in N'$ are defined respectively as follows:

$$\begin{aligned}
\operatorname{sk}(a) &= \{x \in N' : x \sim a\},\\
\operatorname{con}(a) &= \{x \in N' : x \leftrightarrow a\},\\
\operatorname{er}(a) &= N' \cap \{f(a) : f \in F\}.
\end{aligned}$$

Thus a sky consists of numbers which are not too different in magnitude to be accessible from each other by standard functions. I shall show below (Theorem 4.4) that con(a) consists precisely of the images of a under standard permutations. A sky is always made up of whole constellations. If it is a single constellation it is said to be *linked*.

The set SK[$^*N$] of all the skies in N' is ordered in a natural way: $\text{sk}(a) < \text{sk}(b)$ iff $x < y$ for all $x \sim a$, $y \sim b$, i.e. iff $a \ll b$.

The following results are closely related to [1971] Theorem 3.4, Lemma 8.4, and will be used in the sequel.

1.2. LEMMA. *Let a be any infinite number in any* $^*N$. *Then*

(i) *For all* $f \in F_0$, $f(a) \sim a$.
(ii) *If* $b \sim a$, *then there exists* $f \in F_0$ *such that* $f(a) = f(b)$.

Proof. (i) It is immediate from the definitions that $a \nearrow f(a)$. To show that $f(a) \nearrow a$ we define a kind of inverse to f as follows:

For all $n \in N$, $f_1(n) =$ the largest m for which $f(m) \leqslant n$.

f_1 is well defined (except for values of n below the range of f, which don't matter) because $f^{-1}[1, n]$ is finite for all n, by the definition of F_0. Moreover $f_1(f(n)) \geqslant n$ for all n, so by the defining property of a nonstandard model $f_1(f(a)) \geqslant a$, proving that $f(a) \nearrow a$ as required.

(ii) The proof in [1971] Lemma 8.4, applies. (F_1 is the set of unbounded monotonic functions: $N \to N$, a subset of F_0.)

The main results of [1971] related the skies of a basic ultrapower to the following classification of filters on N.

1.3. DEFINITION. *Let* κ, λ *be any cardinals and let* $\mathfrak{F}$ *be a filter on* N. $\mathfrak{F}$ *will be called* $\kappa\lambda$-*sparse if, for every partition of* N *into countably many sets* $D_1, D_2, D_3, \ldots$, *all of power* $< \kappa$ *(some of them may be empty), either some* $D_m \in \mathfrak{F}$ *or there is an* $\mathfrak{F}$ *set* S (i.e. $S \in \mathfrak{F}$) *such that* $S \cap D_m$ *has power* $|S \cap D_m| < \lambda$ *for all* m. *The set of all* $\kappa\lambda$-*sparse fufs will be denoted by* $S[\kappa\lambda]$.

Sparse filters were studied by Choquet [1968a and b], as well as by other writers. He calls

$\aleph_1\aleph_0$-sparse filters *δ-stable* (or *absolutely* 1-*simple*),
$\aleph_0 2$-sparse filters *rare*,
$\aleph_1 2$-sparse filters *absolute*,

and I shall normally use this terminology from now on. Using CH Choquet proved that $S[\aleph_1 2]$, $S[\aleph_1\aleph_0] - S[\aleph_0 2]$ and $S[\aleph_0 2] - S[\aleph_1\aleph_0]$ are all non-empty, so δ-stability and rarity are independent. Rudin [1956] had previously shown the existence of δ-stable fufs; they are P-points in $\beta N - N$

and their existence makes $\beta N - N$ inhomogeneous. (See [1971] Lemma 4.3 for some other characteristic properties.)

The connection with skies is given in the following result. Note first that a basic ultrapower $N^N/\mathcal{U}$ always has a highest sky, namely $\mathrm{sk}(u)$ where $u = (1, 2, 3, \ldots)/\mathcal{U}$.

1.4. THEOREM. *Let $\mathcal{U}$ be any fuf on N and let $^*N = N^N/\mathcal{U}$. Then*

(a) *$N' = {}^*N - N$ is a single sky iff $\mathcal{U}$ is δ-stable.*

(b) *The highest sky of N' is linked iff $\mathcal{U}$ is rare.*

(c) *N' is a single constellation iff $\mathcal{U}$ is absolute.*[1])

Proof. See [1971] Theorem 4.2. For convenience I shall give here the proof of (a).

Let $a = (a_1, a_2, a_3, \ldots)/\mathcal{U} = (a_n)/\mathcal{U}$ be any number of $^*N$. For each $m \in N$ let $D_m = \{n : a_n = m\}$. The D_m partition N and $|D_m| < \aleph_1$ holds trivially. It is easily seen that a is finite iff some $D_m \in \mathcal{U}$. On the other hand, if $a \in \mathrm{sk}(u)$ so that $f(a) \geqslant u$ for some $f \in F$ then $f(a_n) \geqslant n$ $\mathcal{U}$-a.e., i.e. $S = \{n : f(a_n) \geqslant n\} \in \mathcal{U}$. But $S \cap D_m$ is always finite, as $f(a_n)$ is constant on each D_m.

Conversely, given $S \in \mathcal{U}$ with $|S \cap D_m| < \aleph_0$ for all m, we can define f by

$$f(m) = \text{the largest number in } S \cap D_m$$
$$(\text{or } = 1 \text{ if } S \cap D_m = \phi).$$

Then $f(a_n) \geqslant n$ at least whenever $n \in S$, thus $\mathcal{U}$-a.e., so $f(a) \geqslant u$. We thus find that $\mathcal{U}$ is $\aleph_1\aleph_0$-sparse iff every $a \in {}^*N$ is either finite or in $\mathrm{sk}(u)$, i.e. iff $^*N - N$ is a single sky.

1.5. We can now deduce that (CH) there are basic models with just one sky, which can be linked or unlinked. Basic models with many skies are obtained by iterating the ultrapower construction; I shall amplify this a little as the idea is used in what follows.

If $^*M$ is any nonstandard model of M and $\mathcal{U}$ any fuf on N, then $^*M_1 = ({}^*M)^N/\mathcal{U}$ is another nonstandard model of M. $^*M_1$ has a sub-structure M_1 isomorphic to $M^N/\mathcal{U}$, consisting of all entities of the form $(a_n)/\mathcal{U}$ with each a_n standard. This is called the *lower half* of $^*M_1$, the rest being the *upper half*. In particular the *lower numbers* of $^*N_1 = ({}^*N)^N/\mathcal{U}$ are numbers $(a_n)/\mathcal{U}$ with each a_n finite. It is easy to see that if a is an infinite lower number and b

[1]) I have recently found another connection between $\mathcal{U}$ and $\mathrm{SK}[{}^*N]$: (d) $\mathrm{con}(u)$ is co-initial in $\mathrm{sk}(u)$ iff $\mathcal{U}$ is rapid (in the sense of Mokobodzki [1967–1968], or see Choquet [1968b]).

an upper number then $a \ll b$; thus $^*N_1$ has at least one sky more than $N^N/\mathcal{U}$. In this way one obtains basic models with 2, 3, 4, ..., n, ... skies, or with c skies, SK[$^*N$] being discretely ordered with first and last element in every case. Mathias [1970] has shown further that there are basic ultrapowers with no lowest sky.

If in the above construction $^*M$ was a basic ultrapower $M^N/\mathcal{U}_0$ then $^*M_1 = (M^N/\mathcal{U}_0)^N/\mathcal{U}$ can be shown (Kochen [1961]) to be isomorphic to the (essentially basic) ultrapower $M^{N\times N}/\mathcal{U}_0 \times \mathcal{U}$, where $\mathcal{U}_0 \times \mathcal{U}$ is a fuf on $N \times N$ defined by

$$\begin{aligned} S \in \mathcal{U}_0 \times \mathcal{U} \quad &\text{iff} \quad \{m:(m,n) \in S\} \in \mathcal{U}_0 \quad \text{for } \mathcal{U}\text{-almost all } n, \\ \text{i.e.} \quad &\text{iff} \quad \{n:\{m:(m,n) \in S\} \in \mathcal{U}_0\} \in \mathcal{U}. \end{aligned}$$

1.6. Theorem 1.4 generalises to arbitrary nonstandard models in the following way: If a is any infinite number in any $^*N$, it is easily verified that the family

$$\mathcal{U}_a = \{S \subseteq N : a \in {}^*S\}$$

is a fuf on N, and for any $f, g \in F$, $f(a) = g(a)$ iff $\{n : f(n) = g(n)\} \in \mathcal{U}_a$. Thus er($a$) is isomorphic (in a sense intuitively obvious and defined in [1971] Theorem 3.6) to $N^N/\mathcal{U}_a - N$. We thus have

1.7. THEOREM. *For any infinite a in any* $^*N$,
(a) er(a) $\subseteq$ sk(a) *iff* $\mathcal{U}_a$ *is* δ*-stable,*
(b) er(a) $\cap$ sk(a) = con(a) *iff* $\mathcal{U}_a$ *is rare,*
(c) er(a) = con(a) *iff* $\mathcal{U}_a$ *is absolute,*
where $\mathcal{U}_a = \{S \subseteq N : a \in {}^*S\}$.[1])

1.8. When $^*M$ is an enlargement, we find that $^*N$ has no highest sky, though (CH) there may be a lowest sky. SK[$^*N$] is densely ordered above a certain point. If $^*M$ is κ-saturated with $\kappa > c$, SK[$^*N$] is densely ordered without first or last element and all the skies are unlinked. (See [1971] sections 6 and 7.) The latter results also apply to models which are *adequately saturated* in the sense of the following definition; such models can be constructed without using GCH, e.g. by forming an ultralimit of successive enlargements: see Luxemburg [1969] pp. 32–34. I shall write $\Phi_2(s, x, y)$ to mean that the binary relation s is satisfied by x and y. The domain of s, $D(s) = \{x$: for some y, $\Phi_2(s, x, y)\}$.

1) Also (d) con(a) is coinitial in sk(a) iff $\mathcal{U}_a$ is rapid.

1.9. DEFINITION. *Let κ be any infinite cardinal. The nonstandard model $^*M$ of M will be said to be κ-adequately saturated* (κ-AS) *if the following holds for every internal binary relation s of $^*M$: if there is a set A consisting of standard elements of $D(s)$, with $|A| < \kappa$ and such that s is concurrent on A (i.e. for every finite set $\{x_1, \ldots, x_k\} \subseteq A$ there exists $y \in {}^*M$ such that $\Phi_2(s, x_i, y)$ holds for $i = 1, \ldots, k$), then for every such A there exists $y_1 \in {}^*M$ such that $\Phi_2(s, x, y_1)$ holds for all $x \in A$. $^*M$ will be called adequately saturated* (AS) *if it is κ-AS for some $\kappa > c$.*

The difference between the above and ordinary saturation lies in the restriction that A must consist of standard elements.

If X, Y are any sets the notation $X \subseteq' Y$ will mean that X is almost contained in Y, i.e. $X - Y$ is finite.

2. Filter monads. Filter monads play an important role in Non-Standard Analysis, particularly in topological contexts. They have been extensively studied by Luxemburg [1969] pp. 18–86.

Let X be any infinite set belonging to any structure M (not necessarily based on N), and let $^*M$ be any non-standard model of M. For any filter $\mathfrak{F}$ on X the *monad* of $\mathfrak{F}$ in $^*M$ is defined as

$$\mu(\mathfrak{F}) = \cap\,({}^*S : S \in \mathfrak{F}).$$

This may well be non-empty even when $\mathfrak{F}$ is free so that $\cap(S : S \in \mathfrak{F}) = \phi$. In fact enlargements are completely characterised by the fact that in them all proper filters have non-empty monads (Luxemburg [1969] p. 37). In that case filters are characterised by their monads: for every filter $\mathfrak{F}$ on X,

$$\mathfrak{F} = \{S \subseteq X : \mu(\mathfrak{F}) \subseteq {}^*S\},$$

and many properties of filters are reflected in their monads, which makes these a valuable aid to the understanding of topology.

If $^*M$ is not an enlargement, then some monads are empty, but provided $^*M$ is a proper extension of M not all monads are empty. I shall illustrate this with two examples and then consider the question: for what $\mathfrak{F}$ is $\mu(\mathfrak{F}) \neq \phi$ in every proper extension of M? For the first example we need

2.1. DEFINITION. *A point $a \in {}^*X$ will be called serial if there is a countable subset S of X with $a \in {}^*S$.*

It is obvious that all points of $^*N$ are serial. Also if $^*X = X^N/\mathscr{U}$ then all points of $*X$ are serial, for if $a = (a_n)/\mathscr{U}$ then $S = \{a_n : n \in N\}$ is a countable subset of X and $a \in *S$.

Now suppose X is uncountable and let

$$\mathfrak{F} = \{S \subset X : |X - S| \leqslant \aleph_0\}.$$

It is easy to see that $\mathfrak{F}$ is a filter and that $\mu(\mathfrak{F})$ consists of all the non-serial points of $*X$, so $\mu(\mathfrak{F})$ is empty in every basic model.

On the other hand if we take the Frechet filter on N,

$$\mathscr{F}\imath = \{S \subseteq N : |N - S| < \aleph_0\},$$

we find that $\mu(\mathscr{F}\imath) = *N - N$, which is non-empty in every proper extension of arithmetic. It is not hard to see that the same applies to any filter of the form $f(\mathscr{F}\imath)$ with $f : N \to X$, and to any filter which has such an $f(\mathscr{F}\imath)$ as a refinement. I shall show, assuming CH, that if $|X| \leqslant c$, no other free filters on X have guaranteed non-empty monads. I shall assume that N is embedded in X and shall call $*M$ a *proper extension of* M (and $*X$ likewise of X) iff $*N - N \neq \emptyset$. (In the case when X is of measurable cardinal Luxemburg [1962] has shown that it is possible for $*N - N$ to be empty while $*X - X$ is non-empty; we want to exclude this possibility.)

2.2. THEOREM. *The filter* $\mathfrak{F}$ *on* X *has non-empty monad in every proper extension iff for every fuf* $\mathscr{U}$ *on* N *there is a map* $f : N \to X$ *such that* $f(\mathscr{U}) \supseteq \mathfrak{F}$.

Proof. The condition is necessary, for every basic $*M = M^N/\mathscr{U}$ is a proper extension. If in such $*M$, $\mu(\mathfrak{F})$ has a point $a = (a_n)/\mathscr{U}$ say, let $f : N \to X$ be the map for which $f(n) = a_n$. Then for all $S \in \mathfrak{F}$, $a \in *S$, so that $\{n : f(n) \in S\} \in \mathscr{U}$, i.e. $f^{-1}[S] \in \mathscr{U}$. But this means that $S \in f(\mathscr{U})$ for all $S \in \mathfrak{F}$, so $f(\mathscr{U}) \supseteq \mathfrak{F}$.

To prove sufficiency, let a be any number in $*N - N$ and let $\mathscr{U}_a$ be the fuf of sets containing a. Let $f : N \to X$ be such that $f(\mathscr{U}_a) \supseteq \mathfrak{F}$. Then $f(a) \in *X$ and since $a \in \mu(\mathscr{U}_a)$ $f(a) \in \mu(f(\mathscr{U}_a))$, so $f(a) \in \mu(\mathfrak{F})$.

2.3. Before going further we have to consider a rather trivial complication arising from the fact that $\mathfrak{F}$ may not be free, in which case we have $\emptyset \neq \cap(S : S \in \mathfrak{F}) \subseteq \mu(\mathfrak{F})$. In particular this holds when $\mathfrak{F}$ is a principal filter, i.e. $\mathfrak{F}$ is the set of all supersets of some (non-empty) $S_0 \subseteq X$. In that case $\mu(\mathfrak{F}) = *S_0$. However $\mathfrak{F}$ may be neither free nor principal. The following result deals with this situation and enables us from then on to consider free filters only.

2.4. THEOREM. *Every filter* $\mathfrak{F}$ *is free or principal or is the intersection of a free filter* $\mathfrak{F}_1$ *with a principal filter* $\mathfrak{F}_2$, *in which case* $\mu(\mathfrak{F}) = \mu(\mathfrak{F}_1) \cup \mu(\mathfrak{F}_2)$.

Proof. Suppose $\mathfrak{F}$ is neither free nor principal and let $S_0 = \cap(S : S \in \mathfrak{F})$ and $\mathfrak{F}_1$ be the principal filter generated by S_0. Since $\mathfrak{F}$ is not principal, $S_0 \notin \mathfrak{F}$ so that $S - S_0 \neq \emptyset$ for all $S \in \mathfrak{F}$. The sets $S - S_0 : S \in \mathfrak{F}$ therefore generate a filter $\mathfrak{F}_2$ which is easily seen to be free. Furthermore the $\mathfrak{F}$ sets are precisely those which belong to both $\mathfrak{F}_1$ and $\mathfrak{F}_2$; finally $\mu(\mathfrak{F}_1 \cap \mathfrak{F}_2) = \mu(\mathfrak{F}_1) \cup \mu(\mathfrak{F}_2)$ is easily verified (c.f. Luxemburg [1969] p. 44, Theorem 2.3.2).

2.5. THEOREM. *Let* $\mathfrak{F}$ *be a free filter on* X *and* $^*X$ *any proper extension of* X. *The following statements are equivalent:*

(a) $\mathfrak{F}$ *has a countably based refinement.*

(b) $\mathfrak{F}$ *has an elementary refinement.*

(c) *There is an infinite set* $S_0 \subseteq X$ *such that* $S_0 \subseteq' S$ *for all* $S \in \mathfrak{F}$, *i.e. such that* $\emptyset \neq {}^*S_0 - S_0 \subseteq \mu(\mathfrak{F})$.

Proof. (a) $\Rightarrow$ (b). Let $\mathfrak{F}' \supseteq \mathfrak{F}$ be generated by the sets S_n, $n \in N$. We can arrange that $S_1 \supset S_2 \supset S_3 \ldots$, the inclusions being proper in each case, as $\mathfrak{F}$ is free. For each n let a_n be any point of $S_n - S_{n+1}$. The tails of the sequence $(a_n : n \in N)$ generate a filter $\mathfrak{F}'' \supseteq \mathfrak{F}$ which (by definition) is elementary.

(b) $\Rightarrow$ (c). Given the sequence $(a_n : n \in N)$ whose tails generate a refinement $\mathfrak{F}''$ of $\mathfrak{F}$ let $S_0 = \{a_n : n \in N\}$, the range of the sequence. This is infinite as $\mathfrak{F}$ is free, and $S_0 \subseteq' S$ for all $S \in \mathfrak{F}''$, so for all $S \in \mathfrak{F}$. But this implies that $^*S_0 - S_0 \subseteq {}^*S$ for all $S \in \mathfrak{F}$, so $\emptyset \neq {}^*S_0 - S_0 \subseteq \mu(\mathfrak{F})$.

(c) $\Rightarrow$ (a). Given S_0 satisfying (c) let $S_0' = \{a_n : n \in N\}$ be a countable subset of S_0. The tails of $(a_n : n \in N)$ form a countable base for a refinement of $\mathfrak{F}$.

2.6. DEFINITION. *A free filter which satisfies any and hence all of the conditions of Theorem* 2.5. *will be said to be ample.*

It is immediate from Theorem 2.5(c) that, if $\mathfrak{F}$ is an ample filter on X, then $\mu(\mathfrak{F}) \neq \emptyset$ in every proper extension of M. That ampleness is also a necessary condition in the case $|X| \leqslant c$ will now be shown using CH; the use of CH is fairly essential, for we find that the result being proved itself implies the existence of δ-stable fufs (P-points). We shall take $X = \mathbf{R}$ without loss of generality, as cardinality is the only thing that matters.

2.7. THEOREM. *Let* AN *be the statement: "For every free filter* $\mathfrak{F}$ *on* R, *if* $\mu(\mathfrak{F})$ *is non-empty in every proper extension* $^*M$ *of* M, *then* $\mathfrak{F}$ *is ample*". *Then*

(i) CH *implies* AN,

(ii) AN *implies that there is a* δ*-stable fuf on* N.

Proof. (i) Suppose $\mathfrak{F}$ is not ample, so that for every infinite $S_0 \subseteq R$ there is an $\mathfrak{F}$ set S such that $S_0 - S$ is infinite. We construct a fuf $\mathscr{U}$ on N such that for all $f: N \to R, f(\mathscr{U}) \not\supseteq \mathfrak{F}$. There are c such f and we well order them into $(f_\alpha : \alpha < \Omega)$, where Ω is the first uncountable ordinal (assuming $|\Omega| = c$, i.e. CH); we take f_0 to be the identity, $f_0(n) = n$. We then construct by induction a sequence $(N_\alpha : \alpha < \Omega)$ of infinite subsets of N with the following properties:

(a) $\forall \alpha < \beta < \Omega, \quad N_\beta \subseteq' N_\alpha$: the sequence is *almost decreasing*.

(b) $\forall \alpha < \Omega \quad \exists S_\alpha \in \mathfrak{F}$ such that $f_\alpha[N_\alpha] \cap S_\alpha = \emptyset$.

To do this let N_0 be any infinite subset of N such that $N - N_0 \in \mathfrak{F}$, thus satisfying (b). Now suppose that $(N_\beta : \beta < \alpha)$ has been constructed with the desired properties. As $\alpha < \Omega$ the family $\{N_\beta : \beta < \alpha\}$ is finite or countable, so using (a) we can construct an infinite set $A_\alpha \subseteq N$ such that $A_\alpha \subseteq' N_\beta$ for all $\beta < \alpha$. If $f_\alpha[A_\alpha]$ is finite we take $N_\alpha = A_\alpha$. Otherwise let $S_\alpha \in \mathfrak{F}$ be such that $f_\alpha[A_\alpha] - S_\alpha$ is infinite (using the non-ampleness of $\mathfrak{F}$). We then take

$$N_\alpha = \{n \in A_\alpha : f_\alpha(n) \notin S_\alpha\}.$$

This is infinite and $\subseteq' N_\beta$ for $\beta < \alpha$, and $f_\alpha[N_\alpha] \cap S_\alpha = \emptyset$, so the existence of (N_α) follows by induction. If $\mathscr{U}$ is any fuf containing the N_α then (b) ensures that $f(\mathscr{U}) \not\supseteq \mathfrak{F}$ for every $f \in R^N$ so that (i) follows from Theorem 2.2.

(ii) For each $k \in N, f \in F$, let $S_{k,f} \subseteq N \times N$ be given by

$$S_{k,f} = \{(m, n) : m > k \quad \text{and} \quad f(m) < n\}.$$

The sets $S_{k,f}$, $k \in N, f \in F$, generate a filter $\mathfrak{F}$ whose monad consists of all pairs (a, b) of infinite numbers with $a \ll b$. Now it is not hard to see that $\mathfrak{F}$ is not ample: given any infinite $S_0 \subseteq N \times N$ we can construct $S \in \mathfrak{F}$ such that $S_0 - S$ is infinite. It then follows from AN that there is a basic $^*M = M^N/\mathscr{U}$ in which $\mu(\mathfrak{F}) = \emptyset$, so that $N^N/\mathscr{U}$ has only one sky, whence $\mathscr{U}$ is δ-stable by Theorem 1.4(a).

2.8. *Remarks.* (1) I do not know whether the existence of P-points implies AN.

(2) The following counterexample shows that AN need not hold with R replaced by a set of power $> c$. Let I be a set of power 2^c and let $X = N \times I$. Let $(\mathscr{U}_i : i \in I)$ be a listing of all fufs on N, and let the filter $\mathfrak{F}$ on X be defined as follows:

$S \in \mathfrak{F}$ iff for all $i \in I$, $\{n : (n, i) \in S\} \in \mathscr{U}_i$. It is easy to see that $\mathfrak{F}$ is not ample. However $\mu(\mathfrak{F}) \neq \emptyset$ in every proper extension, because if $\mathscr{U}$ is any fuf on N then $\mathscr{U} = \mathscr{U}_i$ for some $i \in I$ and we take $f: N \to X$ given by $f(n) = (n, i)$, so that $f(\mathscr{U}) \supseteq \mathfrak{F}$ follows immediately.

(3) Ample filters can always be further refined, e.g. by forming the tails of $(a_{2n}: n \in N)$. Thus no fufs are ample.

2.9. *The transformation of monads.* We now consider the question: Is the image $f[\mu(\mathfrak{F})]$ of a filter monad $\mu(\mathfrak{F})$ under a standard mapping f again a monad? We may expect the image to be related to the monad of $f(\mathfrak{F})$. I shall write $f\mu\mathfrak{F}$ and $\mu f\mathfrak{F}$ for $f[\mu(\mathfrak{F})]$ and $\mu(f(\mathfrak{F}))$ from now on.

2.10. THEOREM.[1]) *Let X, Y be any sets in a structure M, $\mathfrak{F}$ a filter on X, f a map from X to Y, and $^*M$ any nonstandard model of M. Then*

(i) $f\mu\mathfrak{F} \subseteq \mu f\mathfrak{F}$.

(ii) *If $^*M$ is an enlargement, $\mu f\mathfrak{F}$ is the smallest monad containing $f\mu\mathfrak{F}$; thus $f\mu\mathfrak{F}$ is not a monad unless $f\mu\mathfrak{F} = \mu f\mathfrak{F}$.*

(iii) *$f\mu\mathfrak{F} = \mu f\mathfrak{F}$ iff the following condition is satisfied:*

(C) *For every $y \in \mu f\mathfrak{F}$, if $f^{-1}[y] \cap {}^*S \neq \emptyset$ for all $S \in \mathfrak{F}$ then $f^{-1}[y] \cap \mu\mathfrak{F} \neq \emptyset$.*

Proof. (i) Let $y \in f\mu\mathfrak{F}$. Then $y = f(x)$ for some $x \in \mu\mathfrak{F}$. For every $S \in \mathfrak{F}$, $x \in {}^*S$ so $y \in f[{}^*S]$, hence $y \in \mu f\mathfrak{F}$.

(ii) Let $\mathfrak{F}'$ be any filter such that $\mu\mathfrak{F}' \supseteq f\mu\mathfrak{F}$. For every $S \in \mathfrak{F}'$, ${}^*S \supseteq \mu\mathfrak{F}' \supseteq f\mu\mathfrak{F}$, so $f^{-1}[{}^*S] \supseteq \mu\mathfrak{F}$. Since $^*M$ is an enlargement $\mathfrak{F}$ is characterised by its monad, thus $f^{-1}[S] \in \mathfrak{F}$, so $S \in f(\mathfrak{F})$. As S was any set of $\mathfrak{F}'$, $\mathfrak{F}' \subseteq f(\mathfrak{F})$ and so $\mu f\mathfrak{F} \subseteq \mu\mathfrak{F}'$, proving (ii).

(iii) Suppose $y \in \mu f\mathfrak{F}$; this holds iff $y \in f[{}^*S]$ for all $S \in \mathfrak{F}$, i.e. iff $f^{-1}[y]$ meets all such ${}^*S$. If (C) holds we then have $f^{-1}[y]$ meets $\mu\mathfrak{F}$, so $y = f(x)$ for some $x \in \mu\mathfrak{F}$, then $y \in f\mu\mathfrak{F}$ as required. If (C) fails for some $y \in \mu f\mathfrak{F}$, then $y \notin f\mu\mathfrak{F}$ as $f^{-1}[y] \cap \mu\mathfrak{F}$ then $= \emptyset$.

Before going on to examine when condition (C) is satisfied, we shall consider here an important general result (due to Luxemburg) of which (C) is a special case.

2.11. THEOREM. *Let $\mathfrak{F}$ be any filter on X, let $^*M$ be a κ-AS model of M with $\kappa > |\mathfrak{F}|$, and let A be any internal subset of $^*X$. If A meets $^*S$ for every $S \in \mathfrak{F}$ then A meets $\mu(\mathfrak{F})$.*

[1]) Part (ii) and a result related to (iii) are derived by Machover and Hirschfeld [1969] 5.1.9–10.

Proof. (See Luxemburg [1969] p. 55, Theorem 2.7.10.) Let the binary relation s_3 be satisfied by (S, a) whenever S is an internal subset of $^*X$ and $a \in A \cap S$. By hypothesis s_3 is concurrent on $\mathfrak{F}$, whence the result follows.

The above theorem may fail to hold in an enlargement; see Example 2.7.4 in Luxemburg [1969] p. 53, or see 3.2 below for a simpler example.

2.12. THEOREM. *Condition* (C) *is satisfied whenever either*
(a) $^*M$ *is* κ-AS *with* $\kappa > |\mathfrak{F}|$,
or (b) f *is such that for some* $k \in N$, $f^{-1}[y] < k$ *for all* $y \in Y$ (*in particular if* f *is* 1–1).

Proof. (a) follows from Theorem 8.11 and the fact that the sets $f^{-1}[y]$ are internal.

For (b), observe that if $f^{-1}[y] < k$ for all $y \in Y$, the same holds for all $y \in {}^*Y$. Let $y \in \mu f \mathfrak{F}$ and suppose that $f^{-1}[y] \cap \mu\mathfrak{F} = \emptyset$. This will entail $f^{-1}[y] \cap {}^*S = \emptyset$ for some $S \in \mathfrak{F}$, which gives the result by contraposition. Indeed, let $f^{-1}[y] = \{x_1, x_2, \ldots, x_m\}$ say, with $m < k$. For $i = 1, \ldots, m$ $x_i \notin \mu\mathfrak{F}$ so there exists $S_i \in \mathfrak{F}$ with $x_i \notin {}^*S_i$. Then $S = S_1 \cap S_2 \ldots \cap S_m \in \mathfrak{F}$ and $f^{-1}[y] \cap {}^*S = \emptyset$ as asserted.

I shall give below (3.5 and 3.10) examples in which condition (C) fails so that $f\mu\mathfrak{F}$ is not a monad.

3. Monads and skies in $^*N$. We begin with some simple properties of monads in $^*N$.

3.1. THEOREM. *Let* $\mathscr{U}$ *be a fuf (or any free filter) on* N *and let* $^*M$ *be an enlargement or an* AS *model of* M. *Then*
(i) $|\mu(\mathscr{U})| = |{}^*N|$ *and* $\mu(\mathscr{U})$ *is cofinal in* N'.
(ii) *If* $^*M$ *is* AS $\mu(\mathscr{U})$ *is coinitial in* N'.

Proof. (i) I shall show the existence of a strictly increasing function $p: {}^*N \to {}^*N$ such that $p[{}^*N] \subseteq \mu(\mathscr{U})$. Let r be the binary relation which is satisfied by (S, f) iff $S \in {}^*\mathscr{U}$, f is a strictly increasing function: $^*N \to {}^*N$ and $f[{}^*N] \subseteq S$. Given any k elements $^*S_1, \ldots, {}^*S_k$ of $\mathscr{U}$ let $S_0 = S_1 \cap \ldots \cap S_k$. Then S_0 is infinite, so there exists f such that $({}^*S_0, {}^*f)$ satisfies r, and hence so does $({}^*S_i, {}^*f)$, $i = 1, \ldots, k$. Thus r is concurrent on $\mathscr{U}$; but r is standard, so are the sets of $\mathscr{U}$ and $|\mathscr{U}| = c$, so the assumptions on $^*M$ ensure the existence of p as defined above. Since p is strictly increasing its range is cofinal in and has the same power as $^*N$, so the same is true of $\mu(\mathscr{U})$.

(ii) Let a be any number of N'. Then for every $S \in \mathscr{U}$, $[1, a] \cap {}^*S \neq \emptyset$, and it follows from Theorem 2.11 that $[1, a] \cap \mu(\mathscr{U}) \neq \emptyset$.

3.2. A simple example will show that (ii) above can fail in an enlargement. Thus let $\mathscr{U}_1$, $\mathscr{U}_2$ be fufs such that in $N^N/\mathscr{U}_2$ $\mu(\mathscr{U}_1) = \emptyset$. Let ${}^*M$ be any enlargement of M and let ${}^*M_2 = {}^*M^N/\mathscr{U}_2$. Then in ${}^*M_2$ $\mu(\mathscr{U}_1)$ contains only upper numbers, so is not coinitial in N'. Indeed, if a is a lower number (i.e. a comes from $N^N/\mathscr{U}_2 - N$), then $\mu(\mathscr{U}_1) \cap [1, a] = \emptyset$ even though $[1, a]$ meets ${}^*S$ for all $S \in \mathscr{U}$, so that we have a counterexample to Theorem 2.11.

3.3. *The monad of* $\mathscr{U}_1 \times \mathscr{U}_2$: *A counterexample*. For any fufs $\mathscr{U}_1$, $\mathscr{U}_2$ on N, $\mathscr{U}_1 \times \mathscr{U}_2$ denotes the fuf on $N \times N$ defined in 1.5 above. I shall here obtain an expression for its monad, which is of some interest in itself and which also furnishes a counterexample to Theorem 2.10(iii); i.e. we find a map f and an enlargement in which $f\mu(\mathscr{U}_1 \times \mathscr{U}_2)$ is not a monad.

The exact range of a number $a \in N'$ was defined in 1.1 above. $b < \operatorname{er}(a)$ means that $b < x$ for all $x \in \operatorname{er}(a)$, i.e. b is so much smaller than a that for any $f \in F$, $f(a)$ is either greater than b or finite.

3.4. THEOREM. *If* $\mathscr{U}_1$, $\mathscr{U}_2$ *are fufs on* N *and* $\mathscr{U} = \mathscr{U}_1 \times \mathscr{U}_2$,

$$\mu\mathscr{U} = \{(a_1, a_2) : a_1 \in \mu\mathscr{U}_1, a_2 \in \mu\mathscr{U}_2 \quad \text{and} \quad a_2 < \operatorname{er}(a_1)\}.$$

Proof. That $\mu\mathscr{U} \subseteq \mu\mathscr{U}_1 \times \mu\mathscr{U}_2$ is fairly obvious. Indeed, if (say) $a_1 \notin \mu\mathscr{U}_1$, let $S_1 \in \mathscr{U}_1$ be such that $a_1 \notin {}^*S_1$ and let S_2 be any $\mathscr{U}_2$ set. Then $S_1 \times S_2 \in \mathscr{U}$ but $(a_1, a_2) \notin {}^*S_1 \times S_2$, so $\notin \mu\mathscr{U}$. Further, suppose that $a_1 \in \mu\mathscr{U}_1$, $a_2 \in \mu\mathscr{U}_2$ but that $a_2 \nless \operatorname{er}(a_1)$, say $h(a_1) \leqslant a_2$ with $h \in F$, $h(a_1) \in N'$. For each $n \in N$ let $S_n = \{m : h(m) > n\}$. Then since $h(a_1)$ is infinite $a_1 \in {}^*S_n$, so that $S_n \in \mathscr{U}_1$ for all n (as $\mathscr{U}_1$ is ultra and $a_1 \in \mu\mathscr{U}_1$). Thus $S = \bigcup_{n=1}^{\infty} (S_n \times n)$ belongs to $\mathscr{U}$. But $S_{a_2} = \{m \in {}^*N : h(m) > a_2\}$ and $h(a_1) \leqslant a_2$, so $a_1 \notin S_a$ and $(a_1, a_2) \notin {}^*S$, so $(a_1, a_2) \notin \mu\mathscr{U}$.

Now suppose that $a_1 \in \mu\mathscr{U}_1$, $a_2 \in \mu\mathscr{U}_2$ and $a_2 < \operatorname{er}(a_1)$, and let S be any $\mathscr{U}$ set. We shall show that $(a_1, a_2) \in {}^*S$, thus completing the proof. For each $n \in N$ let $S_n = \{m : (m, n) \in S\}$ and $S'_n = S_n - [1, n]$, and define $h \in F$ as follows:

$$h(m) = \text{the smallest } n \text{ such that } S_n \in \mathscr{U}_1 \text{ and } m \notin S'_n.$$

The definition is good because $S \in \mathscr{U}$, so that $S_n \in \mathscr{U}_1$ for $\mathscr{U}_2$-almost all n, while $m \notin S'_n$ whenever $n \geqslant m$. Also $a_1 \in {}^*S'_n$ whenever $S_n \in \mathscr{U}_1$, so $h(a_1)$ must be infinite. Therefore $a_2 < h(a_1)$ by hypothesis. Now $S_0 = \{n : S_n \in \mathscr{U}_1\} \in$

$\mathscr{U}_2$ and $a_2 \in \mu\mathscr{U}_2$, so $a_2 \in {}^*S_0$, whence (by transfer to ${}^*M$) $S_{a_2} \in {}^*\mathscr{U}_1$. Since $a_2 < h(a_1)$ and $h(a_1)$ is the smallest v such that $S_v \in {}^*\mathscr{U}_1$ and $a_1 \notin S_v$, it follows that $a_1 \in S_{a_2}$, so that $(a_1, a_2) \in {}^*S$ as asserted.

3.5. Now let $p: N \times N \to N$ be the projection onto the first co-ordinate: $p(m, n) = m$. It is easily seen that $p(\mathscr{U}) = \mathscr{U}_1$. Let ${}^*M$ be any enlargement of M and let ${}^*M_1 = {}^*M^N/\mathscr{U}_1$. The number $u_1 = (1, 2, 3, \ldots)/\mathscr{U}_1$ is a lower number in ${}^*N_1$ and belongs to the monad of $\mathscr{U}_1$ in ${}^*M_1$ (because, for any $S \subseteq N$, $u_1 \in {}^*S$ iff $\{n : n \in S\} \in \mathscr{U}_1$, i.e. iff $S \in \mathscr{U}_1$). Also $\mathrm{er}(u_1)$ consists of all the infinite lower numbers of ${}^*N_1$. Thus there is no infinite $a_2 < \mathrm{er}(u_1)$, so that $\mu\mathscr{U}$ has no point (u_1, a_2). It follows that $u_1 \notin p\mu\mathscr{U}$ although $u_1 \in \mu\mathscr{U}_1 = \mu p\mathscr{U}$. Thus $p\mu\mathscr{U}$ is a proper subset of $\mu p\mathscr{U}$ and is not a monad.

The example can be sharpened a little by considering instead of $N \times N$ the set $X' = \{(m, n) : m \geqslant n\}$ and taking $\mathscr{U}'$ to be the trace of $\mathscr{U}$ on X. The projection $p' = p|X'$ has the property that $p'^{-1}[n]$ is finite for all n, while $\mu\mathscr{U}' = \mu\mathscr{U}$ and $p'\mu\mathscr{U}' \neq \mu p'\mathscr{U}'$ as above. [If we then take for $\mathscr{U}_1$ a rare fuf, so that $\mu\mathscr{U}_1 \cap \mathrm{sk}(u_1) = \{u_1\}$ (see 3.6 below), we can construct a counter-example to [1971] Theorem 8.7(b) as follows:

Let the 1–1 correspondence $q: X' \to N$ be defined by $q(m, n) = \frac{1}{2}m(m-1) + n$. q is chosen so that $f = p' \circ q^{-1}$ is a monotonic unbounded function: $N \to N$, i.e. $f \in F_1$. Let $\mathscr{V}_1 = q(\mathscr{U})$, let $v = q(u_1, u_1)$ and let

$$\mathscr{V}_2 = \{S \subseteq N : v \in {}^*S\}.$$

Then $f(\mathscr{V}_1) = p'(\mathscr{U}) = \mathscr{U}_1$, and $f(\mathscr{V}_2)$ also equals $\mathscr{U}_1$, since $f(v) = u_1$. Now $v \in \mu\mathscr{V}_2$, which thus meets $\mathrm{sk}(v)$. But $\mu\mathscr{V}_1$ does not meet $\mathrm{sk}(v)$, for if (say) v_1 belonged to $\mu\mathscr{V}_1 \cap \mathrm{sk}(v)$, then we would have $f(v_1) \in \mathrm{sk}(f(v)) \cap f\mu\mathscr{V}_1 = \mathrm{sk}(u_1) \cap f\mu\mathscr{V}_1$, which is impossible because $f\mu\mathscr{V}_1 \subseteq \mu\mathscr{U}_1 - \{u_1\}$ which does not meet $\mathrm{sk}(u_1)$ as $\mathscr{U}_1$ is rare. Thus $f(\mathscr{V}_1) = f(\mathscr{V}_2)$ with $f \in F_1$, but $\mu\mathscr{V}_1$ and $\mu\mathscr{V}_2$ do not meet the same skies: $\mathrm{SM}[\mathscr{V}_1] \neq \mathrm{SM}[\mathscr{V}_2]$ in the notation of [1971].]

3.6. In [1971] I showed that, in an enlargement of M, a rare ($\aleph_0$2-sparse) filter on N is characterised by the fact that its monad has at most one point in any sky[1]); and (CH) no union of c or less fuf monads

[1]) An analogous characterisation of absolute fufs is as follows: $\mathfrak{F}$ is absolute iff, in any enlargement, whenever $a, b \in \mu\mathfrak{F}$ and $a < b$, $a < \mathrm{er}(b)$. This is not hard to prove directly, but occurred to me, via Theorem 3.4 above, from a result of A. Louveau (Ultrafiltres absolus, to appear in *Seminaire Choquet*): $\mathfrak{F}$ is absolute iff $\mathfrak{F} \times \mathfrak{F} = \mathfrak{F}^{(2)}$, the trace of $\{S \times S : S \in \mathfrak{F}\}$ on $\{(m, n) : m < n\}$.

meets every sky (Theorems 8.5 and 8.9). Here we shall consider what filters $\mathfrak{F}$ are such that $\mu\mathfrak{F}$ meets every sky. Not surprisingly the answers depend on the type of model being considered. There is however a simple sufficient condition, which is also necessary in a certain sense.

3.7. THEOREM. *Let $\mathfrak{F}$ be a free filter on N.*

(a) *If $\mathfrak{F}$ is ample, then in any $*N$ $\mu\mathfrak{F}$ meets every sky.*

(b) *If $\mathfrak{F}$ is not ample and if* AN *is true, then there exists an enlargement in which $\mu\mathfrak{F}$ does not meet every sky.*

Proof. (a) Let $\mathfrak{F}$ be ample and S_0 be such that $\phi \neq *S_0 - S_0 \subseteq \mu\mathfrak{F}$ (Theorem 2.5(c)). Let S_0 be listed as $\{k_n : n \in N\}$ with $k_1 < k_2 < k_3 \ldots$. Then $*S_0 - S_0 = \{k_\nu : \nu \in N'\}$ and this meets every sky; for if f is defined by $f(n) = k_n$ then for all $a \in N'$ $a \leqslant k_a$ and $a \nearrow k_a$ since $k_a = f(a)$, so $a \sim k_a$. Therefore $\mu\mathfrak{F}$ meets every sky.

(b) If $\mathfrak{F}$ is not ample then (AN) there is a basic model $M^N/\mathscr{U}$ in which $\mu\mathfrak{F}$ is empty, so meets no skies. If $*M$ is any enlargement, then $*M^N/\mathscr{U}$ is another enlargement in which $M^N/\mathscr{U}$ is embedded. $\mu\mathfrak{F}$ then consists entirely of upper numbers and meets no skies in the lower half of $*N^N/\mathscr{U}$, which proves the theorem.

It should be noted that a non-ample filter monad may meet every sky in a given enlargement, though not in all enlargements. We find in particular that in the case of AS models the condition can be slightly relaxed.

3.8. DEFINITIONS. (1) *A free filter $\mathfrak{F}$ on N will be called sub-ample if there is a function $f \in F_0$ such that $f(\mathfrak{F})$ is ample.*

(2) *A nonstandard model $*M$ of arithmetic will be called rich if every filter on N has a non-empty monad in $*N$.*

It is clear that, in particular, enlargements and AS models are rich.

3.9. THEOREM. *Let $\mathfrak{F}$ be a free filter on N.*

(a) *If $\mathfrak{F}$ is sub-ample then in any* AS *model $\mu\mathfrak{F}$ meets every sky.*

(b) (CH) *If $\mathfrak{F}$ is not sub-ample, and if $*M$ is any rich model, then $\mu\mathfrak{F}$ does not meet all the skies of $*N$.*

Proof. (a) Let $f \in F_0$ be such that $f(\mathfrak{F})$ is ample. Then $\mu f\mathfrak{F}$ meets all skies of $*N$. If $*M$ is AS we have $f\mu\mathfrak{F} = \mu f\mathfrak{F}$, from Theorems 2.10 and 2.12, so that $f\mu\mathfrak{F}$ meets every sky. But from Lemma 1.2 f maps every sky into itself, so that $\mu\mathfrak{F}$ and $f\mu\mathfrak{F}$ meet precisely the same skies. Thus $\mu\mathfrak{F}$ meets all skies.

(b) I shall show first, using CH and an argument similar to that used in deriving AN, that if $\mathfrak{F}$ is not sub-ample then there is a fuf $\mathscr{U}$ on N such that for every $f \in F_0$, $f(\mathscr{U}) \not\supseteq f(\mathfrak{F})$. It will then follow that no sky met by $\mu\mathscr{U}$ (which is non-empty in a rich model) is met by $\mu\mathfrak{F}$.

Let F_0 be well-ordered to $(f_\alpha : \alpha < \Omega)$ with $f_0(n) = n$. Taking N_0 to be any infinite set such that $N - N_0 \in \mathfrak{F}$ we define an almost decreasing sequence $(N_\alpha : \alpha < \Omega)$ to satisfy

(P) $\quad \forall \alpha < \Omega, \ \exists S_\alpha \in \mathfrak{F} \quad$ such that $\quad f_\alpha[N_\alpha] \cap f_\alpha[S_\alpha] = \emptyset.$

Given $(N_\beta : \beta < \alpha)$ we construct $A_\alpha \subseteq' N_\beta$ as before. As A_α is infinite and $f_\alpha \in F_0$, $f_\alpha[A_\alpha]$ is infinite. Since $f_\alpha(\mathfrak{F})$ is not ample, by hypothesis, there is an $S \in f_\alpha(\mathfrak{F})$ such that $f_\alpha[A_\alpha] - S$ is infinite. By definition of $f_\alpha(\mathfrak{F})$ this means that for some $S_\alpha \in \mathfrak{F}$, $f_\alpha[A_\alpha] - f_\alpha[S_\alpha]$ is infinite. We take $N_\alpha = \{n \in A_\alpha : f_\alpha(n) \notin f_\alpha[S_\alpha]\}$. This is infinite, $N_\alpha \subseteq' N_\beta$ for all $\beta < \alpha$ and $f_\alpha[N_\alpha] \cap f_\alpha[S_\alpha] = \emptyset$, so that (P) is satisfied. Hence if $\mathscr{U}$ is any fuf containing $(N_\alpha : \alpha < \Omega)$, $f(\mathscr{U}) \not\supseteq f(\mathfrak{F})$ for all $f \in F_0$.

Now let $a \in \mu(\mathscr{U})$. If $\mu(\mathfrak{F})$ meets sk(a), suppose that $b \in \mu\mathfrak{F} \cap$ sk(a). Using Lemma 1.2(ii) let $f \in F_0$ be such that $f(a) = f(b)$. Then $f\mu\mathscr{U}$ meets $f\mu\mathfrak{F}$ so from Theorem 2.10(i) $\mu f\mathscr{U}$ meets $\mu f\mathfrak{F}$. Since $f(\mathscr{U})$ is a fuf this means that $f(\mathscr{U}) \supseteq f(\mathfrak{F})$, which contradicts the result just established and so proves the theorem.

3.10. *Example*. I shall now give an example of a filter which is sub-ample but not ample, so that in a certain enlargement its monad fails to meet all skies, even though in an AS model $\mu\mathfrak{F}$ must meet every sky. We incidentally obtain another counterexample to Theorem 2.10(iii).

First, let the partition (D_m) of N be defined as follows: $D_1 = \{1\}$, $D_2 = \{2, 3\}$, $D_3 = \{4, 5, 6\}$ etc., so that $|D_m| = m$. Let f be defined by $f(n) = m$ where $n \in D_m$; then $f \in F_0$. The filter $\mathfrak{F}$ is defined to be that generated by all sets $S \subseteq N$ such that $N - S$ consists of a single point from each D_m. It is easy to see that $\mathfrak{F}$ is free and $f(\mathfrak{F}) = \mathscr{F}r$, the Frechet filter on N, which is certainly ample. However, if S_0 is any infinite set $\subseteq N$ let S_0' consist of the first number in every non-empty $S_0 \cap D_m$. Then $N - S_0' \in \mathfrak{F}$ and $S_0 - (N - S_0') = S_0'$ is infinite; thus $\mathfrak{F}$ itself is not ample. From Theorem 3.7(b) there is an enlargement in which $\mu\mathfrak{F}$ does not meet every sky. As f leaves skies invariant $f\mu\mathfrak{F}$ also misses some skies, but $f\mathfrak{F}$ is ample, so $\mu f\mathfrak{F}$ meets every sky; thus $f\mu\mathfrak{F}$ is a proper subset of $\mu f\mathfrak{F}$, so is not a monad.

4. Accessible functions: serial points. In this and the following sections the relation of upward accessibility will be extended to the finite numbers. I shall say that $m \nearrow n$ holds for all $m, n \in N$. Thus for *all* $a, b \in {}^*N$, $a \nearrow b$ iff there is an $f \in F$ such that $f(a) \geqslant b$.

4.1. DEFINITION. *Let* $^*M$ *be any non-standard model of arithmetic,* A *any (internal or external) subset of* $^*N$, *and* p *any internal function:* $^*N \to {}^*N$. p *will be said to be accessible on* A *if* $n \nearrow p(n)$ *for all* $n \in A$. *If there is a single function* $f \in F$ *such that* $p(n) \leqslant f(n)$ *for all* $n \in A$, p *will be said to be uniformly accessible (u.a.) on* A.

The question that immediately suggests itself is: Under what circumstances does accessibility imply uniform accessibility? The following result is not as general as one would like, but gives enough for the application in section 5. Note that a set is a monad iff it is an intersection of standard sets.

4.2. THEOREM. *Let* $^*M$ *be an* AS *model of* M, *let* $\mathfrak{F}$ *be any filter on* N *and let the internal function* $p: {}^*N \to {}^*N$ *be accessible on* $\mu(\mathfrak{F})$. *Then there is an* $\mathfrak{F}$ *set* S_0 *such that* p *is u.a. on* $^*S_0$*–a fortiori* p *is u.a. on* $\mu(\mathfrak{F})$.

Proof. We take the contrapositive. Thus suppose that, for all $S_0 \in \mathfrak{F}$, p is not u.a. on $^*S$. Let s be the binary relation such that $\Phi_2(s, (S, f), a)$ holds in $^*M$ iff $S \in {}^*\mathfrak{F}$, $f \in {}^*F$, $a \in S$ and $p(a) > f(a)$. By the above supposition s is concurrent on $\mathfrak{F} \times F$ which has power c and consists of standard entities. Thus the saturation of $^*M$ guarantees the existence of $a_s \in {}^*N$ such that, for all $S_0 \in \mathfrak{F}$, $f \in F$, $a_s \in {}^*S_0$ and $p(a_s) > f(a_s)$, so that p is not accessible on $\mu\mathfrak{F}$, which proves the theorem.

A counterexample to the above in the case of an enlargement is not hard to find. If $^*M$ is an enlargement in which $^*N$ has a lowest sky (see Puritz [1971] §6), let a be a number in this sky and let p be the constant function with value a for all n. p is accessible on N' (which is the monad of $\mathscr{F}\imath$) but is not u.a. on N, as is easily verified by considering the infinite numbers below a.

I have made very little progress in considering the interesting case (for a general $^*M$) when p is accessible on the whole of $^*N$. In a single-skied basic model this implies that p is u.a. on $^*N$, but I do not know whether this holds in other models.

4.3. *Serial points and their constellations.* In 2.1 I defined, for an arbitrary infinite set X, an element a of $^*X$ to be serial if there exists a countable set $S \subseteq X$ with $a \in {}^*S$. Such a set S can of course be arranged as a sequence

$(a_n : n \in N)$ with all the a_n distinct, and then for some $\nu \in {}^*N$ $a = a_\nu$. However the choice of S is not unique, nor is the way of arranging S into a sequence. Thus the number ν is not uniquely determined by a, and it seems interesting to characterise the set of all ν such that for some $(a_n : n \in N)$, $a = a_\nu$. Remembering that a permutation of N is a 1–1 map of N onto N we begin with

4.4. THEOREM. *Let ν be any infinite number in any ${}^*N$. Then* $\text{con}(\nu) = \{\pi(\nu) : \pi$ *any permutation of* $N\}$.

Proof. It is obviously sufficient to show that if $\nu' \leftrightarrow \nu$ then $\nu' = \pi(\nu)$ for some permutation π. Suppose then that $f(\nu) = \nu'$, $g(\nu') = \nu$, $f, g \in F$. Let $S = \{n \in N : g(f(n)) = n\}$, and let S_1 consist of the 1st, 3rd, 5th etc. numbers in S and S_2 of the 2nd, 4th, 6th etc. Then $\nu \in {}^*S$ so $\nu \in {}^*S_1$ or ${}^*S_2$, say $\nu \in {}^*S_1$. Now f restricted to S is 1–1, so $f[S_1]$ and $f[S_2]$ are infinite and disjoint. Let h be any 1–1 correspondence between $N - S$ and $N - f[S_1]$, and define $\pi : N \to N$ by

$$\pi(n) = \begin{cases} f(n) & \text{for } n \in S_1 \\ h(n) & \text{for } n \in N - S_1. \end{cases}$$

π is 1–1 and its range is $f[S_1] \cup (N - f[S_1]) = N$. Furthermore $\pi(\nu) = f(\nu) = \nu'$ since $\nu \in {}^*S_1$, whence the result follows.

4.5. THEOREM. *Let X be any infinite set in a structure M, and ${}^*M$ be any non-standard model of M. Let a be a serial element of ${}^*X - X$ and let* con_a *denote the set of all $\nu \in {}^*N$ such that there exists a sequence $(a_n : n \in N)$ of distinct elements of X with $a_\nu = a$; then* con_a *is a constellation of* ${}^*N$.

Proof. Let (a_n) be a 1–1 sequence and ν a number such that $a_\nu = a$. Since a_n is standard for $n \in N$ and a is non-standard, $\nu \in N'$. If ν' is any member of $\text{con}(\nu)$ then by Theorem 4.4 we have $\nu = \pi(\nu')$ for some permutation π on N. Now let $a'_n = a_{\pi(n)}$ for each n. Then (a'_n) is a rearrangement of (a_n) and $a'_{\nu'} = a_{\pi(\nu')} = a_\nu = a$, showing that $\text{con}(\nu) \subseteq \text{con}_a$. On the other hand every rearrangement of (a_n) is derived from a permutation of N, so that rearrangement cannot give numbers outside $\text{con}(\nu)$.

Now suppose that (a'_n) is another 1–1 sequence such that for some $\nu' \in N'$, $a'_{\nu'} = a$. If S, S' are the ranges of (a_n), (a'_n) then $S'' = S \cap S'$ must be infinite, as $a \in {}^*S'' - S''$. Let S'' now be arranged in a sequence (a''_n) following the order of (a_n); thus $a''_n = a_{f(n)}$ where

$$f(1) < f(2) < f(3) \ldots .$$

If $\nu'' \in N'$ is such that $a''_{\nu''} = a_\nu = a$, then since $a''_{\nu''} = a_{f(\nu'')}$ we have $\nu = f(\nu'')$

as the a_n are distinct. But f is 1–1, so there exists $g \in F$ such that $g(v) = v''$. Thus $v \leftrightarrow v''$. Again, if we order S'' following the order of (a'_n) we find $a = a'_{v'} = a'''_{v'''}$ say, and $v' \leftrightarrow v'''$ holds in the same way. But (a'''_n) is a rearrangement of (a''_n), and so $v'' \leftrightarrow v'''$, whence $v \leftrightarrow v'$, which establishes the result.

4.6. THEOREM. *Let a, a' be serial points of $^*X$. Then* $\text{con}_a = \text{con}_{a'}$ *iff a and a' are connected by a standard permutation of $^*X$.*

Proof. If $a' = \pi(a)$ and $a = a_v$ say, then $a' = a'_v$ where $a'_n = \pi(a_n)$, so $\text{con}_a = \text{con}_{a'}$. Conversely assuming $\text{con}_a = \text{con}_{a'}$ let S and S' be countable sets such that $a \in {}^*S$, $a' \in {}^*S'$ and such that $X - S$, $X - S'$ are both infinite and hence of equal power. (This last condition is fulfilled automatically unless $|X| = \aleph_0$; even in that case it is easily secured.) Let S and S' be ordered to give (a_n) and (a'_n) in such a way that, for some $v \in \text{con}_a$, $a = a_v$, $a' = a'_v$. Now let h be any 1–1 correspondence between $X - S$ and $X - S'$ and define $\pi : X \to X$ by

$$\begin{aligned} \pi(a_n) &= a'_n \quad &&\text{for} \quad n \in N \\ \pi(x) &= h(x) \quad &&\text{for} \quad x \in X - S. \end{aligned}$$

This is a permutation and satisfies $\pi(a) = a'$ as required.

4.7. *Remarks.* The above results show that the theory of constellations (and also of skies) is not dependent on the particular ordering of the natural numbers, so that the theory applies to the non-standard extension of any countable set A (as well as to the serial points of a $^*X$ with $|X| > \aleph_0$). Constellations in fact are defined with no reference to ordering at all, while the concept of a sky does involve the idea of the set A being ordered isomorphically to $(N, <)$, though it is immaterial what particular ordering is chosen; different orderings are obtainable from each other by permutations of A, and these leave skies (though not galaxies) invariant. We shall see in the next section that this invariant association of serial points with skies is displayed in the expression for the monad of a serial point.

It is also worth noting that the functions of F_0 can be characterised by an order-independent property: if $f \in F_0$, $n \in N$, $f^{-1}[n]$ is a finite set.

5. Monads in a metric space. As mentioned in section 2 the notion of a filter monad is of considerable use in the study of topology. The filters that arise there are the neighbourhood filters of points of the space or of subsets of it, as well as filters whose convergence properties are being investigated.

Let (X, τ) be a topological space, τ denoting the set of all open subsets of X. Following Luxemburg [1969] p. 59 we define the τ-monad[1]) of an arbitrary point $a \in {}^*X$ to be

$$\mu_\tau(a) = \cap({}^*S : \exists V \in \tau \quad \text{such that} \quad a \in {}^*V \subseteq {}^*S).$$

This is the intersection of all standard open sets to which a belongs, and is easily seen to be a filter monad. If the space is metric with distance function ρ and if x is a *standard* point then it is easy to see that

$$\mu(x) = \{y \in {}^*X : \rho(x, y) \simeq 0\},$$

where $\rho \simeq 0$ means that ρ is infinitesimal, i.e. is less than every standard positive number. Thus $\mu(x)$ is simply the "infinitesimal ball" surrounding x. Robinson in [1966] p. 100 uses the above expression as the definition of $\mu(x)$ even in the case when x is a non-standard point of ${}^*X$; this disagrees with Luxemburg's more general definition of $\mu_\tau(a)$. In fact the infinitesimal ball surrounding a non-standard point is not in general a filter monad at all, though it is of considerable interest in connection with the uniform structure defined by ρ; it turns out (Luxemburg [1969] p. 76) that the ball *is* a monad precisely in the case when x is pre-near-standard, in which case $\mu(x)$ is the monad of a Cauchy filter on X. But even then $\mu(x)$ does not coincide with Luxemburg's monad. It therefore seemed to me of some interest to find out what Luxemburg's monad "looks like", and I have found it possible to do this for a serial point in an AS model of a metric space, using the notion of accessibility defined in previous sections. I still have no conception about the monads of the non-serial points.

5.1. We begin by considering the relatively simple case where $X = N$ and the topology is discrete. The discrete monad $\mu_d(n)$ of a standard number n is just the singleton $\{n\}$. However if $a \in N'$, $\mu_d(a) = \cap({}^*S : a \in {}^*S)$ is the monad of a fuf $\mathcal{U}_a$, which in general contains infinitely many points; in fact I showed in Theorem 3.1 that if ${}^*M$ is AS $\mu(\mathcal{U}_a)$ is both co-initial and cofinal in N' and has the same power as ${}^*N$.

5.2. In considering a general metric space X with metric taking values in R^+, it will be convenient to extend the notion of accessibility to ${}^*R^+$. Thus if $a, b \in {}^*R^+$ I shall say that $a \nearrow b$ or $a \ll b$ according as $[a] \nearrow$ or $\ll [b]$, where $[x]$ denotes the greatest integer $\leqslant x$. This means that a sky of ${}^*R^+$

[1]) The τ will often be omitted for brevity, likewise I shall write $\mu(a)$ for $\mu_\tau(a)$ where this is safe.

is got simply by filling in the spaces between the integers of a sky of $*N$. (This is in some respects a rather crude way of associating a sky with a number in $*R^+$, for if one allows arbitrary standard functions: $*R \to *R$ to operate on a given $a \in *R^+$ one may get answers way above the sky of $[a]$.) I shall also adopt the convention that $1/0 = \infty$ and that $a \ll \infty$ for all $a \in *R^+$.

The following idea provides the nucleus of our characterisation of monads in $*X$.

5.3. DEFINITION. *Let a be any point in* $*X$, *and* ν *any number in* $*N$. *The* ν*-core round* a, $\mathrm{cor}_\nu(a)$ *is defined to be the set of all* $b \in *X$ *such that* $\nu \ll 1/\rho(a, b)$.

When ν is finite $\mathrm{cor}_\nu(a)$ is just the infinitesimal ball round a, otherwise it consists of points whose distance from a is "inaccessibly less than" $1/\nu$. We come now to the main result.

5.4. THEOREM. *Let* (X, ρ) *be a metric space in a structure* M. *Let* $*M$ *be an* AS *model of* M, *and let* $a \in *X$ *be a serial point, i.e. let there be a sequence* $(a_n : n \in N)$ *of distinct points of* X *and a number* $\nu \in N'$ *such that* $a = a_\nu$. *Then the monad of* a *in the* ρ *topology is given by*

$$\mu(a) = \cup(\mathrm{cor}_{\nu'}(a_{\nu'}) : \nu' \in \mu_d(\nu)).$$

If $\{a_n : n \in N\}$ *is discrete in* X *then the cores that make up* $\mu(a)$ *are disjoint.*

Proof. Let V be any open set such that $a \in *V$, and let $S \subseteq N$ be the set of all n such that $a_n \in V$. Since $\nu \in *S$, $\mu_d(\nu) \subseteq *S$ so for each $\nu' \in \mu_d(\nu)$, $a_{\nu'} \in *V$. Since V is open there is an $f \in F$ such that, for each $n \in S$, all points x with $\rho(a_n, x) < 1/f(n)$ belong to V. The same holds in $*M$ for all $n \in *S$, which easily shows that $\mathrm{cor}_{\nu'}(a_{\nu'}) \subseteq \mu(a)$ whenever $\nu' \in \mu_d(\nu)$, thus establishing half the desired result.

The other half is not so easy and needs the saturation. Suppose that $b \in *X$ is such that $b \notin \mathrm{cor}_{\nu'}(a_{\nu'})$ holds for all $\nu' \in \mu_d(\nu)$. We have now to show that $b \notin \mu(a)$ by constructing an open set V with $a \in *V$ and $b \notin *V$.

Let the internal function $p : *N \to *N$ be defined as follows:

$$p(n) = \left[\frac{1}{\rho(a_n, b)}\right] \text{ for all } n.$$

For all $\nu' \in \mu_d(\nu)$ $b \notin \mathrm{cor}_{\nu'}(a_{\nu'})$, so that $\nu' \not\ll 1/\rho(a_{\nu'}, b)$. Thus p is accessible on $\mu_d(\nu)$, which is a filter monad. Hence by Theorem 4.2 p is u.a. on $*S_0$ for some $S_0 \in \mathscr{U}_\nu$; thus there exists $f \in F$ such that $\rho(a_n, b) > 1/f(n)$ for all

$n \in {}^*S_0$, and $\mu_d(v) \subseteq {}^*S_0$. We now define the open set V as follows: for each $n \in S_0$ let B_n be the open ball of centre a_n and radius $1/f(n)$; then $V = \cup(B_n : n \in S)$. Clearly $a = a_v \in {}^*V$ as $v \in {}^*S_0$, and also from the above definitions of S_0 and f the point b lies outside B_n for each $n \in {}^*S_0$, so $b \notin {}^*V$ as required.

Now suppose that $\{a_n : n \in N\}$ is discrete. Then there is a function $g \in F$ such that the balls of centre a_n and radius $1/g(n)$ are disjoint. This holds true in $^*M$, and for each v' the ball round $a_{v'}$ contains $\text{cor}_{v'}(a_{v'})$; thus these cores are disjoint.

5.5. *Example.* Let X be the space R of reals with the usual metric and let $a = 1/v$, $v \in N'$. We have

$$\mu(a) = \cup\left(\text{cor}_{v'}\left(\frac{1}{v'}\right) : v' \in \mu_d(v)\right).$$

This is a proper subset of $\mu(0)$ (which is the infinitesimal ball round a) and consists of many disjoint cores, each “infinitely smaller” than $\mu(0)$.

5.6. *The monad of a σ-compact set.* Let (X, τ) be a topological space and let A be an arbitrary (internal or external) subset of $^*X$. Following Luxemburg [1969] p. 59 again, we define the τ-monad of A to be

$$\mu_\tau(A) = \cap({}^*S: \quad \text{for some} \quad V \in \tau, A \subseteq {}^*V \subseteq {}^*S).$$

This is again a filter monad, the filter being the “neighbourhood filter” of A.[1]) When A is a singleton $\{a\}$, $\mu_\tau(\{a\}) = \mu_\tau(a)$ as defined above. Luxemburg has obtained some results on the relation between the monad of a set A and the monads of the points of A, as follows:

5.7. THEOREM. *Let (X, τ) be a topological space in a structure M and let $^*M$ be a κ-AS model of M, with $\kappa > |M|$. Then*

(a) *If $S \subseteq {}^*X$ is internal, $\mu_\tau(S) = \cup(\mu_\tau(a) : a \in S)$.*

(b) *$A \subseteq X$ is compact iff $\mu_\tau(A) = \cup(\mu_\tau(x) : x \in A)$.*

Proof. (a) Luxemburg [1969] p. 60, Theorem 3.2.2.

(b) Luxemburg [1969] p. 64, Theorem 3.5.2.

Note that (b) is expressed in terms of monads of standard points (infinitesimal balls in the case of a metric space), whereas (a) uses monads of

[1]) It is worth noting that if $A \subseteq X$, $\mu_\tau(A) = \mu_\tau({}^*A)$.

non-standard points as well, which makes the result much harder to visualise. I shall here extend (b) to the case of a σ-compact set, giving the result in terms of cores rather than the monads of non-standard points.

5.8. DEFINITION. *For any point a, any set S and any number n,* $B_n(a)$ *will denote the open ball of centre a and radius* $1/n$, *and* $B_n(S)$ *will denote* $\cup(B_n(a):a \in S)$. *(This can refer to X or *X according to context.)*
$\mathrm{cor}_n(S)$ *will denote* $\cup(\mathrm{cor}_n(a):a \in S)$.

It is evident from the definitions that for any $f \in F$, $\mathrm{cor}_n(S) \subseteq B_{f(n)}(S)$.

5.9. THEOREM. *Let* (X, ρ) *be a metric space in a structure M and *M be an* AS *model of M. Let A be any σ-compact subset of X, i.e.* $A = \bigcup_{n\in N} A_n$ *with each* A_n *compact. Then*

$$\mu(A) = \bigcup_{\nu\in {}^*N} \mathrm{cor}_\nu(A_\nu) = \Big[\bigcup_{n\in N} \mu(A_n)\Big] \cup \Big[\bigcup_{\nu\in N'} \mathrm{cor}_\nu(A_\nu)\Big].$$

Proof. Let V be any open neighbourhood of A. For each $x \in A$ let $d(x) = \rho(x, X - V) = \inf_{y\notin V} \rho(x, y)$. As is well known d is continuous. Since V is open, d never vanishes on A, hence $1/d$ is continuous on A, and so in particular on each A_n. But the A_n are compact, so $1/d$ is bounded on each A_n. This means that there is an $f \in F$ such that $1/d(x) < f(n)$ whenever $x \in A_n$. It follows that $\bigcup_{n\in N} B_{f(n)}(A_n) \subseteq V$ so that $\bigcup_{\nu\in {}^*N} B_{f(\nu)}(A_\nu) \subseteq {}^*V$, which implies that $\bigcup_{\nu\in {}^*N} \mathrm{cor}_\nu(A_\nu) \subseteq {}^*V$ and gives half the result.

For the other half we first observe the following facts relating to the standard theory. If $C \subseteq X$ is compact and $b \notin C$, then $\rho(b, x)$, $x \in C$, is a continuous function of x and attains its minimum at some point x_0 of C: thus $\rho(b, C) = \rho(b, x_0)$ with $x_0 \in C$. This also applies in $^*X$, not only to the compact sets A_n, $n \in N$, but to the "*-compact" A_ν, $\nu \in N'$. Now let b be any point outside $\bigcup_{\nu\in {}^*N} \mathrm{cor}_\nu(A_\nu)$. We have to construct an open set V with $b \notin {}^*V \supseteq {}^*A$. For each $\nu \in {}^*N$ let $\rho(b, A_\nu) = \rho(b, x_\nu)$, $x_\nu \in A_\nu$. Since $b \notin \mathrm{cor}_\nu(x_\nu)$, $\nu \nearrow 1/\rho(b, x_\nu)$ so that $[1/\rho(b, x_\nu)]$ is accessible on $^*N$. Thus (Theorem 4.2) there exists $f \in F$ such that $f(\nu) \geqslant 1/\rho(b, x_\nu)$, i.e. $\rho(b, x_\nu) \geqslant 1/f(\nu)$ for all $\nu \in {}^*N$. Now let

$$V = \bigcup_{n\in N} B_{f(n)}(A_n).$$

V is a union of open balls and $V \supseteq A$, but it is clear that $b \notin B_{f(\nu)}(A_\nu)$ holds for all ν, so that $b \notin {}^*V$, as required.

The alternative expression for $\mu(A)$ is immediate from Theorem 5.7(b).

5.10. *Examples.* (1) Let $X = R \times R$ with the usual metric and let A be the real axis $y = 0$. Taking (say) $A_n = [-n, n] \times \{0\}$ and bearing in mind that if $\nu_2 > \nu_1$, $\mathrm{cor}_{\nu_2}(a) \subseteq \mathrm{cor}_{\nu_1}(a)$, we get

$$\mu(A) = \left\{(x, y) : |x| \ll \frac{1}{|y|}\right\}.$$

(2) If we delete the origin from A to give $A' = \{(x, y) : x \neq 0 \text{ and } y = 0\}$ the monad tapers down near the origin: we find (using e.g. $A'_n = ([-n, -1/n] \cup [1/n, n]) \times \{0\})$

$$\mu(A') = \left\{(x, y) : x \neq 0 \quad \text{and} \quad x \simeq 0 \quad \text{and} \quad \frac{1}{|x|} \ll \frac{1}{|y|} \right.$$
$$\left. \text{or} \quad x \not\simeq 0 \quad \text{and} \quad |x| \ll \frac{1}{|y|}\right\}.$$

5.11. *Uniform spaces.* The basic theory of uniform spaces has been cast into nonstandard form by Luxemburg [1969] pp. 72–82, and has been considerably developed by Machover and Hirschfeld [1969] pp. 48–79; it is well adapted to this treatment. As is well known a uniform space is a set X together with a filter $\mathscr{E}$ on $X \times X$, which is required to satisfy certain conditions, and whose elements are called *entourages*. Luxemburg and Hirschfeld have shown that a filter $\mathscr{E}$ on $X \times X$ gives a uniformity iff $\mu(\mathscr{E})$ is the graph of an equivalence relation: thus if for $a, b \in {}^*X$ we define $a \simeq b$ to mean that $(a, b) \in \mu(\mathscr{E})$ the relation $\simeq$ must be reflexive, symmetric and transitive on ${}^*X$. The previous use of $\simeq$ in ${}^*R$ is a special case of this, the uniformity there being that defined by the usual metric. The following result, which is obtained rather easily from Example 5.10(1), characterises another uniformity on R that induces the same topology.

5.12. THEOREM. *The finest uniformity on R compatible with the usual topology is given by $\simeq_0$ where*

$$x \simeq_0 y \quad \text{iff} \quad |x + y| \ll 1/|x - y|.$$

Proof. Let Δ be the diagonal of $R \times R$, $\Delta = \{(x, x) : x \in R\}$. For a uniformity to be compatible with the usual topology, it is not hard to see that all the entourages must be neighbourhoods of Δ in the usual topology of $R \times R$. Thus the finest such uniformity is the filter of all neighbourhoods of Δ; and its monad is obtained by rotating the solution of Example 5.10(1) through 45°, whence the result follows.

It is also known that a uniform space can always be defined in terms of a family D of semi-metrics on X. (A semi-metric is like a metric except that $d(x, y) = 0$ need not imply that $x = y$.)

When this is done the monad of $\mathscr{E}$ can be expressed as follows (Luxemburg [1969] p. 79):

$$a \simeq b \quad \text{iff} \quad (a, b) \in \mu(\mathscr{E}) \quad \text{iff} \quad d(a, b) \simeq 0 \quad \forall d \in D.$$

That this defines an equivalence reaction on $^*X$ is immediately obvious. Also the topology associated with the uniformity is easily defined by giving the monads of standard points: if $a_0 \in X$,

$$\mu(a_0) = \{x : x \simeq a_0; \quad \text{i.e.} \quad d(x, a_0) \simeq 0 \quad \forall d \in D\}.$$

This clearly generalises the infinitesimal ball monad that characterises a metric topology. It seems reasonable therefore to expect that Theorems 5.4 and 5.9 can also be generalised to uniform spaces. I have found this to be true under slightly stronger assumptions on $^*M$, but the generalisation is less straightforward than I at first supposed. We find ourselves having to take into account some of the non-standard elements of $^*D$, which do not appear at all in the expressions for $\mu(\mathscr{E})$ and $\mu(a_0)$.[1])

The extent of the generalisation is shown by the following definition of a ν-core.

5.13. DEFINITION. *Let (X, D) be a uniform space. For any $a \in {}^*X$, $\nu \in {}^*N$ we define*

$$\mathrm{cor}_\nu(a) = \{x \in {}^*X : \textit{for all } d \in D \textit{ and for all serial } d \in {}^*D \textit{ with } \mathrm{sk}_d \leqslant \mathrm{sk}(\nu),\ \nu \ll 1/d(a, x)\},$$

where sk_d is the sky of $^*N$ that contains con_d.

It will prove helpful in the sequel to bear in mind that standard elements of $^*D$ are serial, and to consider the sky of a standard element to be N (and likewise to agree that $\mathrm{sk}(n) = N$ if $n \in N$: this fits in well with the de-

[1]) Since writing this I have become acquainted with Young's [1972] treatment of topology by semifields. Following Antonovskii, Young shows that every topology can be defined by a family of quasi-metrics (these are generalised from semi-metrics by removing the condition $d(x, y) = d(y, x)$). The monad of a standard point is exactly as given above for a uniform space, and the subsequent discussion, which makes no use of symmetry, applies in full, so that we in fact obtain the monad of a serial point in a general topological space.

finition of skies but would have been rather inconvenient in earlier sections). We then have

$$\mathrm{cor}_v(a) = \{x \in {}^*X : \text{for all serial } d \in {}^*D \text{ with } \mathrm{sk}_d \leqslant \mathrm{sk}(v), v \ll 1/d(a,x)\}.$$

We will also find it helpful to extend D to a kind of semi-lattice as follows: for any $d_1, d_2 \in D$ define $d = d_1 \vee d_2 = \sup(d_1, d_2)$ by

$$d(x, y) = \max(d_1(x, y), d_2(x, y)) \quad \text{for all} \quad x, y \in X.$$

It is easily verified that d is a semi-metric, but d may not belong to D. We therefore define $\bar{D}$ to consist of all sups of finite collections of elements of D. $\bar{D}$ is the smallest set containing D and closed under $\vee$, and we have moreover

5.14. LEMMA (i) *D and $\bar{D}$ define the same uniformity.*

(ij) *$\mathrm{cor}_v(a)$ is unaltered when D is replaced by $\bar{D}$.*

Proof. (i) Let $d \in \bar{D}$. Then there exist $d_1, \ldots, d_k \in D$ such that $d = \sup(d_1, \ldots, d_k)$, and it is immediate that for any $a, b \in {}^*X$, $d(a, b) \simeq 0$ iff $d_i(a, b) \simeq 0$ for $i = 1, \ldots, k$. Thus $a \simeq b$ holds in ${}^*(X, \bar{D})$ iff it holds in ${}^*(X, D)$.

(ij)[1]) Let $\overline{\mathrm{cor}_v}(a)$ denote the result of replacing D by $\bar{D}$ in Definition 11.12. Clearly $\overline{\mathrm{cor}_v}(a) \subseteq \mathrm{cor}_v(a)$, and we have to show that the reverse inclusion holds.

Let $x \in \mathrm{cor}_v(a)$, and suppose that d is a serial member of ${}^*\bar{D}$ with $\mathrm{sk}_d \leqslant \mathrm{sk}(v)$. Let $\bar{D}_0 = (d_n : n \in N)$ be a 1–1 sequence of elements of $\bar{D}$ such that, for some $p \in {}^*N$, $d = d_p$. Each $d_n = \sup(d_{n1}, \ldots, d_{nk_n})$ say, with each $d_{ni} \in D$. Then $\mathrm{sk}(p) \leqslant \mathrm{sk}(v)$, and by listing the d_{ni} in a single sequence we easily see that $\mathrm{sk}_{d_{pi}} \leqslant \mathrm{sk}(v)$, so that by hypothesis $v \ll 1/\mathrm{d}_{pi}(a, x)$, for $i = 1, \ldots, k_p$. But $d_p(a, x) = d_{pi}(a, x)$ for some $i \in [1, k_p]$, so $v \ll 1/d_p(a, x)$; thus $x \in \overline{\mathrm{cor}_v}(a)$ as required.

5.15. THEOREM. *Let (X, D) be a uniform space*[2]) *in a structure M, and let ${}^*M$ be a κ-AS model of M, where $\kappa > \max(c, |D|)$. Let $a = a_v$ be any serial point of ${}^*X$. Then the monad of a is given by*

$$\mu(a) = \cup(\mathrm{cor}_{v'}(a_{v'}) : v' \in \mu_d(v)).$$

Proof. Let V be any open set with $a \in {}^*V$. Then the set $S = \{n : a_n \in V\}$

[1]) May well be an immediate consequence of (i); but how to prove this?

[2]) Or any topological space: see footnote on page 234.

has $a_\nu \in {}^*S$, so that $\mu_d(\nu) \subseteq {}^*S$. Also for each $n \in S$ there exist elements $d_{n1}, \ldots, d_{nk_n} \in D$ and an integer $f(n)$ such that

$$B_n = \{x : d_{ni}(x, a_n) < 1/f(n) \quad \text{for } i = 1, \ldots, k\} \subseteq V,$$

(for otherwise a_n would not be an interior point of V).

It is clear that, for each $\nu' \in \mu_d(\nu)$ and $i = 1, \ldots, k_{\nu'}$, $d_{\nu' i}$ is serial with sky $\leqslant$ sk(ν'), and hence $\mathrm{cor}_{\nu'}(a_{\nu'}) \subseteq B_{\nu'}$, so that

$$\cup(\mathrm{cor}_{\nu'}(a_{\nu'}) : \nu' \in \mu_d(\nu)) \subseteq {}^*V.$$

For the second half of the proof I shall assume that D has been extended to $\bar{D}$; as shown above this affects neither the form nor the content of the result. Also $|\bar{D}| = |D|$ unless both are finite.

Suppose now that $b \in \mu(a)$. Let Δ be the set of all sequences of elements of $\bar{D}$ and $\mathcal{U}_\nu$ be the fuf on N associated with ν, and define the binary relation s as follows: $\Phi_2(s, (S, D_0, f), n)$ holds iff $S \in {}^*\mathcal{U}_\nu$, $D_0 \in {}^*\Delta$, $f \in {}^*F$, $n \in S$ and $f(n) < 1/d_n(a_n, b)$, where $D_0 = (d_m : m \in {}^*N)$. To prove that s is concurrent on $A = \mathcal{U}_\nu \times \Delta \times F$, let $({}^*S_i, D_0^i, f_i)$, $i = 1, \ldots, k$, be k members of A. Let $S = S_1 \cap \ldots \cap S_k$, $f(n) = \max(f_i(n) : i = 1, \ldots, k)$ for all n, and let D_0 be the sequence $(d_n : n \in N)$ where

$$d_n = \sup(d_m^i, m = 1, \ldots, n, i = 1, \ldots, k).$$

For each $n \in S$ let $V_n = \{x \in X : d_n(a_n, x) < 1/f(n)\}$. Then $V = \cup(V_n : n \in S)$ is an open set and $a = a_\nu \in {}^*V$. Hence by hypothesis $b \in {}^*V$, so that for some $n \in {}^*S$, $d_n(a_n, b) < 1/f(n)$. But this implies that $f_i(n) < 1/d_n^i(a_n, b)$ for $i = 1, \ldots, k$, so that $\Phi_2(s, ({}^*S_i, D_0^i, f_i), n)$ holds for $i = 1, \ldots, k$, showing that s is concurrent on A. But the elements of A are all standard, $|A| = \max(c, |\Delta|) = \max(c, |D|) < \kappa$, and ${}^*M$ is κ-AS. It follows that there exists $\nu_1 \in {}^*N$ which satisfies s simultaneously on A. Thus $\nu_1 \in \mu_d(\nu)$ and for every sequence $D_0 = (d_n)$

$$\nu_1 \ll 1/d_{\nu_1}(a_{\nu_1}, b).$$

Now let d be any serial member of ${}^*D$ with $\mathrm{sk}_d \leqslant \mathrm{sk}(\nu_1)$. Thus let $d = d_p$ say with $\mathrm{sk}(p) \leqslant \mathrm{sk}(\nu_1)$, and let $f_1 \in F$ be such that $f_1(\nu_1) \geqslant p$. Define the sequences $(\bar{d}_n)$ from (d_n) as follows:

$$\bar{d}_n = \sup(d_m : m = 1, \ldots, f_1(n)).$$

Then $\bar{d}_{\nu_1} \geqslant d_p$ and $\nu_1 \ll 1/\bar{d}_{\nu_1}(a_{\nu_1}, b)$ so that $\nu_1 \ll 1/d_p(a_{\nu_1}, b)$; thus

$$b \in \mathrm{cor}_{\nu_1}(a_{\nu_1}) \subseteq \cup(\mathrm{cor}_{\nu'}(a_{\nu'}) : \nu' \in \mu_d(\nu)),$$

which completes the proof of the theorem.

A precisely analogous result holds for the monad of a σ-compact set, but as the details are tedious rather than illuminating I shall omit them, and conclude with an illustration.

5.16. *Hilbert space*. The weak topology w on a Hilbert space H over the complex field C is derivable from a uniformity (H, D), where $D = \{d_h : h \in H\}$ and d_h is given by

$$d_h(x, y) = |x - y, h|,$$

the modulus of the inner product of $x - y$ with h. This means that in $^*H$ $x \simeq y$ iff $|x - y, {}^*h| \simeq 0$ for all $h \in H$, i.e. iff $x - y \underline{\wr}\, H$, $x - y$ is "almost perpendicular" to H. The monad of 0 is given by

$$\mu_{\mathrm{w}}(0) = \{x \in {}^*H : x \underline{\wr}\, H\},$$

and monads of other standard points are just translates of this.

Let us now assume that H is separable, with an orthonormal basis $(e_n : n \in N)$. In $^*H$ every vector x has an expansion

$$x = \sum_{n \in {}^*N} c_n e_n$$

with each $c_n \in {}^*C$, and if $\|x\|$ is finite, then it is not hard to show that $x \underline{\wr}\, H$ iff $c_n \simeq 0$ for all finite n. (This is a special case of Theorem 5.17 below.) However this does not give a full characterisation of $\mu_{\mathrm{w}}(0)$, as in general there are infinite vectors $\underline{\wr}\, H$ (I say "in general" because the set of infinite vectors $\underline{\wr}\, H$ is the monad of a filter which by the uniform boundedness principle is not ample, so that there exists a basic $^*M$ in which this monad is empty); for instance, if $^*N$ is big enough to have infinite numbers $\nu_1 \ll \nu_2$, then $\nu_1 e_{\nu_2} \underline{\wr}\, H$, as is not hard to verify; but $\nu_2 e_{\nu_1}$ actually has an infinite inner product with every standard vector $h = \sum a_n e_n$ for which $a_{\nu_1} \neq 0$. (See Puritz [1972] for further details.)

A similar limitation will be seen to apply to the following attempt at characterising a ν-core in the weak topology.

5.17. THEOREM. *Let H be a separable Hilbert space, with orthonormal basis $(e_n : n \in N)$, in a structure M, and let $^*M$ be any non-standard model of M, ν any number of $^*N$, and a any point of $^*H$. For any $x \in {}^*H$ let $x - a = \sum_{^*N} c_n e_n$. Then in the weak topology of H the following hold*:

(i) *If $x \in \mathrm{cor}_\nu(a)$, $\nu \ll 1/|c_n|$ for all n with* $\mathrm{sk}(n) \leqslant \mathrm{sk}(\nu)$.

(ii) *The converse to* (i) *holds provided* $\mathrm{sk}(\|x - a\|) \leqslant \mathrm{sk}(\nu)$.

Proof. (i) is immediate from Definition 5.13 and the fact that $|c_n| = d_{e_n}(x, a)$.

For (ii) I shall assume that $a = 0$, without any loss of generality. Suppose then that $x = \sum_{*N} c_n e_n$, that $f_1(v) \geqslant \|x\|$, $f_1 \in F$, and that $v \ll 1/|c_n|$ whenever $v \nearrow n$. Let $h = h_p = \sum_{n \in {}^*N} a_{pn} e_n$ be any serial point of $^*H$, with $v \nearrow p$. a_{pn} is a standard function of p and n, and

$$|x, h| \leqslant \textstyle\sum_{n \in {}^*N} |a_{pn}\, c_n| = s \quad \text{say.}$$

We need to show that $v \ll 1/s$, i.e., given any $f \in F$, that $s < 1/f(v)$.

For any $m \in {}^*N$ let $s_m = \sum_{n=1}^{m-1} |a_{pn}\, c_n|$, $r_m = \sum_{n=m}^{\infty} |a_{pn}\, c_n|$. By Schwartz's inequality

$$r_m \leqslant \|x\| \cdot \left\| \sum_{n=m}^{\infty} a_{pn}\, e_n \right\|,$$

and the second factor $\to 0$ in $^*R$ as $m \to \infty$ in $^*N$; thus given $k \in {}^*N$, there exists a least m_{pk} such that $\|\sum_m^{\infty} a_{pn}\, e_n\| < 1/k$ for all $m \geqslant m_{pk}$; and m_{pk} is (the value of) a standard function of p and k. We now choose $k = k_v = 2f(v)\, f_1(v)$, with f, f_1 as mentioned above. Then $m_0 = m_{pk_v}$ is a standard function of p and v, and as $v \nearrow p$, $v \nearrow m_0$. Moreover $r_{m_0} < 1/2f(v)$.

We now want to show the same for s_{m_0}. Let $\bar{a} = \max(a_{pn} : n < m_0)$ and $\bar{c} = \max(c_n : n < m_0)$. Then $s_{m_0} \leqslant m_0 \bar{a} \cdot \bar{c}$, and since $v \nearrow p, m_0$, $v \nearrow m_0 \bar{a}$, say $f_2(v) \geqslant m_0 \bar{a}$. But $\bar{c} =$ some c_n with $v \nearrow n$, so $v \ll 1/\bar{c}$. In particular this means that $\bar{c} < 1/2f_2(v)f(v)$ whence $s_{m_0} < 1/2f(v)$ as required.

References

Choquet, G., 1968a, Construction d'ultrafiltres sur *N*, *Bull. Sci. Math.* (2) 92, pp. 41–48.

Choquet, G., 1968b, Deux classes remarquable d'ultrafiltres sur *N*, *Bull. Sci. Math.* (2) 92, pp. 143–153.

Kochen, S., 1961, Ultraproducts in the Theory of Models, *Ann. Math.* 74, pp. 221–261.

Luxemburg, W. A. J., 1962, *Non-Standard Analysis* (Math. Dept., California Institute of Technology, Pasadena).

Luxemburg, W. A. J., Editor, 1969, *Applications of Model Theory to Algebra, Analysis and Probability* (Holt, Rinehart and Winston, New York).

Machover, M. and Hirschfeld, J., 1969, *Lectures on Non-Standard Analysis*, Lecture Notes in Mathematics (Springer, Berlin).

Mathias, A. R. D., 1970, private communication, and Happy Families.

Mokobodzki, G., 1967–1968, *Séminaire Choquet; Initiation à l'Analyse*, 7e année (Sécretariat mathématique, Paris).

Puritz, C. W., Almost Perpendicular Vectors, *this volume*.

Puritz, C. W., 1971, Ultrafilters and Standard Functions in Non-Standard Arithmetic, *Proc. London Math. Soc.* (3), 22, pp. 705–733.

Robinson, A., 1966, *Non-Standard Analysis*, Studies in Logic and the Foundations of Mathematics (North-Holland, Amsterdam).
Rudin, W., 1956, Homogeneity Problems in the Theory of Čech Compactifications, *Duke Math. J.* 23, pp. 409–419.
Young, L., 1972, Functional Analysis – A Non-Standard Treatment with Semifields, *this volume*.

Received 30 March 1971

ADDITIONAL REMARKS ON THE THEORY OF MONADS

K. D. STROYAN
California Institute of Technology
and The University of Wisconsin

0. Introduction. The purpose of this note is to place Luxemburg's [1969] theory of monads (also see Machover and Hirschfeld [1969]) in the setting of a distributive lattice or ring of sets and to apply this theory to further study of compactifications. In particular, the hull-kernel topologies and the Wallman compactification can be viewed in this setting. This extends the study of the Čech-Stone compactification from Luxemburg [1969] and Robinson [1969].

We also make some general observations about monadic topologies, for example, they are necessarily compact. Finally, we show that all Hausdorff compactifications can be viewed this way by constructing the Samuel compactification, which is a topological (as opposed to uniform space) version of a precompact nonstandard hull.

The author gratefully acknowledges numerous suggestions made by Professor Luxemburg in conversations during preparation of this material.

1. Monads in a distributive lattice. In this section some of the basic theory of filters and ideals of a distributive lattice is developed using nonstandard models. This abstracts the monad theory of Luxemburg [1969] and specializes separately to his discrete monads and neighborhood monads. Special mention of the case of a ring of sets is made.

For the sake of brevity we shall not give proofs of several theorems where only mimicry of proofs in Luxemburg [1969] is required.

Our basic setting is as follows. $\mathscr{X}$ is a superstructure based on a set X. L is an infinite distributive lattice with 0 and 1 which is an element of $\mathscr{X}$. The partial ordering of L is denoted $\leq$, supremum of x and y in L by $x \vee y$, and infimum of x and y by $x \wedge y$. We also shall use sup and inf for these last two concepts especially when more than two elements are considered. It follows that all of the relations $\leq$, $\wedge$, $\vee$, sup, and inf are elements of $\mathscr{X}$ and we denote the corresponding nonstandard extensions in ${}^*\mathscr{X}$ by the same names. $^*\mathscr{X}$ shall be an enlargement of $\mathscr{X}$; the importance of this being that sets with the finite meet property or finite join property have non-degenerate monads. (In fact, this characterizes enlargements as Luxemburg points out.)

If A is a standard set we denote the set of nonstandard extensions of elements of A by $\hat{A} = \{^*a : a \in A\}$, this is the set of standard elements of $^*A$.

1.1. DEFINITION. *The inf-monad of a nonempty subset A of L is denoted* $\mu(A) = \{x \in {}^*L : x \leq a \text{ for every } a \in \hat{A}\}$. *In other words, all the non-standard lattice elements below every standard element of* $^*A$.

The sup-monad of a non-empty subset A of L, is denoted

$$\nu(A) = \{x \in {}^*L : x \geq a \text{ for every } a \in \hat{A}\};$$

the nonstandard lattice elements above every standard element of $^*A$.

Although the assumption that L has a 0 and 1 is not entirely necessary it simplifies the discussion and, in particular, $0 \in \mu(A)$ and $1 \in \nu(A)$ for any nonempty set $A \subseteq L$. We caution the reader that monad means monad of a standard subset of L, a distinction which becomes important, for example, in the study of uniform spaces where the infinitesimals around a remote point may not be a monad.

A subset F of L is called a *filter* provided:

1. $0 \notin F$,
2. $x, y \in F$ implies $x \wedge y \in F$,
3. $x \in F$ and $y \in L$ with $y \geq x$ implies $y \in F$.

A subset I of L is called an *ideal* provided:

1. $1 \notin I$,
2. $x, y \in I$ implies $x \vee y \in I$,
3. $x \in I$ and $y \in L$ with $y \leq x$ implies $y \in I$.

Occasionally it is convenient to allow improper filters and ideals by relaxing condition 1.

Our first result states that (non-degenerate) inf-monads and (proper) filters correspond and that (non-degenerate) sup-monads and (proper) ideals correspond.

1.2. THEOREM. *Let A and B be non-empty subsets of L.*

F1. $\mu(A) = \mu(B) \neq \{0\}$ *if and only if A and B are subbases of the same (proper) filter,* $F(\mu(A)) = \{x \in L : {}^*x \geq m \text{ for every } m \in \mu(A)\}$.

I1. $\nu(A) = \nu(B) \neq \{1\}$ *if and only if A and B are subbases of the same (proper) ideal,* $I(\nu(A)) = \{x \in L : {}^*x \leq n \text{ for every } n \in \nu(A)\}$.

F2. *A filter* F_1 *is finer than the filter* F_2 *if and only if* $\mu(F_1) \subseteq \mu(F_2)$.
I2. *An ideal* I_1 *contains the ideal* I_2 *if and only if* $\nu(I_1) \subseteq \nu(I_2)$.

From F1 and I1 we have, $\mu(F(\mu(A))) = \mu(A)$ and $\nu(I(\nu(A))) = \nu(A)$.

We shall use the operators F and I introduced here quite extensively, moreover they are defined for arbitrary nonstandard sets, for example,

$$F(A) = \{x \in L : {}^*x \geq a \quad \text{for every} \quad a \in A\}, \quad \text{where} \quad A \subseteq {}^*L.$$

We shall only briefly indicate the proof of the theorem. Since ${}^*\mathscr{X}$ is an enlargement, there is a *-finite set L_0 such that $\hat{L} \subseteq L_0$. For each $x \in \mu(A)$ (resp. $\nu(A)$) the set $\{y \in L_0 : y \in {}^*A$ and $y \geq x$ (resp. $\leq$)$\} = A_x$ is *-finite, hence $\inf(A_x)$, resp. $\sup(A_x)$) exists and is $\geq x$ (resp. $\leq x$). Since $A_x \supseteq \hat{A}$ the respective inf or sup is in the monad, thus all the elements of the monad are below (resp. above) *-finite inf's or sup's. If the monad is not a singleton set it follows that A has the finite meet or join property and generates a filter or ideal. Conversely, if A has the finite meet or join property then $\inf(A_0) \neq 0$ or $\sup(A_0) \neq 1$ where $A_0 = {}^*A \cap L_0$ and the monad is not a singleton.

In studying ideals and filters over a lattice one considers the lattice operations inherited from set inclusion on the ideals and filters. Replacing the ideals and filters by the corresponding monads these operations take on a particularily simple form, namely set operations on the monads. Finite unions and intersections of monads are monads and correspond to the infs and sups of the corresponding ideals and filters. For the remainder of this section we shall emphasize the case of inf-monads leaving the dual case to the reader where repetition occurs.

Suppose μ_1 and μ_2 are monads corresponding to filters F_1 and F_2, i.e., $\mu(F_j) = \mu_j$ and $F(\mu_j) = \mu(F_j)$. $F_1 \vee F_2$, the coarsest filter finer than F_1 and F_2, is generated by $F_1 \cup F_2$ so that $\mu(F_1 \vee F_2) = \{x \in {}^*L : x \leq f_1$ and $x \leq f_2$ for every $f_1 \in \hat{F}_1$ and $f_2 \in \hat{F}_2\}$. Hence $\mu(F_1 \vee F_2) = \mu_1 \cap \mu_2$. Similar arguments yield:

$$\mu(F_1 \vee F_2) = \mu(F_1) \cap \mu(F_2), \quad \mu(F_1 \wedge F_2) = \mu(F_1) \cup \mu(F_2),$$

$$\nu(I_1 \vee I_2) = \nu(I_1) \cap \nu(I_2) \quad \text{and} \quad \nu(I_1 \wedge I_2) = \nu(I_1) \cup \nu(I_2).$$

Infinite collections of monads are a little more delicate; we have $\mu(\sup[F_\lambda : \lambda \in \Lambda]) = \cap(\mu(F_\lambda) : \lambda \in \Lambda)$, but in general we can only say $\inf[F_\lambda : \lambda \in \Lambda] = F(\cup(\mu(F_i) : \lambda \in \Lambda)) = \{x \in \hat{L} : x \geq y$ for every $y \in \cup(\mu(F_\lambda) : \lambda \in \Lambda)\}$. (Cf. Luxemburg [1969].)

We wish to emphasize that these remarks are simple examples of how monads can replace filters and ideals. The properties of ideals and filters are reflected in the monads as is further exemplified by *prime monads* and prime filters or ideals. Specifically, an inf-monad μ_0 is *prime* whenever standard elements $x, y \in \hat{L}$ satisfying $x \vee y \geq \mu_0$ (i.e., $x \vee y \geq m$ for every $m \in \mu_0$) necessarily satisfy either $x \geq \mu_0$ or $y \geq \mu_0$. One can easily verify that this means the filter $F(\mu_0)$ is prime, that is, whenever $x, y \in L$ satisfy $x \vee y \in F$ then either $x \in F$ or, $y \in F$. The dual definitions hold for prime sup-monads and ideals where we replace $\vee$ and $\geq$ by $\wedge$ and $\leq$.

Another property reflected in monads is that inclusion minimal (non-degenerate) monads, called *ultramonads*, correspond to ultrafilters and maximal ideals. Also for inf-monads, μ_0 is an ultramonad provided that every $x \in \hat{L}$ satisfies either $x \geq \mu_0$ or $x \perp \mu_0$ (i.e., $x \wedge m = 0$ for every $m \in \mu_0$).

Other properties of monads over a distributive lattice seem woıthy of study and in particular, work beyond Theorem 1.9 concerning properties of ideals and filters when the lattice satisfies special normality conditions is planned by the author. For the applications of this note we are interested in the case where our lattice is a *ring of sets*. A ring of subsets of $X \in \mathscr{X}$ is a subset $\mathscr{E}$ of $\mathscr{P}(X)$ (the power set of X) which is closed under finite union and finite intersection, in particular, $\emptyset, X \in \mathscr{E}$. The reader will see that with $\cup$, $\cap$ and $\subseteq$ in place of $\vee$, $\wedge$ and $\leq$ a ring of sets is a distributive lattice with 0 and 1. Moreover, any distributive lattice can be represented as a ring of sets (though in some cases one may wish to avoid the Stone representation). We lose no generality in working with a ring of sets, but there are special features involved in this representation which we shall exploit, leaving an abstract treatment until results warrant its publication.

One immediate consequence of this representation is that we may replace our monad as a set of sets by a single set.

1.3. Definition ($\mathscr{E}$-monads). *If A is a nonempty subset of $\mathscr{E}$ the $\mathscr{E}$-intersection monad of A,*

$$\mu_{\mathscr{E}}(A) = \cap \hat{A} = \cap({}^*E : E \in A),$$

is related to the inf-monad as $\mu_{\mathscr{E}}(A) = \cup\, \mu(A)$.

The $\mathscr{E}$-union monad of A,

$$\nu_{\mathscr{E}}(A) = \cup \hat{A} = \cup({}^*E : E \in A),$$

is related to the sup-monad as $\nu_{\mathscr{E}}(A) = \cap\, \nu(A)$.

We also extend our notation $F_{\mathscr{E}}(B) = \{E \in \mathscr{E} : {}^*E \supseteq B\}$ and $I_{\mathscr{E}}(B) = \{E \in \mathscr{E} : {}^*E \subseteq B\}$ for filters and ideals over $\mathscr{E}$ where B can be any subset of

$^*X$. Theorem 1.2 above tells us that the $\mathscr{E}$-monad of an $\mathscr{E}$-filter, F, characterizes F and conversely, $F = F_{\mathscr{E}}(\mu_{\mathscr{E}}(F))$. Moreover, it is convenient to introduce the notation $\mu_{\mathscr{E}}(B) = \cap(^*E : {}^*E \supseteq B) = \mu_{\mathscr{E}}(F_{\mathscr{E}}(B))$ for any subset B of $^*X$ and $\nu_{\mathscr{E}}(B) = \nu_{\mathscr{E}}(I_{\mathscr{E}}(B))$. Theorem 1.2 tells us $\mu_{\mathscr{E}}(\mu_{\mathscr{E}}(B)) = \mu_{\mathscr{E}}(B)$.

Following Luxemburg we shall denote the ring of all subsets of X by $\mathscr{D}$ and call it the discrete ring, with discrete monads, discrete filters etc. usually being referred to simply as monads, filters, etc. wherever no confusion seems likely. Notation: $\mu_{\mathscr{D}}$, $F_{\mathscr{D}}$, etc. or simply μ, F etc. $\mathscr{E}$-monads are special discrete monads since $\mathscr{E}$-filters and ideals form bases for discrete filters and ideals. This embedding of $\mathscr{E}$ in $\mathscr{D}$ and $\mathscr{E}$-monads in $\mathscr{D}$-monads is a special consequence of our considering a ring of sets. Thus we may write $\mu_{\mathscr{D}}(F)$, $\mu_{\mathscr{E}}(F)$ or just $\mu(F)$ for an $\mathscr{E}$-filter, F, however if $B \subseteq {}^*X$, $\mu_{\mathscr{E}}(B) \supseteq \mu_{\mathscr{D}}(B)$ and strict inclusion is certainly possible. We exploit this embedding further by introducing the *dual ring* $\mathscr{G}$ of $\mathscr{E}$ as $\mathscr{G} = \{X\backslash E : E \in \mathscr{E}\}$, the set of complements (in $\mathscr{D}$) of elements of $\mathscr{E}$. We now have the corresponding $\mathscr{G}$-monads, $\mu_{\mathscr{G}}$, $F_{\mathscr{G}}$, etc.

1.4. THEOREM. *Every prime $\mathscr{E}$-filter arises as one of the filters $F_{\mathscr{E}}(\{x\})$ for some $x \in {}^*X$. Equivalently, every prime $\mathscr{E}$-monad arises as $\mu_{\mathscr{E}}(\{x\})$ for some $x \in {}^*X$.*

Proof. If $x \in E_1 \cup E_2$, $E_1, E_2 \in \mathscr{E}$ then either $x \in E_1$ or $x \in E_2$ hence each $\mu_{\mathscr{E}}(\{x\})$ is prime and so is $F_{\mathscr{E}}(\{x\})$.

Conversely, let F_0 be a prime $\mathscr{E}$-filter. The prime $\mathscr{E}$-ideal $I_0 = \mathscr{E}\backslash F_0$ generates a prime $\mathscr{G}$-filter F_1 as

$$F_1 = \{G \in \mathscr{G} : G = X\backslash E, E \in \mathscr{E}\backslash F_0\}.$$

Now $\mu_{\mathscr{E}}(F_0) \cap \mu_{\mathscr{G}}(F_1) \neq \emptyset$ because if $E \cap G = \emptyset$, where $E \in F_0$ and $G \in F_1$ then $E \subseteq X\backslash G$, forcing $X\backslash G \in F_0$ and $G \notin F_1$, a contradiction. Taking $x \in \mu_{\mathscr{E}}(F_0) \cap \mu_{\mathscr{G}}(F_1)$ gives us $F_{\mathscr{E}}(\{x\}) = F_0$ because $\mu_{\mathscr{E}}(\{x\})$ is the finest $\mathscr{E}$-monad containing x, making $F_{\mathscr{E}}(\{x\}) \supseteq F_0$ and $F_{\mathscr{E}}(\{x\})$ cannot be strictly finer than F_0 since $x \in \mu_{\mathscr{G}}(F_1)$. (If $x \in E \notin F_0$, then $x \notin \mu_{\mathscr{G}}(F_1)$ by the definition of F_1.)

Essentially this result appears in the discussion of Robinson [1969].

Perhaps some remarks about this theorem are in order here. Take $A \subseteq {}^*X$; $\mu_{\mathscr{E}}(A)$ is the finest $\mathscr{E}$-monad which contains the set A. When we take $x \in \mu_{\mathscr{E}}(F)$ we know therefore that $\mu_{\mathscr{E}}(\{x\}) \subseteq \mu_{\mathscr{E}}(F)$, for any $\mathscr{E}$-filter F. We observed above that $\mu_{\mathscr{E}}(\{x\})$ is prime however, so that we do not expect that $\mu_{\mathscr{E}}(\{x\}) = \mu_{\mathscr{E}}(F)$ in general. In fact, even when F is a prime $\mathscr{E}$-filter and $x \in \mu_{\mathscr{E}}(F)$, strict inclusion is possible, as can be seen by taking $x \in \mu_{\mathscr{E}}(u)$ where u is an $\mathscr{E}$-ultrafilter strictly finer than F.

Of course, when $\mathscr{E}$ is complimented (in particular, when $\mathscr{D} = \mathscr{E}$) we do have $\mu_{\mathscr{E}}(\{x\}) = \mu_{\mathscr{E}}(F)$, whenever F is prime, since then the only prime filters are ultrafilters. Ultramonads have this property because they cannot be further broken down by $\mathscr{E}$-sets. Also ultramonads are either equal or disjoint since an intersection cannot be strictly finer and non-degenerate.

For some rings prime monads will contain several ultramonads, or at least be strictly coarser than an ultramonad, we are assured none the less of an x on the fringes that determines the prime filter which gave rise to the monad.

The prime ideals are given by $I_{\mathscr{E}}(^*X \backslash \{x\})$ *and the prime union-monads by* $v_{\mathscr{E}}(^*X \backslash \{x\})$.

The converse can also be shown without introducing the dual ring $\mathscr{G}$. The following result is based on an idea of Luxemburg and is the only use we make of models more saturated than enlargements in this note.

1.5. THEOREM. *If* $^*\mathscr{X}$ *is a countable ultralimit or a* κ*-saturated model* ($\kappa >$ card $(\mathscr{X})$), *a* $\cup$*-monadic cover of an* $\cap$*-monad can be replaced by a finite subcover. Specifically, let* A *and* B *be subsets of* $\mathscr{E}$. *If* $v_{\mathscr{E}}(A) \supseteq \mu_{\mathscr{E}}(B)$, *then there exist* $\mathscr{E}$*-sets* $a_1, \ldots, a_n \in A$ *such that* $\bigcup_{i=1}^n {}^*a_i \supseteq \mu_{\mathscr{E}}(B)$.

Remark. For $\mathscr{E}$-ideals and $\mathscr{E}$-filters this says that if $v_{\mathscr{E}}(I) \supseteq \mu_{\mathscr{E}}(F)$, then there is an $E \in I$ with $^*E \supseteq \mu_{\mathscr{E}}(F)$ or $E \in F$. Applied to the converse of 1.4 this means $\mu_{\mathscr{E}}(F_0) \backslash v_{\mathscr{E}}(I_0) \neq \emptyset$ and $\mu_{\mathscr{E}}(\{x\}) = \mu_{\mathscr{E}}(F_0)$ for $x \in \mu_{\mathscr{E}}(F_0) \backslash v_{\mathscr{E}}(I_0)$.

To prove 1.5 consider the internal family F of *-finite subsets of $^*(A \times B)$ given by: $\{(a_1, b_1), \ldots, (a_\lambda, b_\lambda)\} \in F$ provided

$$\cup(a_i : i = 1, \ldots, \lambda) \supseteq \cap(b_i : i = 1, \ldots, \lambda).$$

If $C = \{(a_1, b_1), \ldots, (a_\lambda, b_\lambda)\}$ is a *-finite set such that $^\circ C = A \times B$ or $C \supseteq \hat{A} \times \hat{B}$, then $C \in F$ since

$$\cup(a_i : i = 1, \ldots, \lambda) \supseteq \cup \hat{A} = v_{\mathscr{E}}(A) \supseteq \mu_{\mathscr{E}}(B) = \cap \hat{B} \supseteq \cap(b_i : i = 1, \ldots, \lambda).$$

Luxemburg's result [1969, Theorem 2.7.11(a)] states that whenever an internal family F of *-finite sets contains all the *-finite sets which contain all the standard elements, then F contains a standard set (which is finite since it is standard and *-finite). Hence there are $a_1, \ldots, a_n \in A$ and $b_1, \ldots, b_n \in B$ such that $\cup(^*a_i : i = 1, \ldots, n) \supseteq \cap(^*b_i : i = 1, \ldots, n) \supseteq \mu_{\mathscr{E}}(B)$.

Introducing the dual ring $\mathscr{G}$ is unnecessary for the last proof, however we feel it is somewhat more natural than the alternatives especially for the next few results.

$\mathscr{E}$-filters F_1 and F_2 have a common refinement in $\mathscr{E}$ provided $F_1 \vee F_2$ is a proper $\mathscr{E}$-filter, that is, provided $F_1 \cup F_2$ has the finite intersection property (finite intersections are nonempty). *A set $E_0 \in \mathscr{E}$ is compatible with an* $\mathscr{E}$-filter F_1 provided the intersection of E_0 with every element of F_1 is nonempty.

1.6. THEOREM. *$\mathscr{E}$-filters F_1 and F_2 have a common refinement in $\mathscr{E}$ if and only if $\mu_{\mathscr{G}}(\mu_{\mathscr{E}}(F_1)) \cap \mu_{\mathscr{E}}(F_2) \neq \emptyset$.*

Proof. $F_1 \vee F_2$ exists if and only if $\mu(F_1) \cap \mu(F_2) \neq \emptyset$ and of course $\mu_{\mathscr{G}}(\mu(F_1)) \supseteq \mu(F_1)$.

Conversely, if $F_1 \vee F_2$ is improper there exists $E_1 \in F_1$ and $E_2 \in F_2$ with $E_1 \cap E_2 = \emptyset$. Then

$$\mu_{\mathscr{G}}(\mu(F_1)) \subseteq {}^*X \backslash {}^*E_2$$

and

$$\mu_{\mathscr{G}}(\mu(F_1)) \cap \mu(F_2) = \emptyset.$$

1.7. COROLLARY. *$E \in \mathscr{E}$ is compatible with F_1 if and only if*

$$\mu_{\mathscr{G}}({}^*E) \cap \mu_{\mathscr{E}}(F_1) \neq \emptyset.$$

Proof. Let $F_2 = F_{\mathscr{E}}({}^*E)$ and apply the above result.

A sharper result is possible for the prime filters $F_{\mathscr{E}}(\{x\})$.

1.8. THEOREM. *$E \in \mathscr{E}$ is compatible with $F_{\mathscr{E}}(\{x\})$ if and only if $x \in \mu_{\mathscr{G}}(E)$.*

Proof. If $x \notin \mu_{\mathscr{G}}(E)$, there exists $E_0 \in \mathscr{E}$ such that $x \in E_0$ and $E \cap E_0 = \emptyset$. Hence E is not compatible with $F_{\mathscr{E}}(\{x\})$. (Note: $\mu_{\mathscr{G}}(E) = \mu_{\mathscr{G}}({}^*E)$.)

Conversely, if $x \in \mu_{\mathscr{G}}(E)$ then $\mu_{\mathscr{E}}(\{x\}) \cap \mu_{\mathscr{G}}(E) \neq \emptyset$ and the result follows from the preceding theorem.

Remark. As a consequence of this result whenever an $\mathscr{E}$-monad $\mu_{\mathscr{E}}(\{x\})$ contains a unique ultramonad the corresponding $\mathscr{E}$-ultrafilter is given by $\hat{\varphi}(x) = \{E \in \mathscr{E} : x \in \mu_{\mathscr{G}}(E)\}$.

We now turn to a result which was announced in Monteiro [1954]. We hope this proof shows how our formalism leads naturally to properties of filters over a distributive lattice. The dual result is left to the reader.

1.9. Definition. *A ring of sets $\mathscr{E}$ is normal shall mean that if $E_1, E_2 \in \mathscr{E}$ and $E_1 \perp E_2$ ($E_1 \cap E_2 = \emptyset$) then there exist sets $A_1, A_2 \in \mathscr{E}$ satisfying*

1. $A_1 \cup A_2 = X$
2. $E_1 \perp A_2 \quad (A_1 \supseteq E_1)$

and

3. $E_2 \perp A_1 \quad (A_2 \supseteq E_2)$

or equivalently, using the dual ring $\mathscr{G}$, that there exist sets $G_1, G_2 \in \mathscr{G}$ ($G_1 = X \backslash A_2$, $G_2 = X \backslash A_1$) satisfying

1. $G_1 \perp G_2$,
2. $G_1 \supseteq E_1$,

and

3. $G_2 \supseteq E_2$.

This is, of course, akin to the topological notion of normality.

1.10. Theorem. *A necessary and sufficient condition that every prime $\mathscr{E}$-filter has a unique refinement to an $\mathscr{E}$-ultrafilter, or equivalently, that $\mu_{\mathscr{E}}(\{x\})$ contains a unique $\mathscr{E}$-ultramonad for each $x \in {}^*X$, is that $\mathscr{E}$ is a normal ring.*

Proof. Take E_1 and $E_2 \in \mathscr{E}$ with $E_1 \perp E_2$. It is sufficient to show that $\mu_{\mathscr{G}}(E_1) \perp \mu_{\mathscr{G}}(E_2)$ since in this case there exist $G_1, G_2 \in \mathscr{G}$ with $G_1 \supseteq E_1$, $G_2 \supseteq E_2$ and $G_1 \perp G_2$.

If $x \in \mu_{\mathscr{G}}(E_1) \cap \mu_{\mathscr{G}}(E_2)$, then by the preceding result $F_{\mathscr{E}}(\{x\})$ is compatible with both E_1 and E_2, whence a prime $\mathscr{E}$-filter has two separate refinements to ultrafilters.

Conversely, if U_1 and U_2 are distinct $\mathscr{E}$-ultrafilters finer than the prime $\mathscr{E}$-ultrafilter F, there exist sets $E_1 \in U_1$ and $E_2 \in U_2$ such that $E_1 \perp E_2$. If $\mathscr{E}$ is also a normal ring, there are sets A_1 and A_2 satisfying the conditions of the first form of the Definition 1.9 above. Since $X = A_1 \cup A_2$ and since F is prime either A_1 or A_2 is in F. If $A_2 \in F$, then $A_2 \in U_1$ and $A_2 \perp E_1 \in U_1$ or if $A_1 \in F$, then $A_1 \in U_2$ and $A_1 \perp E_2 \in U_2$, so in either case we arrive at a contradiction and F must have a unique refinement when $\mathscr{E}$ is normal.

This result plays an important role in one monadic approach to the Wallman compactification and since normality is also required in order that the Wallman space be Hausdorff we restrict our attention to that case below. A nonstandard approach is possible in the abnormal case, and there the question arises as to when the filters $F_{\mathscr{E}}(\{x\})$ have a unique ultrafilter refinement, or when $\mu_{\mathscr{E}}(\{x\})$ contains a unique $\mathscr{E}$-ultramonad so that we might assign x to a unique $\mathscr{E}$-ultramonad. Since that situation is somewhat complicated considering the knowledge gained, we offer only the following from that study.

1.11. ASSERTION. *A point $x \in {}^*X$ can be assigned to a unique $\mathscr{E}$-ultramonad (in the sense above) if and only if $\mu_{\mathscr{G}}(\mu_{\mathscr{E}}(\{x\})) = \cap(\mu_{\mathscr{G}}(E) : x \in \mu_{\mathscr{G}}(E)$ and $E \in \mathscr{E})$.*

A final remark concerning the question of assigning points to ultramonads is that, in a normal ring, the set of points which go to a certain $\mathscr{E}$-ultramonad is itself both an $\mathscr{E}$-monad and a $\mathscr{G}$-monad.

We believe that monads offer certain conceptual advantages over filters and ideals, and we hope this section has indicated a few of them. A final example is that every $\mathscr{E}$-filter, F, is the inf of the prime $\mathscr{E}$-filters finer than it; proof: $\mu(F) = \cup(\mu_{\mathscr{E}}(\{x\}) : x \in \mu(F))$.

We shall close this section by introducing the notion of the $\mathscr{E}$-chroma of a nonstandard set. Luxemburg [1969] calls the corresponding notion for discrete monads saturation, but since other notions of saturation arise we shall introduce the new terminology.

1.12. DEFINITION. *A set $A \subset {}^*X$ is called $\mathscr{E}$-chromatic provided $\mu_{\mathscr{E}}(\{a\}) \subseteq A$ for every $a \in A$.*

As with our other conventions $\mathscr{D}$-chromatic will be referred to simply as chromatic.

Open sets are characterized as those for which ${}^*A$ is τ-chromatic, where τ is the ring of open sets of a topological space X. An internal chromatic set is necessarily standard in sufficiently saturated models. An $\mathscr{E}$-monad is $\mathscr{E}$-chromatic and, when $\mathscr{E}$ is closed under arbitrary unions, and $\mathscr{E}$-chromatic monad is an $\mathscr{E}$-monad. More on the chromatic properties of sets can be found in Luxemburg [1969].

2. Monadic closure operators. We begin our applications of monads to compactification theory by making the following observation.

2.1. *Let M be a mapping from $\mathscr{P}({}^*X)$ into $\mathscr{P}({}^*X)$ which is monad valued. If M is a closure operator on ${}^*X$ we shall say it is a monadic closure, and then the topology it induces is compact.* To see this, let $(M_\lambda : \lambda \in \Lambda)$ be a family of closed sets with the finite intersection property. Let F_λ denote the filters $F_{\mathscr{D}}(M_\lambda)$.

Given any finite set of λ's, $\lambda_1, \ldots, \lambda_n$ we have

$$\sup(F_{\lambda_1}, \ldots, F_{\lambda_n}) \text{ exists as a proper filter}$$

since $\cap(M_{\lambda_i} : i = 1, \ldots, n) \neq \emptyset$. Thus, for any $f_1, \ldots, f_n$ in $F_{\lambda_1}, \ldots, F_{\lambda_n}$ respectively $\cap f_i \neq \emptyset$. Finally,

$$\mu(\sup(F_\lambda : \lambda \in \Lambda)) = \cap(M_\lambda < \lambda \in \Lambda) \neq \emptyset.$$

Another observation about monadic closures is that $\hat{X}$ *is always dense in* $^*X$ since the finest monad containing $\hat{X}$, $\mu_{\mathscr{D}}(\hat{X}) = {}^*X$.

2.2. Our first example is a nonstandard version of the original construction of Wallman [1938]. Let X be a topological space with the ring of closed sets denoted by σ. The σ-monad operator μ_σ is a monadic closure on $^*X$ and we shall refer to the corresponding topology as *Luxemburg's* S-*topology* (since it follows Luxemburg [1969] and is distinct from the metric S-topology introduced by Robinson [1966]). The standard closed sets form a base for the LS-topology, hence the relative topology inherited by $\hat{X}$ is the standard one. Finally, if X is a T_1-space (accessible space) the LS-topology on the space of σ-ultramonads (identifying points in the same σ-ultramonad) with the relative topology coincides with the classical Wallman space. This last remark is justified more generally below.

Since we are interested in Hausdorff compactifications, henceforth standard topological spaces will be assumed to be Tychonoff spaces. Let X be a Tychonoff space (completely regular, Hausdorff) and denote the ring of open sets by τ. The standard part operation $\mathrm{st}_\tau(x) = y$, for $x \in {}^*X$ provided $y \in X$ and $x \in \mu_\tau(y)$, defines a map from the near standard points of $^*X$, $\mathrm{ns}_\tau({}^*X)$, onto X.

2.3. *The monadic closure* μ_τ on $^*X$ *induces a topology on* $\mathrm{ns}_\tau({}^*X)$ *for which* st_τ *is a closed continuous map onto* X. The quotient space obtained by identifying points of $\mathrm{ns}_\tau({}^*X)$ with equal standard parts is thus homeomorphic to the standard space X. The closure of st_τ follows from a general result of Luxemburg [1969] stating that the standard part of a monad is closed. Continuity of st follows from the observation that if $S \in \sigma$, $\mathrm{st}^{-1}(S) \subseteq \mu_\tau({}^*S) \cap \mathrm{ns}({}^*X)$, a consequence of regularity and the τ-chromaticity of $\mu_\tau({}^*S)$.

This example replaces the local notion of how the standard topology is stored in $^*X$ (as $\mu_\tau(\{x\})$) by a global one.

2.4. Next we give a nonstandard approach to the *hull-kernel topology for prime filters* over a ring of sets $\mathscr{E}$. (The reader may consult Luxemburg and Zaanen [1971] for further information on the hull-kernel topology for filters or ideals.) Let π denote the set of prime $\mathscr{E}$-filters; we know $\pi = \{F_{\mathscr{E}}(\{x\}) : x \in {}^*X\}$. The hull-kernel topology on π is given by the closure

$$\mathrm{cl}(S) = h(k(S)), \quad S \subseteq \pi,$$

where $k(S) = \cap(F : F \in S)$ is the *kernel* of S and, if F_0 is an $\mathscr{E}$-filter, $k(F_0) = \{F \in \pi : F \supseteq F_0\}$ is the *hull* of F_0.

The mapping $x \to F_{\mathscr{E}}(\{x\})$ gives us a way to view π in ${}^*X$. We ask which sets $T \subseteq {}^*X$ correspond to closed sets of π, that is, if

$$S = \{F_{\mathscr{E}}(t) : t \in T\},$$

when is $S = h(k(S))$? Since $h(k(S)) = \{F \in \pi : F \supseteq \cap[F_{\mathscr{E}}(\{t\}) : t \in T]\} = \{F \in \pi : F \supseteq F_{\mathscr{E}}(\mu_{\mathscr{E}}(\cup[\mu_{\mathscr{E}}(t) : t \in T]))\} = \{F \in \pi : \mu(F) \subseteq \mu_{\mathscr{E}}(T)\}$, we see that the points of ${}^*X$ which map onto $h(k(S))$ are the points in $\mu_{\mathscr{E}}(T)$. Therefore S is the hull of its kernel (and closed) when it corresponds to the monad $\mu_{\mathscr{E}}(T)$. Thus, the monadic closure $\mu_{\mathscr{E}}$ induces a topology on ${}^*X$ for which $x \to F_{\mathscr{E}}(\{x\})$ is closed and continuous; the quotient space obtained by identifying points which map onto the same prime filter is homeomorphic to π in the hull-kernel topology.

2.5. *The hull-kernel topology for prime ideals over* $\mathscr{E}$ can be treated similarily to 2.4. The prime ideals are given by $x \to I_{\mathscr{E}}({}^*X \setminus \{x\})$, $x \in {}^*X$. The closure is given by $\mu_{\mathscr{G}}$ where $\mathscr{G}$ is the ring dual to $\mathscr{E}$ as described in section 1.

Our final application of $\mathscr{E}$-monads is to the *Wallman compactification*. Further details on a standard development of this space can be found in Steiner [1968].

The basic construction is simply this: $\mathscr{E}$ is a ring of closed subsets of a topological space X, $\mathscr{E} \subseteq \sigma$. We denote the set of $\mathscr{E}$-ultrafilters with the relative topology inherited from the hull-kernel topology for prime $\mathscr{E}$-filters by $w(\mathscr{E})$ and call it the Wallman space of $\mathscr{E}$. A base for closed sets is thus the collection $\{U\}^E = \{U \in w(\mathscr{E}) : E \in U\}$ where E runs over $\mathscr{E}$.

Without even discussing properties of $\mathscr{E}$ which make $w(\mathscr{E})$ a compactification of X we can give the first nonstandard treatment of $w(\mathscr{E})$. Based on example 2.4 we see that giving the points of ${}^*X$ which lie in $\mathscr{E}$-ultramonads the relative topology inherited from $\mu_{\mathscr{E}}$ as a closure and then identifying points in the same $\mathscr{E}$-ultramonads we obtain a space homeomorphic to $w(\mathscr{E})$.

2.6. Rephrasing this, *the space of $\mathscr{E}$-ultramonads with $\mu_{\mathscr{E}}$ as a closure is homeomorphic to the Wallman space $w(\mathscr{E})$.*

A nonstandard treatment is possible where X is only a T_1-space (accessible space) or where the resulting Wallman space is not Hausdorff. We shall not deal with those cases here, instead we want $w(\mathscr{E})$ to be a Hausdorff compactification of X so that X must be a Tychonoff space to begin with.

When $\mathscr{E}$ is taken to be the zero sets of continuous real-valued functions on X, denoted $\mathscr{Z} = \{f^{-1}(0): f \in C(x)\}$, it is well known that $w(\mathscr{Z})$ is the *Čech-Stone compactification.* (Luxemburg [1969] and Robinson [1969] have considered the Čech-Stone compactification nonstandardly.)

We deal briefly with the question of when $w(\mathscr{E})$ is a Hausdorff compactification of X. As above, it is convenient to introduce the dual ring $\mathscr{G}$ of complements of sets in $\mathscr{E}$. (The dual ring to the zero sets, $\mathscr{Z}$ is denoted $\mathscr{C}$, for co-zero sets.)

We first deal with the question of whether X is contained in $w(\mathscr{E})$ as principal filters over points of X.

LEMMA. *The following are equivalent:*

1. *For each (standard) $x \in \hat{X}$, $F_{\mathscr{E}}(\{x\})$ is an $\mathscr{E}$-ultrafilter.*
2. *For each $x \in \hat{X}$, $\mu_{\mathscr{E}}(\{x\})$ is an $\mathscr{E}$-ultramonad.*
3. *For each $x \in \hat{X}$, $\mu_{\mathscr{E}}(\{x\}) \subseteq \mu_{\mathscr{G}}(\{x\})$.*
4. *For each $x \in G \in \mathscr{G}$, there exists $E \in \mathscr{E}$ with $x \in E \subseteq G$.*
5. *For each $E \in \mathscr{E}$, $^\circ(\mu_{\mathscr{G}}(^*E)) = E$ (here $^\circ$ is the discrete standard part, $^\circ(\mu_{\mathscr{G}}(^*F)) = \mu_{\mathscr{G}}(^*F) \cap \hat{X}$, viewed in the standard model).*

The equivalence of 1. and 4. is from Steiner [1968] where it is also shown that this embedding is continuous and onto a dense subset of $w(\mathscr{E})$. (The latter facts also follow from the nonstandard treatment.)

Proof. 1. and 2. are equivalent by Theorem 1.2.

(2. $\Rightarrow$ 3.): If $x \notin E \in \mathscr{E}$, then $^*E \cap \mu_{\mathscr{E}}(\{x\}) = \emptyset$ and since $\mu_{\mathscr{G}}(\{x\}) = {}^*X \backslash \nu_{\mathscr{E}}(^*X \backslash \{x\})$ 3. holds.

(3. $\Rightarrow$ 4.): Since the discrete filter generated by $F_{\mathscr{E}}(\{x\})$ must be finer than that generated by $F_{\mathscr{G}}(\{x\})$ 4. follows.

(4. $\Rightarrow$ 5.): Let $x \in \hat{X}$ and $x \notin E$. Taking $G = X \backslash E$ and applying 4. we get E_1 such that $x \in E_1 \subseteq G$ and $E \subseteq X \backslash E_1 = G_1 \in \mathscr{G}$ so 5. is true.

(5. $\Rightarrow$ 1.): Theorem 1.8 on compatibility states that $\hat{\varphi}(x) = \{E \in \mathscr{E}: x \in \mu_{\mathscr{G}}(E)\}$ is an $\mathscr{E}$-ultrafilter provided it is a filter, and by 5. $F_{\mathscr{E}}(\{x\}) = \hat{\varphi}(x)$ since $x \in \hat{X}$.

Now we ask further that the embedding of X into $w(\mathscr{E})$ be topological.

It is easy to see that this is related to the equality of $\mu_{\mathscr{G}}(\{x\})$ and $\mu_\tau(\{x\})$ for (standard) $x \in \hat{X}$, since $\mu_\tau(\{x\})$ determines convergence to x in X. As Steiner [1968] points out the required condition is that $\mathscr{E}$ is a base for closed sets which satisfies the properties of the above lemma, or equivalently, that whenever $x \notin S$, S a closed set ($S \in \sigma$), there exist sets E_1 and E_2 in $\mathscr{E}$ such that $x \in E_1$, $S \subseteq E_2$ and $E_1 \perp E_2$. The reader can easily check that this is equivalent to: for each $x \in \hat{X}$, $\mu_{\mathscr{E}}(\{x\}) \subseteq \mu_{\mathscr{G}}(\{x\}) \subseteq \mu_\tau(\{x\})$ (and since $\mathscr{G}$ consists of open sets, the latter inclusion is equality). In this case we say *$\mathscr{E}$ separates points and closed sets*. It follows in this event that $^\circ(\mu_{\mathscr{E}}(S)) = S$ when $S \in \sigma$.

From Theorem 1.10 we know that in order to assign to each $x \in {}^*X$ a unique $\mathscr{E}$-ultramonad, $\mathscr{E}$ must be a normal ring of sets. Another consequence of the normality of $\mathscr{E}$ is that $w(\mathscr{E})$ is Hausdorff. Henceforth we assume $\mathscr{E}$ is a normal ring of closed sets which separates points and closed sets.

2.7. Our second approach to the Wallman compactification is simply this: Take $\mu_{\mathscr{G}}$ *as a closure on* $^*X$. *The mapping* $\hat{\varphi}: {}^*X \to w(\mathscr{E})$ *is closed and continuous, so the quotient space obtained from* $^*X$ *by identifying points associated with the same* $\mathscr{E}$*-ultramonad is homeomorphic to* $w(\mathscr{E})$. (Recall that $\hat{\varphi}(x) = \{E \in \mathscr{E} : x \in \mu_{\mathscr{G}}(E)\}$.) We remark that the same result holds with $\mu_{\mathscr{E}}$ as the closure.

To see this we need first to show that the base $\{U\}^E = \{U \in w(\mathscr{E}) : E \in U\}$ for closed sets of $w(\mathscr{E})$ come from the $\hat{\varphi}$-saturated $\mathscr{G}$-monads $\mu_{\mathscr{G}}(E)$. This is a consequence of Theorem 1.8 which says $\hat{\varphi}(x)$ contains E if and only if $x \in \mu_{\mathscr{G}}(E)$. Thus $\hat{\varphi}$ is continuous.

2.8. *Remark*. For the study of the Wallman compactification we could restrict our attention to $\hat{\varphi}$-saturated $\mathscr{G}$-monads, letting the collection $\mu_{\mathscr{G}}(E)$ (as E runs through $\mathscr{E}$) generate a topology (the coarsest for which $\hat{\varphi}$ is continuous). In this case $\hat{\varphi}$ is automatically closed.

Closure of $\hat{\varphi}$ in the $\mu_{\mathscr{G}}$-topology goes as follows. Our previous treatment of the Wallman space (2.6) tells us that for any $A \subseteq {}^*X$, $\mathrm{cl}_w(\hat{\varphi}(A)) = \hat{\varphi}(\mu_{\mathscr{E}}(A))$ so it is sufficient to show that if $\hat{\varphi}^{-1}(\hat{\varphi}(x))$ intersects $\mu_{\mathscr{E}}(A)$ then it also intersects $\mu_{\mathscr{G}}(A)$ forcing $\hat{\varphi}(\mu_{\mathscr{G}}(A)) = \mathrm{cl}_w(\hat{\varphi}(A))$. We can show that $\hat{\varphi}^{-1}(\hat{\varphi}(x)) = \mu_{\mathscr{G}}(\mu_{\mathscr{E}}(\{x\}))$. This tells us that $\hat{\varphi}(x)$ has a pre-image in $\mu_{\mathscr{G}}(A)$ whenever it has one in $\mu_{\mathscr{E}}(A)$ as a result of Theorem 1.6. (If $\mu_{\mathscr{G}}(\mu_{\mathscr{E}}(\{x\})) \perp \mu_{\mathscr{G}}(A)$ it follows that $\mu_{\mathscr{E}}(\{x\}) \perp \mu_{\mathscr{E}}(A)$, contrary to the conclusion of 1.6.)

By Theorem 1.8 we see that $\hat{\varphi}(x) = \hat{\varphi}(y)$ if and only if $y \in \mu_{\mathscr{G}}(\mu(\hat{\varphi}(x)))$. (We use Theorem 1.10 to assure that $\hat{\varphi}$ is defined on all of $^*X$.) Since

$\mu_{\mathscr{E}}(\{x\}) \supseteq \mu(\hat{\varphi}(x))$ we know $\mu_{\mathscr{G}}(\mu_{\mathscr{E}}(\{x\})) \supseteq \mu_{\mathscr{G}}(\mu(\hat{\varphi}(x)))$. Finally, if $G_0 \in \mathscr{G}$ satisfies $G_0 \supseteq \mu(\hat{\varphi}(x))$ we must have $G_0 \supseteq \mu_{\mathscr{E}}(\{x\})$, since otherwise $E_0 = X \backslash G_0$ is compatible with $F_{\mathscr{E}}(\{x\})$ and as such must be in $\hat{\varphi}(x)$ whence $E_0 \supseteq \mu(\hat{\varphi}(x))$, a contradiction. Thus $\hat{\varphi}^{-1}(\varphi(x)) = \mu_{\mathscr{G}}(\mu_{\mathscr{E}}(\{x\}))$ and our second representation of $w(\mathscr{E})$ is complete.

If we denote by φ the mapping induced on the quotient space from $\hat{\varphi}$ acting on ${}^*X$ and consider X embedded as $\hat{X}$ we have an extension of the usual injection of X into $w(\mathscr{E})$ to a homeomorphism onto $w(\mathscr{E})$

$$\begin{array}{ccc} {}^*X & & \\ \downarrow & \searrow^{\hat{\varphi}} & \\ X \subseteq W & \xrightarrow[\varphi]{} & w(\mathscr{E}). \end{array}$$

3. A monadic approach to the Samuel compactification. The remarks made at the beginning of section 2 pertain to any monadic closure, although the examples given were $\mathscr{E}$-monads with respect to some ring of sets (except in Remark 2.8). Our final example of a monadic closure is not based on monads with respect to a ring of sets, but rather on the infinitesimal operator of a uniform space. Specifically, let X be a Hausdorff uniform space with uniformity u. We denote the *infinitesimals with respect to u by o* so that

$$o(B) = \mu(u)[B] = \{x \in {}^*X : (x, b) \in \mu(u) \quad \text{for some} \quad b \in B\}.$$

(The monad of u is a subset of ${}^*X \times {}^*X$ which is an equivalence relation.)

Now we define

$$\mu^s(A) = \mu_{\mathscr{D}}(o(\mu_{\mathscr{D}}(A))) \quad \text{for} \quad A \subseteq {}^*X$$

and

$$\mu^s(F) = \mu_{\mathscr{D}}(o(\mu(F))) \qquad \text{for a filter} \quad F \text{ over } X.$$

Let S denote the set of symmetric open entourages of u. We define the *envelope* of a filter F over X as: $\langle F \rangle$ is the filter generated by

$$\{V[f] : V \in S \quad \text{and} \quad f \in F\}$$

where $V[f] = \{y \in X : (x, y) \in V \text{ for some } x \in f\}$.

Now if $f \in F$ and $V \in S$ then ${}^*(V[f]) = {}^*V[{}^*f] \supseteq o(\mu(F))$, since ${}^*f \supseteq \mu(F)$ and ${}^*V \supseteq \mu(u)$. Therefore, $\mu(\langle F \rangle) \supseteq \mu^s(F)$.

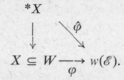

Conversely, if $D \subseteq X$ and ${}^*D \supseteq o(\mu(F))$ there must be standard sets $V \in S$ and $f \in F$ with $V[f] \subseteq D$. This follows from the fact that the standard sentence "there exists $f \in {}^*F$ and there exists $V \in {}^*S$ such that ${}^*D \supseteq V[f]$", holds in $^*\mathscr{X}$ by taking $f \subseteq \mu(F)$ and $V \subseteq \mu(u)$. Interpreted in $\mathscr{X}$ the statement yields the desired result, so $\mu^s(F) = \mu(\langle F \rangle)$. Moreover, we see that a monad is $[\mu(u)]$-saturated if and only if it is the monad of an envelope of a filter and in that case the monad is $\tau(u)$-chromatic where $\tau(u)$ is the induced topology.

It is easy to check that μ^s is a closure on $^*X$ and one other observation is that $a \overset{s}{=} b$ if and only if $\mu^s(\{a\}) = \mu^s(\{b\})$ is an equivalence relation, since $a \overset{s}{=} b$ if and only if $\langle F_{\mathscr{D}}(\{a\}) \rangle = \langle F_{\mathscr{D}}(\{b\}) \rangle$.

Samuel [1948] constructs a space from the discrete Wallman space of X, $w(\mathscr{D})$, by identifying ultrafilters with the same envelope. This corresponds to identification in $^*X$ of $\overset{s}{=}$-equal elements.

3.1. *$^*X$ with μ^s as a closure and $\overset{s}{=}$-equal points identified is isomorphic to the Samuel compactification.*

When u is a precompact uniformity μ^s induces the nonstandard hull topology on $^*X$. (This follows from Samuel's result on the completion.) We see in this case then that saturation of the nonstandard model is not essential for completeness of the nonstandard hull.

Another consequence of this approach to the nonstandard hull is that all Hausdorff compactifications can be viewed as monadic closures on $^*X$ (with identifications.)

References

Luxemburg, W. A. J., 1969, A General Theory of Monads, in: *Applications of Model Theory to Algebra, Analysis and Probability*, ed. W. A. J. Luxemburg (Holt, Rinehart and Winston).

Luxemburg, W. A. J. and Zaanen, A. C., 1971, *Riesz Spaces*, Part I (North-Holland, Amsterdam).

Machover, M. and Hirschfeld, J., 1969, *Lectures on Non-Standard Analysis*, Springer-Verlag Lecture Notes no. 94.

Monteiro, A. A., 1954, L'Arithmétique des filtres et les espaces topologiques, *Symp. Lat. Amer. de Mat. Montevideo*, pp. 129–164.

Robinson, A., 1969, Compactification of Groups and Rings, and Non-Standard Analysis, *J. Symbolic Logic* 34, pp. 576–588.

Robinson, A., 1966, *Non-Standard Analysis*, Studies in Logic and the Foundations of Mathematics (North-Holland, Amsterdam).

Samuel, P., 1948, Ultrafilters and Compactifications of Uniform Spaces, *Trans. Am. Math. Soc.*, pp. 100–132.

Steiner, E. F., 1968, Wallman Spaces and Compactifications, *Fund. Math.* 61, pp. 295–304.

Wallman, H., 1938, Lattices and Topological Spaces, *Ann. Math.* 39, pp. 112–126.

Received 4 May 1971

ULTRAFILTERS AND ULTRAPRODUCTS IN NON-STANDARD ANALYSIS

Greg CHERLIN and Joram HIRSCHFELD[1])
Yale University

The theory of ultrafilters and ultraproducts may be developed in non-standard terms within the framework of Robinson's [1966, pp. 30–48] theory of enlargements.

Ultrafilters on a set may be associated with points in the enlargement of the set and ultrapowers may be identified with subsets of an enlargement. The same method is applied to ultraproducts–enlarging the union of the components in the product. Dealing with ultrapowers however, turns out to be easier than with general ultraproducts, and some of the results concern only ultrapowers. The paper is therefore divided into four sections.

Section 1–Ultrafilters–Begins with a known identification of ultrafilters on a set I with equivalence classes of points in an enlargement I^* of I. Doing so we obtain from $^*I$ the Rudin–Keisler order (R–K) of ultrafilters on I, and we prove the following theorems:

1.12. If $|I| = \lambda$ then any 2^λ elements in the R–K ordering have a common upper bound.

1.16. If $|I| = \omega$ then any (countable) decreasing sequence in the R–K ordering has a lower bound.

Section 2–Ultrapowers–The basic construction is a simultaneous embedding of all ultrapowers of a set M, indexed by a given set I, into a single enlargement $^*M$ of M. We treat M as a model in the language L that has names for all possible (first order) relations on M. In this language every elementary embedding of one ultrapower into another is induced by a simple map on

[1]) While this work was in progress the first author was an N.S.F. Fellow. The work of the second author was supported in part by the National Science Foundation Grant No. GP 18728.

the set of indices 2.6. This yields again the R–K ordering in terms of ultrapowers and elementary embeddings. In particular, we get a model theoretic characterization of minimal and *P*-filters. We conclude the chapter with an example of two properties of models in L that do not contain minimal extensions of *M*.

Section 3 sets up the framework that makes it possible to deal with ultraproducts. This is a modified version of Machover's and Hirschfeld treatment [1969] of Robinson's theory of enlargements.

In *section 4–Ultraproducts*–the theory of ultraproducts is developed. As examples we prove the Compactness Theorem, Frayne's Lemma, and a theorem on the joint embedding property.

We would like to thank Abraham Robinson for his encouragement and advice, and Gabriel Sabbagh for many stimulating conversations.

1. Ultrafilters. Let I be a set and let $\mathfrak{A}$ be a structure that contains I, all subsets of I, all functions from I to I, all filters on I, and the natural numbers. $\mathfrak{A}$ may be constructed as in Robinson [1966] or Machover and Hirschfeld [1969]. Let $^*\mathfrak{A}$ be an enlargement of $\mathfrak{A}$. In $^*\mathfrak{A}$ I is extended to the set $^*I$, every function f on I is extended to the function $^*f$ on $^*I$, and every filter D on I has the property:

1.1. $\mu(D) = \cap\{^*A | A \in D \text{ (} A \text{ is standard)}\} \neq \emptyset$.

For every $\alpha \in {}^*I$ the collection

1.2. $\mathrm{Fil}(\alpha) = \{A \subseteq I | \alpha \in {}^*A \text{ (} A \text{ is standard)}\}$

is an ultrafilter. If D is an ultrafilter then

1.3. $D = \mathrm{Fil}(\alpha)$ iff $\alpha \in \mu(D)$.

Therefore the relation

1.4. $\alpha \sim \beta$ iff $\mathrm{Fil}(\alpha) = \mathrm{Fil}(\beta)$

is an equivalence relation in $^*I$, and the equivalence classes are the monads of ultrafilters. An equivalence class has a unique (standard) element if the ultrafilter is principal, but is infinite (with no standard element) otherwise.

Let D be an ultrafilter on I and f a function from I to I. Then

1.5. $f(D) = \{A \subseteq I | f^{-1}(A) \in D\}$

is an ultrafilter and if $D = \mathrm{Fil}(\alpha)$

1.6. $f(D) = G$ iff $^*f(\alpha) \in \mu(D)$.

The proofs of 1.1–1.6 may be found in Machover and Hirschfeld [1969] or Luxemburg [1969].

1.7. DEFINITION. *For $\alpha, \beta \in {}^*I$ we define $\alpha \to \beta$ if there is a (standard) function $f: I \to I$ such that $^*f(\alpha) = \beta$. We put*

$$I_\alpha = \{\beta \in {}^*I \mid \alpha \to \beta\}$$

and $\alpha \leftrightarrow \beta$ if $\alpha \to \beta$ and $\beta \to \alpha$.

1.8. *Remarks.* i) $\to$ is a reflexive and transitive relation.
ii) $\alpha \to \beta$ iff $I_\alpha \supseteq I_\beta$ (so that $\alpha \leftrightarrow \beta$ iff $I_\alpha = I_\beta$).
ii)′ $\alpha \to \beta$ iff $\beta \in I_\alpha$.
iii) $\alpha \leftrightarrow \beta$ iff $^*h(\alpha) = \beta$ for some h that is 1–1 from I onto I.

Proof. Everything is obvious except the first implication in iii). Assume $\alpha \leftrightarrow \beta$ i.e., $^*f(\alpha) = \beta$ and $^*g(\beta) = \alpha$ for some f and g. Put

$$T = \{a \in I \mid gf(a) = a\}.$$

Then $\alpha \in {}^*T$. If $|T| < \infty$ then α and β are standard and the implication is trivial. If $|T| = \infty$ let $T = T_1 \cup T_2$ where $|T_1| = |T_2| = |T|$ and $T_1 \cap T_2 = \emptyset$. We may assume $\alpha \in {}^*T_1$, and it is now easy to redefine f on $I - T_1$ to obtain a function that is 1–1 and onto.

1.9. The Rudin–Keisler order (R–K) is defined as follows (Booth [1970]): Let βI be the set of ultrafilters on I. For $D, G \in \beta I$ define $D \equiv G$ if there is a 1–1 mapping f from I onto I such that $f(D) = G$. The R–K ordering is the lattice of equivalence classes with the order:
$[D] \leq [G]$ if there is a mapping $f: I \to I$ such that $f(G) = D$.

The important Corollary 1.11 proves that the R–K ordering is really an order. The standard proof may be found in Booth [1970]. Our non-standard proof (of Lemma 1.10) is based on a standard proof pointed out to us by G. Sabbagh.

1.10. LEMMA. *If $\alpha \sim \beta$ and $\alpha \to \beta$ then $\alpha = \beta$.*
Proof. For some f $^*f(\alpha) = \beta$. Define on I the equivalence $a \simeq b$ iff for

some non-negative integers m, n $f^m(a) = f^n(b)$. Let $<$ be a well-ordering of I, and for a in I let $l(a)$ be the first λ such that $\lambda \simeq a$. Then ${}^*l(\alpha) = {}^*l(\beta) = \lambda$, some λ in ${}^*I$.

Let $m(a)$ be the least integer m such that for some n $f^m(l(a)) = f^n(a)$, and $n(a)$ the least n such that $f^{m(a)}(l(a)) = f^n(a)$.

$$\text{Set } \mu = {}^*m(\alpha), \quad \nu = {}^*n(\alpha). \quad \text{Then} \quad {}^*f^{\mu}(\lambda) = {}^*f^{\nu}(\alpha)$$
$$\bar{\mu} = {}^*m(\beta), \quad \bar{\nu} = {}^*n(\beta) \qquad {}^*f^{\bar{\mu}}(\lambda) = {}^*f^{\bar{\nu}}(\beta).$$

From ${}^*f(\alpha) = \beta$ it follows that $\mu \leq \bar{\mu} \leq u + 1$. Also $\alpha \sim \beta \Rightarrow \mu \sim \bar{\mu}$, so $\bar{\mu} \neq \mu + 1$ since one is even and the other is odd. Therefore $\bar{\mu} = \mu$ and

$$ {}^*f^{\mu}(\lambda) = {}^*f^{\nu}(\alpha)$$
$$ {}^*f^{\mu}(\lambda) = {}^*f^{\bar{\nu}}(\beta) = {}^*f^{\bar{\nu}+1}(\alpha).$$

If $\nu > 0$ it follows that $\nu = \bar{\nu} + 1$ since ${}^*f^{\nu}(\alpha) = {}^*f^{\nu-1}(\beta)$, but $\nu \sim \bar{\nu}$ so $\nu \neq \bar{\nu} + 1$. Therefore $\nu = 0$. Since $\bar{\nu} \sim \nu$ $\bar{\nu} = 0$, and thus $\beta = {}^*f^{\mu}(\lambda) = \alpha$, $\beta = \alpha$. q.e.d.

1.11. COROLLARY. *If $f(D) = D$ then there is a set $A \in D$ such that $f|A$ is the identity.*

Proof. Choose $\alpha \in \mu(D)$. Then ${}^*f(\alpha) \sim \alpha$ so that ${}^*f(\alpha) = \alpha$ by 1.10. Hence

$$\{a | f(a) = a\} \in \text{Fil}(\alpha) = D. \qquad \text{q.e.d.}$$

Corollary 1.11 suggests the question:
If $f(D) = g(D)$ is there a set $X \in D$ such that $f|X = g|X$? The following provides a counterexample if D is taken as Fil(α).

1.12. *Example. Let I be infinite, $\Delta = \{(a, a) : a \text{ in } A\}$, $p : I \to I \times I - \Delta$ an enumeration of all ordered pairs with unequal terms, $f = \pi_1 \circ p$, $g = \pi_2 \circ p$. Then there are α, β in ${}^*I$, $\alpha \sim \beta$ such that ${}^*f(\alpha) = {}^*g(\beta)$ and ${}^*f(\alpha) \neq {}^*g(\alpha)$.*

Proof. $\mathscr{S}_p = \{S \subseteq I$: for a, b in S $f(a) \neq g(b)\}$. We show that for any p as specified $\mathscr{S}_p$ generates a proper ideal in $P(I)$, so that any ultrafilter containing $\{I - S : S \in \mathscr{S}_p\}$ affords a suitable pair α, β.

Assume that k is minimal such that for some such p there are $S_1, \ldots, S_k$ in $\mathscr{S}_p$ with $S_1 \cup \ldots \cup S_k = I$. Clearly $k > 1$. Let $I_1 = g(S_k)$ and assume without loss of generality that $|I_1| = |I|$. Let $I_2 = p^{-1}(I_1 \times I_1 - \Delta)$. If $a \in I_2 \cap S_k$ and $p(a) = (x, y)$ then $x = g(b)$ for some b in S_k, so that $f(a) = g(b)$, a, b in S_k. This contradiction shows that $I_2 \cap S_k = \emptyset$. Therefore $I_2 \subseteq S_1 \cup \ldots \cup S_{k-1}$.

Since $|I_1| = |I_2| = |I|$ let $q : I_1 \to I_2$ be 1–1 and onto, and let $\bar{p} = p|_{I_2} \circ q$. Then $\bar{p} : I_1 \to I_1 \times I_1 - \Delta$ is 1–1 and onto. Let $T_j = q^{-1}(S_j \cap I_2)$ for $j = 1, \ldots, k - 1$. Then T_j is in $\mathscr{S}_{\bar{p}}$, $I_1 = T_1 \cup \ldots \cup T_{k-1}$, contradicting the minimality of k over all p. q.e.d.

1.13. To obtain the R–K ordering in $^*I$ we define an equivalence relation on $^*I$:

$$\alpha \equiv \beta \quad \text{if} \quad \alpha \leftrightarrow \beta' \quad \text{for some} \quad \beta' \sim \beta.$$

Let R–K$_1$ be the set of equivalence classes with the order

$$[\alpha] \geq [\beta] \quad \text{if} \quad \alpha \to \beta' \quad \text{for some} \quad \beta' \sim \beta.$$

1.14. THEOREM. *The correspondence* $\psi([\alpha]) = [\mathrm{Fil}(\alpha)]$ *is an isomorphism between the* R–K$_1$ *ordering and the* R–K *ordering.*

Proof. ψ is well defined and is 1–1: $\alpha \equiv \beta$ iff $^*f(\alpha) \sim \beta$ for some permutation of I. By 1.6 this is true iff $f(\mathrm{Fil}(\alpha)) = \mathrm{Fil}(\beta)$, i.e., iff $\mathrm{Fil}(\alpha) \equiv \mathrm{Fil}(\beta)$. ψ is clearly onto, and it is order preserving: $[\alpha] \geq [\beta]$ iff $^*f(\alpha) \sim \beta$ for some $f : I \to I$. Again by 1.6 this is true iff $f(\mathrm{Fil}(\alpha)) = \mathrm{Fil}(\beta)$, or $[\mathrm{Fil}(\alpha)] \geq [\mathrm{Fil}(\beta)]$. q.e.d.

We use next the correspondence established above to obtain some theorems on the R–K ordering.

1.15. THEOREM. *Let* $|I| = \lambda$. *Then any* 2^λ *elements of the* R–K *ordering have a common upper bound.*

Proof. The proof is based on the following theorem by Ketonen [1971]: There exists a family $\mathfrak{F}$ of functions from I to I with the following properties:

i) $|\mathfrak{F}| = 2^\lambda$.

ii) For any $f_1, \ldots, f_n$ in $\mathfrak{F}$ and $i_1, \ldots, i_n$ in I there exists a $j \in I$ such that $f_k = i_k$, $k = 1, \ldots, n$.

Let $\mathfrak{F}$ be such a family and let $\mathfrak{G}$ be a given set of 2^λ ultrafilters. We fix a 1–1 mapping $\psi : \mathfrak{G} \to \mathfrak{F}$, and define the relation

$$\phi(j, \langle D, S \rangle) = [S \in D \to \psi(D)(j) \in S].$$

This is a relation on $I \times \mathfrak{G} \times P(I)$ and it is concurrent: If $\langle D, S \rangle_1, \ldots, \langle D, S \rangle_k$ are given where $D_1, \ldots, D_n$ are all the distinct filters that occur in those pairs and $\mathfrak{S}$ is the set of all distinct sets. We choose

$$i_r \in \cap \{S \mid S \in \mathfrak{S} \wedge S \in D_r\}, \quad r = 1, \ldots, n.$$

By (ii) there is a $j \in I$ such that $\psi(D_r)(j) = i_r$, $r = 1, \ldots, n$, and therefore $\phi(j, \langle D, S\rangle_m)$, $m = 1, \ldots, k$. We conclude that there is a $j \in {}^*I$ such that $\phi(j, \langle D, S\rangle)$ is true for all pairs $\langle D, S\rangle \in \mathfrak{G} \times P(I)$. Therefore ${}^*(\psi(D))(j) \in \mu(D)$ for every $D \in \mathfrak{G}$. By 1.6 we have then $\psi(D)(\mathrm{Fil}(j)) = D$ for every $D \in \mathfrak{G}$ and hence $\mathrm{Fil}(j)$ is the required filter. q.e.d.

1.16. COROLLARY. *Every element of the* R–K *ordering is the first element in some increasing chain of type* $(2^\lambda)^+$.

Proof. It is known that there is no maximal element in the R–K ordering. So we construct the chain by induction, using 1.15 at limit step. This construction will not stop before we reach a chain of length $(2^\lambda)^+$. q.e.d.

1.17. From now on up to the end of this chapter we assume I is countable and we write $\mathcal{N}$ instead of I. Thus we will write for example $\mathcal{N}_\alpha$ instead of I_α (c.f. 1.7). $<$ is some fixed sequencelike order of $\mathcal{N}$ (possibly the order of the natural numbers). Notions like "bounded", "cofinal" refer to this order.

1.18. THEOREM. *Let* $\mathcal{N}_\alpha \supset \mathcal{N}_{\alpha_1} \supset \ldots \supset \mathcal{N}_{\alpha_n} \ldots$, $n < \omega$, *where all* α_i *are non-standard. Then there exists a non-standard* β *such that* $\mathcal{N}_\beta \subset \cap \{\mathcal{N}_{\alpha_i} \mid i < \omega\}$.

Proof. We first note that we may assume that $\alpha_{i+1} < \alpha_i : {}^*f(\alpha_i) = \alpha_{i+1}$ for some $f: I \to I$. Put

$$g(x) = \min\{y \mid f(y) = x\}$$

then ${}^*g(x) \leftrightarrow x$ for all x and $\mathcal{N}_{g(\alpha_{i+1})} = \mathcal{N}_{\alpha_{i+1}}$, while ${}^*g(\alpha_{i+1}) \leq \alpha_i$. Hence we may replace α_{i+1} by ${}^*g(\alpha_{i+1}) - 1$.

Now let ${}^*f_{n+1}(\alpha_n) = \alpha_{n+1}$ and put

$$g_n = f_n \circ \ldots \circ f$$

so that ${}^*g_n(\alpha) = \alpha_n$. Define

1.19. $h(x) = \min\{g_n(x) \mid g_n(x) \geq n \wedge \forall i \leq n \;\; g_i(x) > g_{i+1}(x)\}$

(we look at the sequence $\{g_n(x)\}$ and take the last element up to where the sequence decreases, or the last that is still bigger than its index). h is defined in $\mathfrak{A}$ and fulfills 1.19 also in the enlargement ${}^*\mathfrak{A}$ of $\mathfrak{A}$. Hence for the given α above ${}^*h(\alpha)$ is not standard as for standard n's ${}^*g_n(\alpha) > n$ and $\{{}^*g_n(\alpha)\}$ is decreasing. Put ${}^*h(\alpha) = \beta$. We shall see that this β is really in all $\mathcal{N}_{\alpha_n}$ $n < \omega$, which will prove the theorem.

For any given α_i in the sequence define

$$\bar{g}_n = \begin{cases} \text{identity} & i \geq n \\ f_n \circ \ldots \circ f_i & i < n \end{cases}$$

and define $\bar{h}$ like 1.19 replacing g_n by $\bar{g}_n$. Then it is true in $\mathfrak{A}$ that

$$[y = g_i(x)] \wedge [g_1(x) < x] \ldots \wedge [g_i(x) < g_{i+1}(x)] \rightarrow [h(x) = \bar{h}(y)].$$

The left hand is true in the enlargement for $x = \alpha$ so that $\beta = {}^*h(\alpha) = {}^*\bar{h}(g_i(\alpha)) = {}^*\bar{h}(\alpha_i) \in \mathcal{N}_{\alpha_i}$. q.e.d.

1.20. COROLLARY. *Every decreasing sequence of non principal ultrafilters in* R–K *is bounded from below by a non principal ultrafilter.*

Proof. Assume $\{D_n\}_{n<\omega}$ is given such that $f_{n+1}(D_n) = D_{n+1}$. Choose $\alpha \in \mu(D_0)$ and $\alpha_{n+1} = {}^*f_{n+1}(\alpha_n)$, and the corollary follows from Theorem 1.18. q.e.d.

Note. The standard proof of 1.15 is obvious. The standard proof of 1.18 is not so transparent and we suggest the following "translation" of our proof:

i) If $f(D) = G$ then $g(D) = G$ for some g which has the property $\{x \mid g(x) < x\} \in D$.

ii) If $f_n(D_n) = D_{n+1}$, put g_n such that $g_n(D_0) = D_{n+1}$. By (i) we may assume $A_{n+1} = \{x \in A_n \mid g_{n+1}(x) < g_n(x)\} \in D$.

iii) $\cap A_n = \emptyset$. Define $h(x) = f_n(x)$ where n is the last index for which $x \in A_n$.

iv) Show that $h(D_0)$ is a filter as required.

Next we give a non-standard characterization of minimal and P-filters. As will be seen in section 2 this is really a characterization in terms of ultrapowers.

1.21. DEFINITION. *An ultrafilter D on $\mathcal{N}$ is called minimal (resp. a P-filter) if for any given partition $\mathcal{N} = \cup\{A_i \mid i < \omega\}$ where for all $i < \omega$ $A_i \notin D$, there is a set $A \in D$ such that for all $i < \omega$ $|A \cap A_i| \leq 1$ (resp. $|A \cap A_i| < \infty$).*

1.22. By relating to each partition $\mathcal{N} = \cup A_i$ the function $f(x) = n$ iff $x \in A_n$, and vice versa one proves easily that D is minimal iff every function is either constant or 1–1 on some member of D. I.e., iff D is a minimal non principal ultrafilter in R–K order.

1.23. LEMMA. i) Fil(α) *is minimal iff for every non-standard* $\beta \in \mathcal{N}_\alpha$, $\mathcal{N}_\beta = \mathcal{N}_\alpha$.

ii) Fil(α) *is a P-filter iff for every non-standard* $\beta \in \mathcal{N}_\alpha$, $\mathcal{N}_\beta$ *is cofinal* (1.17) *in* $\mathcal{N}_\alpha$.

Proof. i) is immediate from 1.22.

ii) Assume that $D = \text{Fil}(\alpha)$ is a P-filter, and that $\beta \in \mathcal{N}_\alpha$. $\beta = {}^*f(\alpha)$ for some $f:\mathcal{N} \to \mathcal{N}$. Define a partition

$$A_n = \{x | f(x) = n\}.$$

Since ${}^*f(\alpha) = \beta$ is non-standard none of these sets is in D. Therefore there exists a set $A \in D$ such that for all $i < \omega$ $A \cap A_i$ is finite. This enables us to define the function

$$g(y) = \begin{cases} \max\{x \in A | f(x) = y\} & y \in f(A) \\ 0 & \text{otherwise.} \end{cases}$$

Then $\mathfrak{A} \models x \in A \to gf(x) \geq x$ so that ${}^*g({}^*f(\alpha)) = {}^*g(\beta) \geq \alpha$. To show that $\mathcal{N}_\beta$ is cofinal in $\mathcal{N}_\alpha$: Let $\gamma \in \mathcal{N}_\alpha$, $\gamma = {}^*h(\alpha)$. Put

$$\bar{h}(x) = \max\{h(y) | y \leq g(x)\}.$$

$\bar{h}(x)$ is well defined and ${}^*\bar{h}(\beta) \geq {}^*h(\alpha) = \gamma$.

Conversely: Assume that $\mathcal{N}_\beta$ is cofinal in $\mathcal{N}_\alpha$ for all non standard $\beta \in \mathcal{N}_\alpha$, and let $\mathcal{N} = \cup A_n$ be a partition with no A_n in D. Define the function f: $f(x) = n$ iff $x \in A_n$. ${}^*f(\alpha)$ is non-standard and $\mathcal{N}_{f(\alpha)}$ is cofinal in $\mathcal{N}_\alpha$. Therefore there is a function g such that ${}^*g({}^*f(\alpha)) \geq \alpha$. But then

$$A = \{x | gf(x) \geq x\}$$

is in $D = \text{Fil}(\alpha)$ and for all $x \in A_n \cap A$ we have $g(n) \geq x$ so that $A \cap A_n$ is finite and A is the required set. q.e.d.

1.24. *Note.* Lemma 1.23 was first proved (independently) by Puritz [1972]. Our last example shows that non-standard characterizations of types of filters may be useful for proving combinatorial properties.

1.25. EXAMPLE. *If D is a minimal filter then there is a set $A \in D$ such that $(A + A) \cap A = \emptyset$ where $A + A = \{x + y : x, y \in A\}$, and $+$ is the sum of the natural numbers.*

Proof. Note first that not every filter has this property. Indeed if $\mathcal{S} = \{X \subseteq N | (X + X) \cap X = \emptyset\}$ it is not difficult to show that $\mathcal{S}$ generates a proper ideal in $P(N)$, and thus $D_0 = \{N - X : X \in \mathcal{S}\}$ extends to a ultrafilter D.

Suppose now that a filter D is minimal and for each $X \in D$ $(X + X) \cap X \neq$

$\emptyset$. Then one can find $\alpha, \beta, \gamma \in \mu(D)$ such that $\alpha + \beta = \gamma$. Let $\alpha = 2^\lambda \alpha_1$, $\beta = 2^\nu \beta_1$, $\gamma = 2^\omega \gamma_1$ with $\alpha_1, \beta_1, \gamma_1$ odd. Then $\lambda \sim \nu \sim \omega$. If $\lambda = \nu$ then $\omega = \lambda + 1$, contradicting $\omega \sim \lambda$. Thus $\lambda \neq \nu$, and since $\lambda \sim \nu$ both μ and ν are infinite.

We may assume $\lambda < \nu$. Then $\omega = \lambda$. Since $\alpha \sim \gamma$ and $\alpha, \gamma \to \omega$ it follows that $\mathcal{N} \subsetneq \mathcal{N}_\omega \subset \mathcal{N}_\alpha \cap \mathcal{N}_\gamma$, or by minimality of $\mathcal{N}_\alpha$–that $\mathcal{N}_\alpha \subset \mathcal{N}_\gamma$. Hence there is a function f such that $*f(\gamma) = \alpha$, and by 1.10 $\gamma = \alpha$. Since $\alpha + \beta = \gamma$, $\beta = 0$. As $\beta \in \mu(D)$ this contradicts the assumption that D is not principal. q.e.d.

2. Ultrapowers. To discuss ultrapowers and model theoretic properties we need the following definitions:

2.1. DEFINITION. *Let γ be a cardinal. The full structure of cardinality γ is the structure*

$$\mathfrak{M}(\gamma) = \{M, \{R_\delta\}_{\delta < 2^\gamma}\}$$

where

i) $|M| = \gamma$;

ii) $\{R_\delta\}_{\delta < 2^\gamma}$ *is the set of all possible relations on M.*

Denote by $L(\gamma)$ the appropriate language. Clearly for every γ there is only one such structure up to isomorphism. We fix γ and write $M = M(\gamma)$ and $L = L(\gamma)$.

2.2. Let I be a set of indices, and D a ultrafilter on I. Then $\mathfrak{M}^I/D \succ \mathfrak{M}$ (in L).

2.3. The basic construction in this section is a simultaneous embedding of all ultrapowers of $\mathfrak{M}$ indexed by I, into a single enlargement $*\mathfrak{M}$ of $\mathfrak{M}$. To this end let $\mathfrak{A}$ be a structure that contains M, I, all possible relations on M, all ultrafilters on I and all functions from I to M. Let $L(\mathfrak{A})$ be the appropriate language and $*\mathfrak{A}$ be an enlargement of $\mathfrak{A}$. Every relation R in $L(\gamma)$ has an interpretation in $L(\mathfrak{A})$ which we denote by $\tilde{R}$. Consequently every formula φ in $L(\gamma)$ has the interpretation $\tilde{\varphi}$ in $L(\mathfrak{A})$. We define the structure

$$*\mathfrak{M} = \langle *M, \{R_\delta\}_{\delta < 2^\gamma}\rangle.$$

For any $x_1, \ldots, x_n \in *M$, $*\mathfrak{M} \models R(x_1, \ldots, x_n)$ iff $*\mathfrak{A} \models \tilde{R}(x_1, \ldots, x_n)$. We get immediately by induction on the formulas that $*\mathfrak{M} \models \varphi(x_1, \ldots, x_n)$ iff

$^*\mathfrak{A} \models \hat{\varphi}(x_1, \ldots, x_n)$. ($^*\mathfrak{M}$ should be thought of as an enlargement of $\mathfrak{M}$ ignoring the higher order structure of $\mathfrak{M}$.)

2.4. THEOREM. *Let D be a ultrafilter on I and $\alpha \in \mu(D)$. Define a mapping ψ*

$$\psi : \mathfrak{M}^I/D \to {}^*\mathfrak{M}$$

by $\psi(f/D) = {}^*f(\alpha)$.

Then ψ is an elementary embedding (in $\mathrm{L}(\gamma)$*).*

Proof. Let φ be a formula in L such that

$$\mathfrak{M}^I/D \models \varphi(f_1/D, \ldots, f_n/D).$$

Then for some $A \in D$

$$\mathfrak{M} \models \varphi(f_1(x), \ldots, f_n(x)) \quad x \in A.$$

This may be stated in $\mathrm{L}(\mathfrak{A})$

$$\mathfrak{A} \models \forall_{x \in A}\, \hat{\varphi}(f_1(x), \ldots, f_n(x)).$$

Hence in $^*\mathfrak{A}$ $\;^*\mathfrak{A} \models \forall_{x \in A}\, \hat{\varphi}(f_1(x), \ldots, f_n(x))$, $\alpha \in {}^*A$ so $^*\mathfrak{A} \models \hat{\varphi}(f_1(\alpha), \ldots, f_n(\alpha))$.

By 2.3 now $^*\mathfrak{M} \models \varphi(f_1(\alpha), \ldots, f_n(\alpha))$. q.e.d.

2.5. Like in section 1 we define for every $\alpha \in {}^*I$ the set $M_\alpha = \{{}^*f(\alpha) \mid f: I \to M\}$ and $\mathfrak{M}_\alpha = \langle M_\alpha, \{R_\delta\}_{\delta < 2^\gamma} \rangle$ the structure induced by $^*\mathfrak{M}$. Then if $\alpha \in \mu(D)$ we have from 2.4 $\mathfrak{M}^I/D \simeq \mathfrak{M}_\alpha \prec {}^*\mathfrak{M}$. But choosing different elements $\alpha, \beta \in \mu(D)$ we get two different isomorphic copies of the same ultrapower.

2.6. THEOREM. i) *Let D be an ultrafilter, $h: I \to I$ a mapping such that $h(D) = G$. h induces a mapping*

$$\tilde{h} : \mathfrak{M}^I/G \to \mathfrak{M}^I/D$$

by $\tilde{h}(g/G) = g \circ h/D$.

Then $\tilde{h}$ is an elementary embedding (in L*).*

ii) *If $|I| \leq |M|$ and $\psi : \mathfrak{M}^I/G \to \mathfrak{M}^I/D$ is an elementary embedding then there is a function $h: I \to I$ such that $h(D) = G$ and $\psi = \tilde{h}$.*

Proof. i) Choose $\alpha \in \mu(D)$. Then $\beta = {}^*h(\alpha) \in \mu(G)$. Let $l: \mathfrak{M}_\alpha \simeq \mathfrak{M}^I/D$, $k: \mathfrak{M}_\beta \simeq \mathfrak{M}^I/G$ be the canonical isomorphism. Then $l^{-1} \circ \tilde{h} \circ k : \mathfrak{M}_\beta \to \mathfrak{M}_\alpha$ is simply the inclusion $\mathfrak{M}_\beta \subseteq \mathfrak{M}_\alpha$. But $\mathfrak{M}_\beta \subseteq \mathfrak{M}_\alpha \prec {}^*\mathfrak{M}$ and $\mathfrak{M}_\beta \prec {}^*\mathfrak{M}$ so that $\mathfrak{M}_\beta \prec \mathfrak{M}_\alpha$. Thus $l^{-1} \circ \tilde{h} \circ k$ is an elementary embedding, so $\tilde{h}$ is as well.

ii) If $|I| \leq |M|$ we may assume that $I \subseteq M$ and $^*I \subseteq {}^*M$. Choose

$\alpha \in \mu(D)$, $\beta \in \mu(G)$ and let $l : \mathfrak{M}_\alpha \simeq \mathfrak{M}^I/D$, $k : \mathfrak{M}_\beta \simeq \mathfrak{M}^I/G$, $\overline{\psi} = l^{-1} \circ \psi \circ k : \mathfrak{M}_\beta \to\!\!\to \mathfrak{M}_\alpha$. Let $\beta' = \overline{\psi}(\beta)$. Since $\overline{\psi}$ is an elementary embedding $\beta' \sim \beta$ (c.f. 1.4). In particular $\beta' \in {}^*I$ and since $\beta' \in \mathfrak{M}_\alpha$, $\beta' = {}^*g(\alpha)$ for some $g : I \to M$.

Let $I' = \{x \mid g(x) \in I\}$ then $I' \in D$ since ${}^*g(\alpha) \in {}^*I$. Let $h(x)$ be

$$h(x) = \begin{cases} g(x) & x \in I' \\ x_0 & \text{otherwise} \end{cases}$$

where x_0 is some fixed element of I. Then ${}^*h(\alpha) = \beta'$ and $h(D) = \mathrm{Fil}(\beta') = \mathrm{Fil}(\beta) = G$. Finally if $r : I \to M$ then $\overline{\psi}({}^*r(\beta)) = {}^*r(\beta)$ since $\overline{\psi}$ is an elementary embedding, and ${}^*r(\beta') = {}^*(r \circ f)(\alpha)$ so that $\psi = \tilde{h}$. q.e.d.

2.7. Corollary. *If* $|I| \leq |M|$ *then*

i) $\mathfrak{M}^I/D \simeq \mathfrak{M}^I/G$ *iff* $F \leq G$ *in the* R–K *ordering (c.f.* 1.9).

ii) *Define* $\mathfrak{M}^I/D \leq \mathfrak{M}^I/G$ *if there is an elementary embedding of* $\mathfrak{M}^I/D$ *into* $\mathfrak{M}^I/G$. *Then this order (reduced to isomorphism classes) is canonically isomorphic to the* R–K *ordering.*

2.8. Corollary. *If* $\delta = |I| \leq |M|$ *then any* 2^δ *ultrapowers of* $\mathfrak{M}$ *indexed by* I *may be simultaneously embedded into a single ultrapower* $\mathfrak{M}^I/D$.

Proof. 1.15 and 2.6. q.e.d.

2.9. To be able to state the results for general models of $\mathrm{L}(\gamma)$ we need the following observations:

i) Let $\mathfrak{N} \succ \mathfrak{M}$. By Frayne's Lemma $\mathfrak{N}$ may be elementarily embedded in some ultrapower $\mathfrak{M}^I/D$. If the set I is in $\mathfrak{A}$ then by 2.4 we may assume that

$$\mathfrak{M} \prec \mathfrak{N} \prec {}^*\mathfrak{M}.$$

ii) Let $\mathfrak{N} \succ \mathfrak{M}$ and $\alpha \in \mathfrak{N}$. Put

$$\mathfrak{N}_\alpha = \{f(\alpha) \mid f \text{ is a function in } \mathrm{L}(\gamma)\}.$$

Then by taking $I = M$ in 2.4 it is clear that $\mathfrak{N}_\alpha$ is the smallest submodel of $\mathfrak{N}$ containing α and $\mathfrak{N}_\alpha \simeq \mathfrak{M}^M/\mathrm{Fil}(\alpha)$. From now on to the end of this chapter $\mathfrak{N} = \langle \mathcal{N}, \{R_\delta\}_{\delta < 2^\omega} \rangle$ will denote the full structure of cardinality ω (c.f. 2.1) and $<$ will denote some fixed sequencelike order of $\mathcal{N}$ (possibly the order of the natural numbers). Notions like "bounded" or "cofinal" refer to this order.

2.10. Theorem. *Let* D *be a non principal ultrafilter on* $\mathcal{N}$.

i) D *is minimal iff* $\mathfrak{N}^{\mathcal{N}}/D$ *does not contain any submodel except* $\mathfrak{N}$.

ii) *D is a P-filter iff every submodel of* $\mathfrak{N}^{\mathcal{N}}/D$ *(except* $\mathfrak{N}$*) is cofinal in* $\mathfrak{N}^{\mathcal{N}}/D$.

Proof. i) is immediate from 2.7 and 2.9.

ii) Choose $\alpha \in \mu(D)$. By 1.23 D is a P-filter iff $\mathcal{N}_\beta$ is cofinal in $\mathcal{N}_\alpha$ for all non-standard $\beta \in \mathcal{N}_\alpha$. By 2.6 this is true iff every model $\mathfrak{N}^{\mathcal{N}}/G$ which is elementary embedded in $\mathfrak{N}^{\mathcal{N}}/D$ is cofinal in $\mathfrak{N}^{\mathcal{N}}/D$. By 2.9 we may replace $\mathfrak{N}^{\mathcal{N}}/G$ by an arbitrary submodel. q.e.d.

2.11. THEOREM. *Let* $\mathfrak{M} \succ \mathfrak{N}$ *such that* $\mathfrak{M}$ *does not contain a submodel of the form* $\mathfrak{N}^{\mathcal{N}}/D$ *where D is minimal (resp. a P-filter). Then the following are true:*

i) *For every* $\alpha \in \mathfrak{M} - \mathfrak{N}$ *there is a submodel that does not contain* α *(resp. and is bounded by* α*).*

ii) *There is a decreasing sequence*

$$\mathfrak{M} \supsetneqq \mathfrak{M}_1 \supsetneqq \dots \supsetneqq \mathfrak{M}_\delta \supsetneqq \dots, \delta < \omega_1,$$

of submodels of $\mathfrak{M}$ *(resp. such that for every* α $\mathfrak{M}_\alpha$ *is an initial segment of* $\mathfrak{M}$*).*

Proof. i) Put $\mathfrak{N}_\alpha$ like in 2.9. As $\mathfrak{N}_\alpha$ is not isomorphic to an ultrapower $\mathfrak{N}^I/D$ where D is minimal (resp. a P-filter), there is a submodel that does not contain α (and is bounded by α) by 1.20.

ii) The sequence may now be constructed by induction using 1.18 at limit steps. To replace a given submodel $\mathfrak{M}'$ by an initial segment of $\mathfrak{M}$ we notice that

$$\{\beta \in \mathfrak{M} \mid \exists\alpha(\alpha \in \mathfrak{M}' \wedge \alpha \geq \beta)\}$$

is such a submodel. q.e.d.

3. A set theoretic framework for the nonstandard theory of ultraproducts. We work in a set theory that has arbitrarily large sets of distinct individuals (objects which are not sets). All languages are forms of first order predicate calculus with identity corresponding to a given similarity type. If $\mathcal{M} = \langle M, \{R_a\}_{a\in A}\rangle$ is a relational system and L is an appropriate language, we will say $|\mathcal{M}| = M$ and assume for m in M that $\boldsymbol{m}$ is a constant denoting m in L, and $\boldsymbol{R_a}$ is a predicate symbol denoting R_a.

If S is a set let $E(S) = S \cup P(S)$ ($P(S)$ is the power set of S) and define inductively $E_0(S) = S$, $E_{n+1}(S) = E(E_n(S))$, $E_\omega(S) = \bigcup_{n=0}^{\infty} E_n(S)$. Let ε be the membership relation on $E_\omega(S)$, $\varepsilon_n = \varepsilon \mid E_n(S)$, $e_n = E_n(S)$. Full $S = \langle E_\omega(S), \{\varepsilon_n e_n\}_{n\in N}\rangle$, and let $\mathrm{L} = \mathrm{L}(S)$ be the language appropriate to Full S, containing a name for every element of $E_\omega(S)$. The *index* of ε_n or e_n is just n.

A relational system $\mathcal{M}$ is a *strong extension* of S iff $\mathcal{M} \equiv$ Full S. $\mathcal{M}$ is *graded* iff for each m in $|\mathcal{M}|$ there is an integer n such that $\mathcal{M} \models \boldsymbol{e}_n(\boldsymbol{m})$. A formula $p(x, y)$ in L is *concurrent* over $\mathcal{M}$ iff for each $m_1, \ldots, m_n$ in $|\mathcal{M}|$ there is a b such that $\mathcal{M} \models p(\boldsymbol{m}_i, \boldsymbol{b})$ for $i = 1, \ldots, n$. A strong extension $\mathcal{M}$ of S is an *enlargement* of S iff for each $p(x, y)$ in L concurrent over Full S there is a b in $|\mathcal{M}|$ such that for every c in $E_w(S)$ $\mathcal{M} \models p(\boldsymbol{b}, \boldsymbol{c})$. Such an element b is called a *bound* for p.

Relativization. If p is a formula in L $=$ L(S) and N is an integer we define the relativization $p|_N$ of p to $E_N(S)$ inductively as follows:

$$p|_N = p \quad \text{if} \quad p \text{ is atomic},$$
$$(p \mathbin{\&} q)|_N = p|_N \mathbin{\&} q|_N,$$
$$(-p)|_N = -(p|_N),$$
$$(\mathrm{Ex}\, q)|_N = \mathrm{Ex}(\boldsymbol{e}_N(x) \mathbin{\&} q|_N).$$

3.1. Lemma. *Suppose $p = p(x_1, \ldots, x_k)$ is a formula in* L. *Then there is an integer N such that for n larger than N,* Full $S \models (x_1, \ldots, x_k)(p \equiv p|_N)$.

Proof. Taking N larger than the indices of the relations in p and such that for each constant symbol $\boldsymbol{c}$ of p, c is in $E_N(S)$, the result is fairly clear. q.e.d.

3.2. Lemma. *Suppose $\mathcal{M}$ is a strong extension of S, and set $M = |\mathcal{M}|$, $M_n = \{m \text{ in } M : \mathcal{M} \models \boldsymbol{e}_n(\boldsymbol{m})\}$, $M_\omega = \bigcup_{n=0}^{\infty} M_n$, and $\mathcal{M}_\omega = \langle M_\omega, \{\varepsilon_n|_{M_\omega}, e_n|_{M_\omega}\}_{n\in N}\rangle$. Then $\mathcal{M}_\omega$ is a graded strong extension of S and an elementary substructure of $\mathcal{M}$. $\mathcal{M}_\omega$ is an enlargement of $S \Leftrightarrow \mathcal{M}$ is an enlargement of S.*

Proof. Let p be a sentence in the language L augmented by names for elements of M_ω. Let the constants of p be $\boldsymbol{c}_1, \ldots, \boldsymbol{c}_k$ where $c_1, \ldots, c_k$ are in M_ω. Choose N large so that Full $S \models (x_1, \ldots, x_k)(p \equiv p|_N)$ where the constants of p have been replaced by variables. It follows that $\mathcal{M} \models (x_1, \ldots, x_k)(p(x_1, \ldots, x_k) \equiv p(x_1, \ldots, x_k)|_N)$. Further, the same sentence holds in $\mathcal{M}_\omega$; this last claim is not immediate, but is easily verified. It is claimed finally that $\mathcal{M}_\omega \models p|_N(\boldsymbol{c}_1, \ldots, \boldsymbol{c}_k)$ if and only if $\mathcal{M} \models p|_N(\boldsymbol{c}_1, \ldots, \boldsymbol{c}_k)$. But this is quite clear by the definition of $p|_N$ and of M_ω.

Thus $\mathcal{M}_\omega < \mathcal{M}$. To show that $\mathcal{M}_\omega$ is a strong extension of S it now suffices to prove that for c in $E_\omega(S)$, the interpretation in $\mathcal{M}$ of $\boldsymbol{c}$ is in M_ω, which is obvious.

Now if $\mathcal{M}_\omega$ is an enlargement of S it is clear that $\mathcal{M}$ is as well, with bounds in $\mathcal{M}$ given by bounds in $\mathcal{M}_\omega$.

Conversely if $\mathcal{M}$ is an enlargement and $p(x, y)$ is concurrent over Full S, choose N so that Full $S \models (x, y)(p(x, y) \equiv p(x, y)|_N)$. Let b in $|\mathcal{M}|$ be a bound for p. If $\mathcal{M} \models \boldsymbol{e}_N(\boldsymbol{b})$ then b is in M_ω and b is a bound for p in $\mathcal{M}_\omega$. Otherwise any element outside of M_N acts as a bound for p in $\mathcal{M}$; choose any such b in M_ω. q.e.d.

3.3. LEMMA. *Let $\mathcal{M}$ be a graded strong extension of S, and retain the notation of Lemma 3.2. Assume that M_0 is a set of individuals. Then $\mathcal{M}$ is isomorphic with a substructure of* Full M_0.

Proof. Note that the assumption that M_0 contains only individuals involves no loss of generality.

Define inductively $U_n : M_n \to E_n(M_0)$ by:

i) U_0 is the identity on M_0.

ii) $$U_{n+1}(m) = \begin{cases} m & \text{if } m \text{ is in } M_0, \\ \{U_n(c) : \mathcal{M} \models c\boldsymbol{\varepsilon}_{n+1}\boldsymbol{m}\} & \text{if } m \text{ is in } M_{n+1}/M_0. \end{cases}$$

We then have:

1) $U_n : M_n \to E_n(M_0)$.

2) U_n is 1–1.

3) U_n is an isomorphism with respect to ε_i and e_i for $i = 1, \ldots, n$.

4) $U_{n+1}|_{M_n} = U_n$.

Verification of these claims is trivial. Any information needed about $\mathcal{M}$ is obtained by transfer from Full S.

It follows from 1)–4) that $U = \bigcup_{n=0}^{\infty} U_n$ is the desired isomorphism.

Suppose now that $\mathcal{M}$ is a graded strong extension of S and $T \subseteq S$. Define $p_n(x) = x\, \boldsymbol{e}_{n+1}\, \boldsymbol{E}_n(\boldsymbol{T})$.

Let $M_n|_T = \{m \text{ in } M_n : \mathcal{M} \models p_n(\boldsymbol{m})\}$, $M|_T = \bigcup_{n=0}^{\infty} M_n|_T$, $\varepsilon_n|_T = \varepsilon_n|_{M|_T}$, $e_n|_T = e_n|_{M|_T}$, and $\mathcal{M}_T = \langle M|_T, \{\varepsilon_n|_T, e_n|_T\}_{n \in N}\rangle$.

3.4. LEMMA. *If $\mathcal{M}$ is a graded strong extension of $S \supseteq T$ with interpretation $v_{\mathcal{M}}$, then $\mathcal{M}_T$ is a graded strong extension of T with respect to the induced interpretation. If $\mathcal{M}$ is an enlargement of S then $\mathcal{M}_T$ is an enlargement of T.*

Proof. Note that for c in $E_\omega(T)$, $\mathcal{M} \models p_n(c)\ \&\ (x)(p_n(x) \Rightarrow \boldsymbol{e}_n(x))$ so $v_{\mathcal{M}}(\boldsymbol{c})$ is in $M_n|_T$.

Consider the following relativization process. For q a formula in L(S) and n an integer, define inductively:

$$q|_{n,T} = q \quad \text{for } q \text{ atomic},$$
$$(-q)|_{n,T} = -(q|_{n,T}),$$
$$(q_1\ \&\ q_2)|_{n,T} = q_1|_{n,T}\ \&\ q_2|_{n,T},$$
$$(\text{Ex}q)|_{n,T} = \text{Ex}\,(p_n(x)\ \&\ q|_{n,T}).$$

$\mathcal{M}|_T$ is clearly graded. To show that $\mathcal{M}_T$ is a strong extension of T, fix s in L(T) and choose N as in Lemma 3.1. Clearly Full $T \models s \Leftrightarrow$ Full $S \models s|_{N,T} \Leftrightarrow \mathcal{M} \models s|_{N,T} \Leftrightarrow \mathcal{M}|_T \models s$. Thus $\mathcal{M}|_T >$ Full T as desired.

Now assume that $\mathcal{M}$ is an enlargement of S. Let $s(x, y)$ be concurrent over Full T. Choose N as above and let $t(x,y)$ be $(s(x,y) \,\&\, p_N(x)) \vee (-p_N(y))$. Then t is concurrent over Full S and so has a bound b in $\mathcal{M}$. Then by definition of t, b will be a bound for s in $\mathcal{M}|_T$. q.e.d.

4. Ultraproducts. Let $\{M_a\}_{a\in A}$ be a collection of sets, $S = (\bigcup_{a\in A} M_a) \cup A$, $\mathcal{M}$ an enlargement of S with interpretation $v_{\mathcal{M}}$. Applying Lemmas 3.2 and 3.3 assume $\mathcal{M}$ is a substructure of Full M_0. For c in $E_\omega(S)$ let ${}^*c = v_{\mathcal{M}}(c)$, e.g. ${}^*S = M_0$.

Let $M_n \to E_{n+1}(S)$ be the function $M_n(a) = E_n(M_a)$. Then ${}^*M_n : {}^*A \to {}^*E_{n+1}(S)$. For α in ${}^*A$ let $M_n(\alpha) = \{{}^*f(\alpha) : f \in \times_{a\in A} E_n(M_a)\}$; this is consistent with the original definition of $M_n(\alpha)$ for $\alpha \in A$.

Fix α in ${}^*A$. Set

$$ {}^*\mathcal{M}_\alpha = \left\langle \bigcup_{n=0}^{\infty} {}^*M_n(\alpha), \{\varepsilon_n|_{|{}^*\mathcal{M}_\alpha|}, e_n|_{|{}^*\mathcal{M}_\alpha|}\}_{n\in N} \right\rangle. \quad \text{Set} $$

$$ \mathcal{M}_\alpha = \left\langle \bigcup_{n=0}^{\infty} M_n(\alpha), \{\varepsilon_n|_{|\mathcal{M}_\alpha|}, e_n|_{|\mathcal{M}_\alpha|}\}_{n\in N} \right\rangle. $$

Then for a in A, ${}^*\mathcal{M}_a = \mathcal{M}|_{{}^*M_a}$, $\mathcal{M}_a =$ Full M_a.

4.1. THEOREM. i) *For* α *in* ${}^*A$ $\mathcal{M}_a \prec {}^*\mathcal{M}_\alpha$.

ii) *Suppose* $X \subseteq A$, $\alpha \in {}^*X$, $p(x, y, {}^*f_1(\alpha), \ldots, {}^*f_n(\alpha))$ *is a formula in the language of* $\mathcal{M}_\alpha$, $p(x, y, z) = p(x, y, f_1(z), \ldots, f_n(z))$ *expressed in* L(S), *and for* a *in* X *suppose* $p(x, y, a)$ *is concurrent on* $\mathcal{M}_\alpha$. *Then* p *has a bound in* ${}^*\mathcal{M}_\alpha$.

iii) *Assume that for each* a $M_a = M$, *a fixed set. Then* $\mathcal{M}_\alpha$, ${}^*\mathcal{M}_\alpha$ *are strong extensions of* M, ${}^*\mathcal{M}_\alpha$ *is an enlargement of* M.

Proof. i) Fix s a sentence in L(S) with constants in $\mathcal{M}_\alpha$, $s = s({}^*f_1(\alpha), \ldots, {}^*f_n(\alpha))$. Replace the constants of s by variables to get $s(y_1, \ldots, y_n)$, and write s in Skolem open form as $(z_1, \ldots, z_p)t(y_1, \ldots, y_n, z_1, \ldots, z_p, \phi_1, \ldots, \phi_r)$.

Let $A_1 = \{a$ in A: Full $M_a \models s(f_1(a), \ldots, f_n(a))\}$ and for a in A_1 let $\phi_j(a; z_1, \ldots, z_p)$ be functions: Full $(M_a)^p \to$ Full M_a such that for $c_1, \ldots, c_p$ in Full M_a, Full $M_a \models t(f_1(a), \ldots, f_n(a), c_1, \ldots, c_p, \phi_1(a; c_1, \ldots, c_p), \ldots, \phi_r(a; c_1, \ldots, c_p))$.

Choose N larger than the indices of the relations in s (cf. Lemma 3.1) and such that for each i f_i is in $\times_{a\in A} M_N(a)$.

Let $g_j(a; z_1, \ldots, z_p) = \phi_j(a; z_1, \ldots, z_p)|_{(M_n(a))^p}$, and assume without loss of generality that $\mathrm{rg}(g_j(a; z_1, \ldots, z_p)) \subseteq M_N(a)$ for a in A_1, $j = 1, \ldots, r$.

Suppose ${}^*\mathcal{M}_\alpha \models s$. Fix $c_1, \ldots, c_p$ in $|\mathcal{M}_\alpha|$. It suffices to find $d_1, \ldots, d_r$ in $|\mathcal{M}_\alpha|$ such that $\mathcal{M}_\alpha \models t({}^*\boldsymbol{f}_1(\boldsymbol{\alpha}), \ldots, {}^*\boldsymbol{f}_n(\boldsymbol{\alpha}), \boldsymbol{c}_1, \ldots, \boldsymbol{c}_p, \boldsymbol{d}_1, \ldots, \boldsymbol{d}_r)$. Assume without loss of generality that $c_1, \ldots, c_p$ are in $M_N(\alpha)$, and have the form $c_k = {}^*h_k(\alpha)$ where h_k is in $\times_{a \in A} M_N(a)$.

For $j = 1, \ldots, r$ let

$$u_j(a) = \begin{cases} g_j(a; h_1(a), \ldots, h_p(a)) & a \text{ in } A_1 \\ \text{any element of } M_N(a) & a \text{ not in } A_1. \end{cases}$$

Then Full $S \models (x)(x\ \varepsilon_1\ A_1 \Rightarrow t(f_1(x), \ldots, f_n(x), h_1(x), \ldots, h_p(x), u_1(x), \ldots, u_r(x)))$. This last sentence is not in L(S) as written, but it may easily be expressed in L(S) by means of the usual sorts of circumlocutions (Machover and Hirschfeld [1969] p. 5).

$\boldsymbol{\alpha}\ \varepsilon_1\ \boldsymbol{A}_1$, because by means of an obvious relativization procedure we may construct a formula $v(x)$ such that for a in A [Full $S \models v(z)$] $\Leftrightarrow$ [Full $M_a \models s(\boldsymbol{f}_1(\boldsymbol{a}), \ldots, \boldsymbol{f}_n(\boldsymbol{a}))$], and at the same time [$\mathcal{M} \models v(a)$] $\Leftrightarrow$ [${}^*\mathcal{M}_\alpha \models t({}^*\boldsymbol{f}_1(\boldsymbol{\alpha}), \ldots, {}^*\boldsymbol{f}_n(\boldsymbol{\alpha}))$].

Thus $\mathcal{M} \models t(\boldsymbol{f}_1(\boldsymbol{\alpha}), \ldots, \boldsymbol{f}_n(\boldsymbol{\alpha}), \boldsymbol{h}_1(\boldsymbol{\alpha}), \ldots, \boldsymbol{h}_p(\boldsymbol{\alpha}), \boldsymbol{u}_1(\boldsymbol{\alpha}), \ldots, \boldsymbol{u}_r(\boldsymbol{\alpha}))$, and therefore $\mathcal{M} \models t({}^*\boldsymbol{f}_1(\boldsymbol{\alpha}), \ldots, {}^*\boldsymbol{f}_n(\boldsymbol{\alpha}), {}^*\boldsymbol{h}_1(\boldsymbol{\alpha}), \ldots, {}^*\boldsymbol{h}_p(\boldsymbol{\alpha}), {}^*\boldsymbol{u}_1(\boldsymbol{\alpha}), \ldots, {}^*\boldsymbol{u}_r(\boldsymbol{\alpha}))$, and taking $d_1, \ldots, d_r$ to be ${}^*u_1(\alpha), \ldots, {}^*u_r(\alpha)$, we obtain $\mathcal{M}_\alpha \models t({}^*\boldsymbol{f}_1(\boldsymbol{\alpha}), \ldots, {}^*\boldsymbol{f}_n(\boldsymbol{\alpha}), \boldsymbol{c}_1, \ldots, \boldsymbol{c}_p, \boldsymbol{d}_1, \ldots, \boldsymbol{d}_r)$ as desired.

ii) N is as usual an integer so large that $f_1, \ldots, f_n$ are in $E_N(S)$ and the indices of the relations in p are less than N. In the usual way one can define a relativization $p_{\mathrm{rel}}(x, y, z)$ of $p(x, y, z)$ to $M_N(z)$.

Let M be so large that $\times_{a \in A} M_N(a)$ is in $E_M(S)$. Let $t(u, v)$ be

$$v\ \boldsymbol{\varepsilon}_{\boldsymbol{M}} \times_{a \in A} \boldsymbol{M}_{\boldsymbol{N}}(\boldsymbol{a}) \Rightarrow u\ \boldsymbol{\varepsilon}_{\boldsymbol{M}} \times_{a \in A} \boldsymbol{M}_{\boldsymbol{N}}(\boldsymbol{a})$$

$(z)(z\ \varepsilon_1\ X \Rightarrow p_{\mathrm{rel}}(u(z), v(z), z))$ expanded out suitably in L(S). t is easily seen to be concurrent on Full S. Let η be a bound for t in $\mathcal{M}$. Then $\eta(\alpha)$ is in ${}^*M_N(\alpha)$ and $\eta(\alpha)$ is a bound for p in ${}^*\mathcal{M}_\alpha$.

iii) If Full $M \models s$, use relativization to express in Full S that Full $M_x \models s$ for each x. By transfer to $\mathcal{M}$ ${}^*\mathcal{M}_\alpha \models s$. Thus ${}^*\mathcal{M}_\alpha$ is a strong extension of M, and an enlargement by ii). By i), $\mathcal{M}_\alpha$ is a strong extension of M. q.e.d.

Now suppose that for each a in A $\mathfrak{M}_a = \langle M_a, \{R_b^a\}_{b \in B}\rangle$ is a relational system, where R_b^a is a relation of rank n_b on M_a, and suppose L is an appropriate first order language for the structures $\mathfrak{M}_a$. We modify the definition of S, taking $S = \bigcup_{a \in A} M_a \cup A \cup B$.

For b in B define f_b in $X_{a\in A}\, E_N(M_a)$ for some larger N by $f_b(a) = R^a_b$. Then $*f_b(\alpha)$ is a relation of rank n_b on $*M_\alpha$, denoted $*R^\alpha_b$, and $*R^\alpha_b$ is an element of $\mathcal{M}_\alpha$. Interpreted as a relation in $\mathcal{M}_\alpha$ $*R^\alpha_b$ becomes $R^\alpha_b = *R^\alpha_b \cap (M_\alpha \times M_\alpha)$.

Set $*\mathfrak{M}_\alpha = \langle *M_\alpha, \{R^\alpha_b\}_{b\in B}\rangle$, $\mathfrak{M}_\alpha = \langle M_\alpha, \{R^\alpha_b\}_{b\in B}\rangle$.

4.2. THEOREM. $\mathfrak{M}_\alpha \prec *\mathfrak{M}_\alpha$.

Proof. This is essentially a corollary to Lemma 3.5, since any sentence in $\mathfrak{M}_\alpha$ may be interpreted in $\mathcal{M}_\alpha$. In fact, passing from $\mathcal{M}_\alpha$ to $\mathcal{M}$ (again compare Lemma 3.5) one can obtain:

4.2′. THEOREM. *For s defined in $\mathfrak{M}_\alpha$,*

$s = s(*\boldsymbol{f}_1(\boldsymbol{\alpha}), \ldots, *\boldsymbol{f}_n(\boldsymbol{\alpha}), \boldsymbol{R}^\alpha_{b_1}, \ldots, \boldsymbol{R}^\alpha_{b_p})$, *and*

$s_a = s(\boldsymbol{f}_1(\boldsymbol{a}), \ldots, \boldsymbol{f}_n(\boldsymbol{a}), \boldsymbol{R}^a_{b_1}, \ldots, \boldsymbol{R}^a_{b_b})$, *the following are equivalent*:

i) $\mathfrak{M}_\alpha \models s$

ii) $*\mathfrak{M}_\alpha \models s$

iii) $\alpha \in *\{a : \mathfrak{M}_a \models s_a\}$.

Theorem 4.3 below is a generalization of Theorem 2.4. It relates the structures $\mathfrak{M}_\alpha$ to ultraproducts.

4.3. THEOREM. *Let D be an ultrafilter on A, $\alpha \in \mu(D)$ (c.f. 1.1). Then there is a natural isomorphism $p : X_{a\in A}\, \mathfrak{M}_a/D \simeq \mathfrak{M}_\alpha$, (c.f. 2.5), defined by $p(f/D) = *f(\alpha)$.*

Proof. p is well defined, since if $f/D = g/D$ then $X = \{a \text{ in } A : f(a) = g(a)\}$ is in D, so α is in $*X$, and therefore $*f(\alpha) = *g(\alpha)$.

Now if R is a relation and $X_{a\in A}\, \mathfrak{M}_a/D \models \boldsymbol{R}(\boldsymbol{f}_1/\boldsymbol{D}, \ldots, \boldsymbol{f}_n/\boldsymbol{D})$ then $X = \{a \text{ in } A : \mathfrak{M}_a \models \boldsymbol{R}(\boldsymbol{f}_1(\boldsymbol{a}), \ldots, \boldsymbol{f}_n(\boldsymbol{a}))\}$ is in D, so α is in $*X$, and therefore $*\mathfrak{M}_\alpha \models \boldsymbol{R}(*\boldsymbol{f}_1(\boldsymbol{\alpha}), \ldots, *\boldsymbol{f}_n(\boldsymbol{\alpha}))$, so the same holds in $\mathfrak{M}_\alpha$. The same holds if the relation R is replaced by $-R$, and since p is obviously onto it is therefore an isomorphism.

4.4. COROLLARY. *If $\alpha \sim \beta$ then $\mathfrak{M}_a \simeq \mathfrak{M}_\beta$.*

In order to treat model theory in this context we may consider the set P_{L} of formulas of the language L (appropriate to $\mathfrak{M}_a$) as a set of individuals, and adjoin it to S. For any integer N let $\mathfrak{M}_a|_N$ be the reduct of $\mathfrak{M}_a$ to relations of rank less than or equal to N. Then $\mathfrak{M}_a|_N$ is in Full S. Thus we have the relation $\models_N$ in Full $S : (\mathfrak{M}_a|_N) \models_N (p(\boldsymbol{c}_1, \ldots, \boldsymbol{c}_m))$ which holds only when the relations in p have ranks less than or equal to N, and when $\mathfrak{M}_a|_N \models p(\boldsymbol{c}_1, \ldots, \boldsymbol{c}_m)$ in the usual sense.

This process can be avoided completely by interpreting $\mathfrak{M}_a|_N \models_N p(\boldsymbol{c}_1, \ldots, \boldsymbol{c}_m)$ as a first order sentence in L(S). In any case a relation $* \models_N$ is induced in $\mathcal{M}$, and the properties of $* \models_N$ all follow by transfer from Full S.

4.5. Lemma. *Let* $* \models \; = \bigcup_{N=0}^{\infty} * \models_N$, and $p = p(*\boldsymbol{f}_1(\boldsymbol{\alpha}), \ldots, *\boldsymbol{f}_n(\boldsymbol{\alpha}))$. *Then* $\mathfrak{M}_\alpha \models p \Leftrightarrow *\mathfrak{M}_\alpha * \models p$.

Proof. We indicate some intermediate equivalences. Assume the relations of p all have rank less than or equal to N. Let $q(a) = p(\boldsymbol{f}_1(\boldsymbol{a}), \ldots, \boldsymbol{f}_n(\boldsymbol{a}))$ interpreted in L(S) in the usual way. Then $\mathfrak{M}_\alpha \models p \Leftrightarrow \alpha$ is in $*\{a : \text{Full } S \models \{\mathfrak{M}_a|_N \models \boldsymbol{q}(\boldsymbol{a})\}\} \Leftrightarrow \mathfrak{M} \models (\mathfrak{M}_\alpha|_N \models \boldsymbol{q}(\boldsymbol{\alpha})) \Leftrightarrow *\mathfrak{M}_\alpha * \models p$.

The only difficulty lies in the first equivalence, which was demonstrated in the proof of Theorem 4.1 i). This lemma can also be derived directly from Theorem 4.1 i), since it is easily seen that $*\mathfrak{M}_\alpha * \models p \Leftrightarrow *\mathfrak{M}_\alpha \models p$. q.e.d.

We conclude this section with proofs of some straightforward standard results from this point of view.

4.6. Example *(Compactness). Let K be a set of sentences in the first order theory* L, *and assume that for finite $F \subseteq K$ there is a model $\mathfrak{M}_F \models F$. Then there is a model $\mathfrak{M} \models K$.*

Proof. For $F \subseteq K$ finite fix $\mathfrak{M}_F \models F$. In an enlargement we may choose a *-finite (Robinson [1966] p. 10, 1. 22) subset $\mathscr{F} \subseteq *K$ such that $K \subseteq \mathscr{F}$. Then $*\mathfrak{M}_{\mathscr{F}} * \models \mathscr{F}$. For s in K, $*\mathfrak{M}_{\mathscr{F}} * \models s$, $*\mathfrak{M}_{\mathscr{F}} \models s$. q.e.d.

4.7. Example *(Frayne's Lemma). If $\mathfrak{M}_1 \equiv \mathfrak{M}_2$ with respect to the vocabulary V then there is an ultrapower $\mathfrak{M}$ of $\mathfrak{M}_2$ and an elementary embedding $\mathfrak{M}_1 \rightarrow\!\!\rightarrow \mathfrak{M}$ (with respect to V).*

Proof. Let $F = \{s_1, \ldots, s_k\}$ be a finite set of sentences satisfied in $\mathfrak{M}_1$, and let $s(\boldsymbol{c}_1, \ldots, \boldsymbol{c}_n, \boldsymbol{d}_1, \ldots, \boldsymbol{d}_m) = s_1 \;\&\; \ldots \;\&\; s_k$ where $\boldsymbol{c}_1, \ldots, \boldsymbol{c}_n$ are the constant symbols which are not in V, and $\boldsymbol{d}_1, \ldots, \boldsymbol{d}_n$ are in V. Then by the elementary equivalence there are $c_1', \ldots, c_n'$ in M_2 such that $\mathfrak{M}_2 \models s(\boldsymbol{c}_1', \ldots, \boldsymbol{c}_n', \boldsymbol{d}_1, \ldots, \boldsymbol{d}_m)$. Let $g_F(c_i) = c_i'$, $g_F(d_j) = d_j$.

Choose $\mathscr{F}$ *-finite, Th $\mathfrak{M}_1 \subseteq \mathscr{F} \subseteq *(\text{Th } \mathfrak{M}_1)$. Then $*g : \text{voc}_i\, \mathscr{F} \rightarrow *\mathfrak{M}_{\mathscr{F}}$. Let $g = *g_{\mathscr{F}}|_{|\mathfrak{M}_1|} \cdot g|\mathfrak{M}_1| \rightarrow *\mathfrak{M}_{\mathscr{F}}$, and by the construction of g, $g : |\mathfrak{M}_1| \rightarrow \mathfrak{M}_{\mathscr{F}}$. That g is an elementary embedding follows from Th $\mathfrak{M}_1 \subseteq \mathscr{F}$. q.e.d.

4.8. Definition. *If M is a collection of similar relational structures then*

Prod M *is the class of structures isomorphic to an ultraproduct of elements of* M.

M has the *joint embedding property* (j.e.p.) iff any two elements of M may be embedded in a third.

M has the *strong embedding property* (s.e.p.) iff the elements of any subset of M may be simultaneously embedded in some element of M.

4.9. EXAMPLE (*Sabbagh* [1971] p. 7, Remark). *If* M *has the j.e.p. (s.e.p.) then* Prod M *has the j.e.p. (s.e.p.).*

Proof. It suffices to deal with the s.e.p., since the j.e.p. is treated analogously and more easily.

Assume then that M has the s.e.p. and that $\{\mathfrak{M}_{\alpha_b}\}_{b\in B}$ are ultraproducts of models $\{\mathfrak{M}_{a_b}\}_{a_b \varepsilon A_b}$ from M, where α_b is in $^*A_b$ for b in B. Let $A = \times_{b\in B} A_b$, and choose α in $^*A$ such that for b in B, $\alpha(b) = \alpha_b$. (To obtain such an α special enlargements must be used, but they always exist. Cf. Machover and Hirschfeld [1969] p. 17, section 4.6.)

For a in A, b in B let $f_{a,b}: \mathfrak{M}_{a(b)} \to \mathfrak{M}_a$ be joint embeddings into some $\mathfrak{M}_a$ in N. If $^*g(\alpha_b)$ is in $^*\mathfrak{M}_{\alpha_b}$, define h_b on A by $h_b(a) = f_{a,b}(g(a(b)))$. Then $^*h_b(\alpha) = {}^*f_{\alpha,b}(^*g(\alpha_b))$, so $^*f_{\alpha,b}(^*g(\alpha_b))$ is in $\mathfrak{M}_\alpha$. Thus $^*f_{\alpha,b}|_{\mathfrak{M}\alpha_b}: \mathfrak{M}_{\alpha_b} \to \mathfrak{M}_\alpha$, and we have the desired embeddings.

4.10. COROLLARY. *For any structure* $\mathfrak{M}$, *and index set* A *of cardinality* K, *any* K *ultrapowers of* $\mathfrak{M}$ *by ultrafilters over* A *may be jointly embedded in an ultrapower of* $\mathfrak{M}$ *by an ultrafilter over* A.

Proof. $A = \times_{b\in B} A_b$ in the above proof can be replaced by $A' = \{a \in A \mid a = a_0$ of a finite set$\}$ where $a_0 \in A$ is a fixed element.

References

Booth, D., 1970, Ultrafilters on a Countable Set, *Ann. of Math. Logic* 2, pp. 1–24.

Ketonen, K., 1971, *Ultrafilters and Independent Sets.*

Luxemburg, W. A. J., 1969, A General Theory of Monads, in: *Applications of Model Theory to Algebra, Analysis and Probability*, ed. W. A. J. Luxemburg (Holt, Rinehart and Winston) p. 18.

Machover, M. and Hirschfeld, J., 1969, *Lectures on Non-Standard Analysis*, Springer-Verlag, Lecture Notes in Mathematics no. 94.

Puritz, C., 1972, Skies, Constellations and Monads, *this volume.*

Robinson, A., 1966, *Non-Standard Analysis* (North-Holland, Amsterdam).

Sabbagh, G., 1971, *A Note on the Embedding Property*, to appear.

Received 22 March 1971

A COMPUTER ORIENTED VERSION OF "NON-STANDARD ANALYSIS"

Anton JENSEN
University of Copenhagen

This is a preliminary report of attempts to develop elementary analysis in a simple "non-standard" framework. The version of "non-standard" analysis which can be found in Robinson [1966] is clearly not immediately applicable to an elementary exposition of analysis despite of the obvious advantages offered by a rigorous use of infinitesimals. A simpler version can be found if one accepts a formalistic interpretation of mathematics. This means that the attention is turned to strings of symbols (expressions) which represent the mathematical objects, the existence and nature of which is inessential for the applications of mathematics.

If a reasonable choice of expressions is made, a compiler can be built, which is able to compute the value of expressions, which are fit for numerical calculation. Therefore, it is well motivated to found an exposition of elementary analysis on a strict definition of (1) which strings of symbols are expressions and (2) what does it mean that an expression has value α with accuracy μ. Theorems are theorems about expressions (which of course may be abbreviated in any convenient way) and not about whatever the expressions represent. This makes it a simple matter to introduce "non-standard" tools such as infinitesimals.

We shall give the basic definitions, state the basic rules without proofs, discuss the implementation on computers, and give a typical example of application.

1. Expressions. Given is an alphabet containing symbols

$$0,\ 1,\ +,\ -,\ \cdot,\ /,\ \mathsf{E},\ \lim,\ (,\ ),\ \rightarrow,\ \uparrow,\ =$$

and a denumerable set of variables

$$a, b, c, \ldots \quad N_1, N_2, \ldots .$$

The variables N_1, N_2, N_3, ... are called *infinits*.

Expressions are 0, 1, all variables and strings of symbols which are built up from these simple expressions using the rules:

If $x, x_1, x_2, \ldots, x_n$ are variables and $u, v, u_1, u_2, \ldots u_n, v_1, v_2, v_3$ are expressions, then the following strings of symbols are expressions ($n \geqq 2$)

$(u + v)$ [the sum of u and v]
$(u - v)$ [the difference of u and v]
$(u \cdot v)$ [the product of u and v]
(u/v) [the quotient of u and v]
(uv) [u applied to v]
$\mathsf{E}(u, v_1, v_2, v_3)$ [v_1 if $u < 0$, v_2 if $u = 0$ and v_3 if $u > 0$]
$\lim(x, u)$ [usually written as $\lim_x u$, the limit of u as $x \to \infty$ through integer values]
$(u_1, u_2, \ldots, u_n)$ [the n-tuple of $u_1, u_2, \ldots, u_n$]
$(x \to u)$ [the function which maps x into u]
$((x_1, \ldots, x_n) \to u)$ [the function which maps $(x_1, \ldots, x_n)$ into u]
$(u \uparrow v)$ [usually written as u^v, u iterated v times].

Notice that the use of brackets garantees that expressions can be decomposed uniquely. The variable x is bound in $\lim(x, u)$ and $(x \to u)$, and the variables $x_1, x_2, \ldots, x_n$ are bound in $((x_1, \ldots, x_n) \to u)$.

Let $u_{x_1, \ldots, x_n}[v_1, \ldots, v_n]$ denote the result of simultaneous substitution of v_1 for x_1, v_2 for x_2, etc. in u (with possible necessary changes of bound variables). Now we can recursively define that an expression u has value $\alpha \pm \mu$, where $\mu > 0$ is a positive rational, iff this is a consequence of the rules:

(1) 0 has value $\alpha \pm \mu$ iff $\alpha \in \mathbf{Q}$ and $\alpha - \mu < 0 < \alpha + \mu$.
(2) 1 has value $\alpha \pm \mu$ iff $\alpha \in \mathbf{Q}$ and $\alpha - \mu < 1 < \alpha + \mu$.
(3) If $\circ$ is $+, -, \cdot$ or $/$ then $(u \circ v)$ has value $\alpha \pm \mu$ iff there exist $\beta, \gamma, \nu, \lambda$ such that u has value $\beta \pm \nu$, v has value $\gamma \pm \lambda$, and
$$\forall p, q \in \mathbf{Q}: \beta - \nu < p < \beta + \nu \wedge \gamma - \lambda < q < \gamma + \lambda \Rightarrow \alpha - \mu < p \circ q < \alpha + \mu.$$
(4) $\mathsf{E}(u, v_1, v_2, v_3)$ has value
v_1 iff u has a value $\alpha \pm \mu$, where $\alpha + \mu < 0$.
v_2 iff u has value $0 \pm \mu$ for all $\mu > 0$.
v_3 iff u has a value $\alpha \pm \mu$, where $\alpha - \mu > 0$.
(5) $\lim(x, u)$ has value $\alpha \pm \mu$ iff
$$u_x[\underbrace{1 + 1 + \ldots + 1}_{n \text{ times}}] \text{ has value } \alpha \pm \mu$$
for almost an n with respect to some prechosen fixed ultrafilter on $\mathbf{N}$.

(6) $(u_1, u_2, \ldots, u_n)$ has value $(\alpha_1, \alpha_2, \ldots, \alpha_n) \pm \mu$ iff u_i has value $\alpha_i \pm \mu$, $i = 1, 2, \ldots, n$.

(7) $((x \to u)v)$ has the same values as $u_x[v]$.

(8) $(((x_1, \ldots, x_n) \to u)(v_1, v_2, \ldots, v_n))$ has the same values as $u_{x_1, \ldots, x_n}[v_1, \ldots, v_n]$.

(9) $((u \uparrow v)w)$ has the same values as

$$\overbrace{(u \ldots (u(uw)) \ldots)}^{n \text{ times}}$$

iff v has value $n \pm \mu$ for all $\mu > 0$ $(u = 0, 1, 2, \ldots)$.

(10) If u_1 has the same values as u_2, and v_1 has the same values as v_2, then $(u_1 v_1)$ has the same values as $(u_2 v_2)$.

With a few extensions such as more convenient bracket rules, decimal constants and vector and matrix arithmetic, the above defined formal language can be used as a programming language. In this language it is allowed to write *definitions*

$$a = u,$$

where a is a variable and u an expression. Later free occurrences of a are to be replaced by u. It is also allowed to write *commands*

$$u \pm \mu,$$

where u is an expression and μ is a positive rational. A value of a command $u \pm \mu$ is an element of a (generalized) interval $[\alpha - \mu, \alpha + \mu]$, such that

$$\lim_{N_{i_1}} \lim_{N_{i_2}} \ldots \lim_{N_{i_n}} u$$

has value $\alpha \pm \mu$, where $N_{i_1}, N_{i_2}, \ldots, N_{i_n}$, $i_1 < i_2 < \ldots < i_n$, are the infinits contained in u. (Notice that any other order type than that of the natural numbers could have been chosen for the infinits.)

The evaluation of commands is in principle done by assigning sufficiently large values

$$\overbrace{1 + 1 + \ldots + 1}^{n}$$

to the lim-bounded variables and the infinits, and evaluating the resultant expression. In *finitely* many commands, each infinit can always be assigned the same natural number in all the commands, and this makes it possible to interprete infinits as fixed sufficiently large numbers, the exact value of which is not known, because we do not know which finitely many commands we are going to be interested in.

2. Basic rules. For expressions x and y we define that $x = y$ if the command $\mathsf{E}(y - x, 0, 1, 0) \pm \frac{1}{2}$ has value 1.

An expression x is called *generalized real* if $x = x$ according to the definition above. The infinits are generalized reals, but $\lim_n n$ is not. Since all expressions satisfy $x = y \Rightarrow y = x$ and $x = y \wedge y = z \Rightarrow x = z$, $=$ is an equivalence relation on the generalized reals. Notice that $x = y \Leftrightarrow \mathsf{E}(y - x, 0, 1, 0) = 1$ for generalized reals. The relation $=$ can obviously be extended, which we shall not do here.

We define that $x < y$ if $\mathsf{E}(y - x, 0, 0, 1) = 1$. With the obvious definitions of $+$, $-$, $\cdot$ and $/$, all the usual axioms of an ordered field are satisfied by the generalized reals. If all unary functions $\mathbf{Q} \to \mathbf{Q}$ are admitted like $+$, $-$, $\cdot$ and $/$, then the generalized reals are essentially an ultralimit (see Kochen [1967]) of $\mathbf{R}$.

An expression, which does not contain infinits, is called *standard* or of *order 0*. Standard generalized reals are called *reals*. The *order* of an expression which does contain infinits is the greatest i such that N_i occurs in the expression. The order of u is denoted $\kappa(u)$, and $\max\{\kappa(u_1), \ldots, \kappa(u_n)\}$ is denoted $\kappa(u_1, u_2, \ldots, u_n)$.

We define that $x \simeq_\kappa y$ (x is near y of order κ) if $|x - y| < \varepsilon$ for all $\varepsilon > 0$ of order $\leqq \kappa$. Here $|u|$ is an abbreviation for $\mathsf{E}(u, -u, u, u)$. The relations $\simeq_\kappa$ are equivalence relations on the generalized reals, and they satisfy

$$x = y \Leftrightarrow x \simeq_\kappa y \text{ for all } \kappa \geqq \kappa(x, y)$$

$$x \simeq_{\kappa+1} y \Rightarrow x \simeq_\kappa y.$$

We define that x is *κ-bounded* if there exists an M of order $\leqq \kappa$ such that $|x| < M$. Notice that $x_1 \simeq_\kappa x_2$ and $y_1 \simeq_\kappa y_2$ imply

$$x_1 + y_1 \simeq_\kappa x_2 + y_2$$

$$x_1, x_2, y_1, y_2 \ \kappa\text{-bounded} \Rightarrow x_1 \cdot y_1 \simeq_\kappa x_2 \cdot y_2$$

$$x_1, x_2 \ \kappa\text{-bounded} \wedge y_1, y_2 \not\simeq_\kappa 0 \Rightarrow x_1/y_1 \simeq_\kappa x_2/y_2$$

and we have the important rule ($\lim_i u_i$ means $\lim(i, u)$ and u_{N_κ} is obtained by substituting N_κ for i in u).

When $\kappa > \kappa(\lim_i u_i)$ *then*

$$u_{N_\kappa} \text{ is } \kappa\text{-bounded iff } u_{N_\kappa} \simeq_\kappa \lim_i u_i.$$

This rule shows that the operator which maps generalized reals u of order $\leqq \kappa$ into

$$\lim_{N_1} \lim_{N_2} \dots \lim_{N_\kappa} u$$

is analogous to the "standard part operator" of Robinson [1966].

If we define

$$p_2 = (x, y) \to y$$
$$\sum = (f, a, b) \to p_2((i, s) \to (i + 1, s + f(i + 1)))^{b-a}(a, f(a))$$
$$\max = (f, a, b) \to p_2((i, m) \to (i + 1, \mathsf{E}(f(i + 1) - m, m, m, f(i + 1))))^{b-a}\,(a, f(a))$$

and use obvious abbreviations, we get the rule:

If

$$\max_{i=a,b} |y_i - z_i| \simeq_\kappa 0$$

and

$$\sum_{i=a}^{b} |x_i| \text{ is } \kappa\text{-bounded}$$

then

$$\sum_{i=a}^{b} y_i x_i \simeq_\kappa \sum_{i=a}^{b} z_i x_i.$$

3. Implementation on computers. The formal language described above has been implemented on a small computer (GIER) and used for teaching purposes at the University of Copenhagen in 1970.*

There is of course no way of producing a compiler which satisfies the semantic requirements of the language 100%. The most obvious reason for this is that a computer cannot handle a free ultrafilter on **N**. But even if the lim-step in the recursive definition of the semantics is changed by replacing the ultrafilter with the Frechét filter on **N** (which yields a non-standard theory similar to the one in Schmieden and Laugwitz [1959]), compilation is impossible (an easy consequence of recursive function theory). Since in both cases only the evaluation of "reasonable" commands is possible, the ultrafilter definition must be preferred, because it ensures simpler properties of the generalized reals.

Commands may be evaluated in the following steps:

(1) Definitions are inserted instead of free variables.

* In 1971 a more satisfactory compiler for the IBM 360 has been made.

(2) Expressions of the form $f(x)$ are evaluated where this can be done by substitution.

(3) The infinits are replaced by lim-bounded variables by the rule in section 2.

(4) All lim-bounded variables are replaced by infinits. In the expression obtained from (3), the sub lim-expressions are nested, and the infinit assigned to a lim-bounded variable has the depth as index. This proces may give rise to error ($\mathsf{E}(\lim_n 1/n, 0, 1, 0) \pm 0.1$ has not the same values as $\lim_n \mathsf{E}(1/n, 0, 1, 0) \pm 0.1$, but usually the transformation is correct). The incorrectness may be eliminated at the price of less efficiency.

(5) All the infinits in the expression obtained from (4) are assigned the value 2, and the resulting expression is evaluated. Then the value assigned to the infinit of highest order is changed to 4, 8, 16, etc. and in each case the expression is evaluated. The process is continued until the limit is found with the desired accuracy, normally using the general extrapolation technique known from numerical analysis as Richardsons [1927] deferred approach to the limit. If more infinits are involved, the next highest is assigned the values 4, 8, 16 etc. The choice of the values 2, 4, 8, 16, ... makes the extrapolation technique successful in most cases. It has the consequence that $(-1)^{N_1}$ has the value 1 with any accuracy; this can be accounted for by saying that the ultrafilter used in the definition of lim has the set of powers of 2 as element.

An example goes as follows: Suppose the definition of $\sum$ in section 2 and the definition

$$\int = (f, a, b) \to \lim_n \sum \left(i \to f\left(a + \frac{b-a}{n} \cdot (i - \tfrac{1}{2}) \right), 1, n \right) \cdot \frac{b-a}{n}$$

and the command

$$\int (x \to 1/x^2, 1, N_1) \pm 0.001$$

are read into the computer in order to compute $\int_1^\infty \mathrm{d}x/x^2$. Then the expressions in the command will be changed to (what corresponds to)

$$\left(\sum_{i=1}^{N_2} \frac{1}{[1 + \{(N_1 - 1)/N_2\} \cdot (i - \frac{1}{2})]^2} \right) \cdot \frac{N_1 - 1}{N_2}$$

and computed as described in (5) above.

All numbers, functions and operators normally used in concrete mathematical analysis can be defined as expressions in the formal language and used for computations, which may involve non-standard numbers and *internal* functions and operators (see Robinson [1966]). *External* functions and operators cannot be defined as expressions.

The formal language is very easily learned and used. The technique may seem inefficient for solving actual computational problems, but it turns out that the translated program can be made very efficient. To some extent this compensates for the need for iterating the computation more times than actually necessary. Another point is, that the repetition of computations makes the evaluation of commands rather "fool proof", because the process does not converge when truncation errors make it impossible to attain the desired accuracy.

The structure of the generalized reals as a nest of extensions of the standard reals may seem more complicated than the simple extensions ordinary used in non-standard analysis (where the complicated structure, however, may be hidden in the choice of a complicated ultrafilter for construction of an ultrapower). But it seems quite natural and unavoidable, when expressions are to be used for computational purposes. The nested structure has also advantages in proofs, where it seems possible to avoid the ε-δ-method to an even larger extent than in ordinary non-standard analysis. This may be seen from the following example, which should be compared to the example given in the end of section 9.6 of Robinson [1963].

4. Example: Differential equations. Assume that (for all $\kappa \in \mathbf{N}_0$)

$$x_1 \simeq_\kappa x_2 \wedge y_1 \simeq_\kappa y_2 \Rightarrow g(x_1, y_1) \simeq_\kappa g(x_2, y_2)$$

for all generalized reals x_1, x_2, y_1, y_2 satisfying

$$0 \leqq x_1 \leqq 1 \wedge -x_1 \leqq y_1 \leqq x_1 \wedge 0 \leqq x_2 \leqq 1 \wedge -x_2 \leqq y_2 \leqq x_2,$$

which simply is the natural way of saying that g is continuous on $\Omega = \{(x, y) | 0 \leqq x \leqq 1 \wedge -x \leqq y \leqq x\}$.

Assume further that $|g(x, y)| \leqq 1$ on Ω.

We want to find a function H such that (for all $\kappa \in \mathbf{N}_0$)

$$x_1 \simeq_\kappa x_2 \wedge x_1 \neq x_2 \Rightarrow \frac{H(x_2) - H(x_1)}{x_2 - x_1} \simeq_\kappa g(x_1, H(x_1))$$

for all x_1, x_2 satisfying $0 \leqq x_1 \leqq 1$ and $0 \leqq x_2 \leqq 1$. Such a function will satisfy

$$0 \leqq x < 1 \Rightarrow (\mathrm{D}H)x = g(x, H(x)),$$

where

$$\mathrm{D} = f \to \left(x \to \lim_n \frac{f(x + 1/n) - f(x)}{1/n}\right).$$

Let

$$h = n \to (x \to p_2(\varphi^{[nx]}(0, 0))),$$

where

$$\varphi = (x, y) \to (x + 1/n, y + g(x, y)/n),$$

and $[nx]$ is the integer part of nx.

Then $-x \leqq g(x, h_n(x)) \leqq x$ for all positive integers n and all $x \in [0, 1]$ (meaning $0 \leqq x \leqq 1$).

If $x_1 \simeq_\kappa x_2$ and $x_1 \neq x_2$, and $N = N_\lambda$, where

$$\lambda = \kappa(x_1, x_2) + 1, \quad \text{then}$$

$$\frac{h_N(x_2) - h_N(x_1)}{x_2 - x_1} \simeq_\kappa g(x_1, h_N(x_1)).$$

This is proved as follows:

Let x_3 and x_4 be the smaller and the larger of x_1 and x_2. Then $x_3 < x_4$ and $x_3 \neq_\lambda x_4$ and $x_3 \simeq_\kappa x_4$. Let $a = [N \cdot x_3]$ and $b = [N \cdot x_4]$. If $a \leqq k < l \leqq b$ and k and l are integers, then

$$\left|h_N\left(\frac{l}{N}\right) - h_N\left(\frac{k}{N}\right)\right| = \left|\sum_{i=k}^{l-1} g\left(\frac{i}{N}, h_N\left(\frac{i}{N}\right)\right)\Big/N\right| \leqq$$

$$\leqq \frac{b - a}{N} \simeq_\lambda x_2 - x_1 \simeq_\kappa 0.$$

Now

$$\frac{h_N(x_4) - h_N(x_3)}{x_4 - x_3} \simeq_\lambda \frac{\sum_{i=a}^{b-1} g\left(\frac{i}{N}, h\left(\frac{i}{N}\right)\right)\Big/N}{(b - a)/N} =$$

$$= \sum_{i=a}^{b-1} g\left(\frac{i}{N}, h_N\left(\frac{i}{N}\right)\right) \cdot \frac{1}{b - a}.$$

Since

$$\sum_{i=a}^{b-1} \left|\frac{1}{b - a}\right| = 1 \text{ is } \kappa\text{-bounded}$$

and

$$\max_{i=a,b-1} \left| g\left(\frac{i}{N}, h_N\left(\frac{i}{N}\right)\right) - g(x_1, h_N(x_1)) \right| \simeq_\kappa 0,$$

because $g(i/N, h_N(l/N)) \simeq_\kappa g(x_1, h_N(x_1))$ for all integers i satisfying $a \leqq i \leqq b$, we get

$$\frac{h_N(x_4) - h_N(x_3)}{x_4 - x_3} \simeq_\kappa \sum_{i=a}^{b-1} g(x_1, h_N(x_1)) \cdot \frac{1}{b-a} = g(x_1, h_N(x_1)).$$

Obviously $-x \leqq h_N(x) \leqq x$ for $x \in [0, 1]$ and consequently $H(x) = \lim_n h_n(x)$ is generalized real, and $H(x) \simeq_x h_N(x)$ for $x \in [0, 1]$. Therefore, if $x_1 \simeq_\kappa x_2$ and $x_1 \neq x_2$ and $x_1, x_2 \in [0, 1]$, then

$$\frac{H(x_2) - H(x_1)}{x_2 - x_1} \simeq_\lambda \frac{h_N(x_2) - h_N(x_1)}{x_2 - x_1} \simeq_\kappa g(x_1, h_N(x_1)) \simeq_\lambda g(x_1, H(x_1)),$$

where λ and N are chosen as above.

References

Kochen, S., 1967, Ultraproducts in the Theory of Models, *Ann. of Math.* 74, p. 221.

Richardson, L. F., 1927, The Deferred Approach to the Limit *I*-Single Lattice, *Trans. Roy. Soc. London* 226, p. 299.

Robinson, A., 1963, *Introduction to Model Theory and to the Metamathematics of Algebra* (North-Holland, Amsterdam).

Robinson, A., 1966, *Non-Standard Analysis* (North-Holland, Amsterdam).

Schmieden, C. and Laugwitz, D., 1959, Eine Erweiterung der Infinitesimalrechnung, *Math. Zeitschr.* 69, p. 1.

Received 16 March 1971